A Word of Appreciation:

We would like to thank those who have donated their bodies without whom this exhibition would not have been possible.

TABLE OF CONTENTS

Wilhelm Kriz

Foreword

KÖRPERWELTEN and thus this catalogue display something unusual: anatomical specimens, produced and preserved according to a new process developed by Gunther von Hagens. This process — called Plastination — even makes it possible to lend rigidity to soft body parts (e.g., individual muscles, organs such as the lungs, or a single nerve). As a consequence, even specimens of the entire body can be inherently stabilised and posed in such a way that they are actually capable of standing, which was formerly restricted to skeletons.

A collection of plastinates was first shown in Germany at the Museum for Technology and Labour in Mannheim during the winter of 1997/98. This exhibition succeeded far beyond the most optimistic expectations.

This applies first of all for the number of visitors. Nearly 780 000 people saw the exhibition within the relatively short period of only four months; toward the end, the exhibition had to remain open around the clock to make this at all possible. Secondly, this applies for the response. A representative sampling of public opinion showed that 95 % of those attending this demonstration of the inner realms of the human body gave it high marks. Critics were few but then all the heftier. The heftiest critics were those who had not even seen the exhibition.

From this mixture of a break that flouted social conventions, enthusiastic acceptance and vehement rejection — and more highly publicized than hardly any other — a public discussion was conducted that was sometimes highly emotional, sometimes seriously pensive and that was ultimately embraced by the entire country. Here I would like to respond to both the acceptance and the criticism as the long-time mentor of Gunther von Hagens and from the vantage point of an anatomist.

There were certainly several reasons for the generally positive resonance among the public. I would like to single out three of them here: 1) The creator of these specimens is an unusual personality; 2) his works show things that are new and never before seen; and 3) exhibiting them also permits those viewers not schooled in medicine to free themselves of a taboo.

The Plastinator

Gunther von Hagens, who produced this exhibition, took over a position as a research assistant at the Institute for Anatomy and Cellular Biology at the University of Heidelberg in 1978. Right at the beginning, he stumbled by chance onto a neglected and fallow field of research, namely using plastics to preserve anatomical specimens. He was fascinated by the possibilities that had remained unused until then to such an extent that he literally sank his teeth into this subject matter right from the start — and thus we come directly to the essence of his personality.

This I had to accept, which was not necessarily difficult for me, because producing durable anatomical specimens is definitely recognised as an essential aspect of our field. It soon became clear that any attempt to dissuade von Hagens and to interest him in another research project would have been in vain. No other quality characterises him as does unswerving dedication to achieving a goal once he has set it for himself. Identification with that goal, which he had then made his own, has attained a level over the course of years that hardly allows of a distinction between the person and the profession. Gunther von Hagens embodies his work.

I have accompanied him in his work at the Institute for almost 20 years. As he enthusiastically reported every bit of progress, no matter how small, immediately and expected that we discuss it extensively, a continual professional conference was virtually the order of the day. This made me his critic as well as his partner and rival in a relationship that has remained free of dissonance over the entire period of our association. His commitment and his dedication grew from year to year; despite many setbacks, despite much that did not work out — his persistence and tenacity could not be shaken. He was thus able to discover and to invent new and more innovative improvements, new modifications of his dissection and preservation technologies that ultimately made production of such spectacular whole-body plastinates as those that were mainly responsible for the success of the Mannheim exhibition.

New Vistas

The second reason for the interest of both the public and the media in KÖRPERWELTEN is, as mentioned above, the fact that the exhibits showed things never seen before. A short historical excursion should make this easier to understand.

Even before Andreas Vesalius (1514–1564) published the first book on anatomy, Leonardo da Vinci (1452–1519) had been dissecting cadavers in order to understand the vital relief of the human body from its structures beneath the surface. Leonardo also drew whatever he discovered this way. This was at a time when nothing could be done to prevent decomposition — not a very pleasant activity, as he noted: "… if you feel like doing such things, your stomach prevents you from it; and if this does not prevent you, then your fears will keep you from associating with quartered and excoriated, dreadful to look at dead people at night." However, anatomical science and modern medicine developed from just such beginnings.

Since the last century, anatomy has made the fine structures of organs and tissue the focus of its research with the aid of the microscope, devoted itself to submicroscopic cell and cellular systems in this century and in the meantime is occupied with molecular structures and their functions— as in all other basic subject areas in medicine. Nevertheless, classic, macroscopic anatomy, still provides an indispensable foundation of medical training. The necessary knowledge is imparted in dissection courses, and with the aid of anatomical models and specimens of varied types.

Collections of such specimens in anatomical and pathological institutes have long since been accessible to laypersons; and there are some that are outstanding, for example at the Charité in Berlin, in Basel, and in Vienna. They frequently arouse the spectre of a horror show as exhibits of abnormalities dominate in many places: a still-born child with anencephaly, in which the brain has not developed properly, and on top of that they are preserved in jars filled with formaldehyde. This is usually the lasting impression imparted to unsuspecting visitors.

This changed radically with the advent of plastinates. In them, skillful dissection of details is combined with innovative preservation and aesthetic presentation. Their production is naturally based on a differentiated process with very many individual steps: originating, testing and developing this innovative process. This in substance is what we have gained from the work of Gunther von Hagens.

However, visitors at an exhibition rarely admire the technology with which an exhibit has been made, but rather the finished product itself. Consequently, I would like to discuss the reasons for the attractiveness of whole-body plastinates using a concrete example, the specimen known as "The Chess Player" or "The Thinker."

This is a body in a sitting position, in which the spinal column and the peripheral nerves are shown in detail. I have heard several professional colleagues offer the opinion that this is the best specimen of the nerves of the spinal column that they have ever seen. Such a specimen thus epitomizes the art of dissection and craftsmanship to perfection.

Up till here, this has had little to do with Plastination. This first comes into play after dissection, namely with the possibility of lending the specimens rigidity and a pose. A specimen can thus gain a natural aspect: This whole-body plastinate awakens the impression that it is sitting to think or to play chess.

This type of anatomical specimens is not only something new, but also opens to everyone an accessibility never before experienced by anyone. Even for medical laypersons, the impression wears off that this is a corpse. It becomes easier for them to overcome their timidity at the sight of the specimens, to approach them and to look at the uncovered and projecting structures of the inner realms of the body. They see things that they have never seen before and that they could not have imagined. They are amazed.

It is surprising that many visitors to KÖRPERWELTEN consider some exhibits to be works of art. As an anatomist, I can attest to the fact that the specimen called The "Chess Player" or "The Thinker" was dissected with a high degree of skill and artistic craftsmanship and that the objective, namely of presenting the peripheral nervous system, has been achieved in an exceptionally brilliant and professional fashion as well as in a highly appealing manner.

Breaking with Taboos

There is also a third reason for the success of public exhibitions of such specimens: they touch on the taboo of death. In our society, death is repressed, so to speak blocked out, and the corpses of other people, at least, are viewed with a revulsive shudder — drilled into us through daily assaults by the same media pictures.

Many people also went to see the Mannheim exhibition with such expectations and experienced that this revulsion actually decreased as they viewed the specimens, was lost completely and instead both amazement and a thirst for knowledge began to manifest themselves.

For each visitor, this was ultimately a personal victory. They had overcome the taboos that surround human corpses. They were able to look at these specimens quietly and with interest in anatomical details. In so doing, they were able to pick out those organs or other tissue structures that particularly touched their lives due to a personal experience with a disease or for any other reason whatsoever. And they succeeded in doing this with frankness and without having to be on the defensive. This transition from expecting revulsion to looking at the specimens freely and uninhibitedly amounts to a personal break with these taboos. Many visitors to KÖRPERWELTEN have spoken about this and thus encouraged family, friends and acquaintances to have the same experience.

Reservations and Answers

And it was just this point, the break with the taboos of death and corpses that also ignited the opposition to the Mannheim exhibition. Although the number of opponents was relatively small, the criticism of individuals was nonetheless all the heftier. Criticism came primarily from academics — from theologians as well as pathologists and anatomists.

It was just this vehement and emotional rejection expressed by several anatomists that appears less and less understandable to me the more time passes since the exhibition. I am not convinced by the explanation frequently offered for it, namely to avert the loss of a kind of "sacrosanct" knowledge. Dissection and autopsies are indeed privileges of physicians; however, knowledge of anatomy has long since ceased to be some kind of elite intellectual property, on which anatomists were able to base their identity.

Whatever the motives were — both the heftiness and types of criticism remain regrettable when it came from the anatomical camp. The reason is that seen with unbiased eyes skill in anatomical dissection and an innovative process of preservation were presented to the public in a very respectable fashion; the general public in turn responded to the Mannheim exhibition with immense interest and by far with a predominantly positive resonance.

The main argument of the opponents of KÖRPERWELTEN was that a public exhibition of authentic human anatomical specimens would violate the dignity of the individual, and more precisely that of the deceased. For an anatomist, this argument has a particular aspect. As mentioned above, dissecting cadavers has been an integral part of studying medicine from time immemorial. In my 30 years of experience in the meantime, I can guarantee that students in anatomical courses have never shown anything but the highest respect for those who had donated the bodies for that purpose.

Visitors to the Mannheim exhibition were also not lacking in showing the same respect. On the contrary, it was constantly apparent and could sometimes even be distinctly felt. Dissecting cadavers within the framework of medical studies has been explained and justified by its expediency in educating future physicians. Nevertheless, in an advanced society today, educating the public in general is not a matter of any less importance or any less ethical priority than academic education. Medical laypersons also have the right to ask questions about how the human body looks on the inside, and they also have a right to want to see it. They have a right to learn where and how a disease occurs and how it might be prevented if possible or where what happens during surgery. To make a pri-

vilege out of this for physicians is no longer justifiable. On the contrary, there is considerable demand for educating laypersons on anatomical facts as well as for an objective, free and open discussion about taboos on death and dealing with dead bodies that have existed until now.

To do justice to the objective of clarification, this KÖRPERWELTEN book includes — in addition to the current catalogue of specimens together with explanations on the anatomy and functions of the human body by Angelina Whalley — contributions on all of the essential questions raised by the Mannheim exhibition: Psychologist Ernst D. Lantermann presents an in-depth look at the methods and results of a visitor poll. State Lutheran bishop Ulrich Fischer represents the criticism based on moral-theological grounds; medical ethicist Axel W. Bauer presents the scientific position in this regard. Philosopher Franz Josef Wetz deals extensively with the term "human dignity," and jurist Brigitte Tag discusses the new legal situation. Finally, art historian Bazon Brock looks at Plastination as practiced by Gunther von Hagens under the aspect of applied science as a cultural achievement. Gunther von Hagens himself explains, inter alia, the technology of his process.

Controversial reactions such as experienced at the time in the Mannheim exhibition only serve to show that information on the natural facts of our bodies will always have to be reasserted. The reason is that expectations of revulsion followed by fascination after all can also be found, for example, in a 260-year-old instructional poem about a comparable event, namely a public anatomical dissection:

Hardly had I cast a glance at that dissected wench, Hardly had I seen that corpse, partially denuded of skin, I could hardly even look at the bloody muscles, when at that very moment a vile and repulsive horror seized me.

However, the sage anatomist had hardly begun, he let us shortly see the wise wonders that forming Nature had given to it, so that my first impression had to make room for a far sweeter one.

Fear, horror, disgust were gone in a moment, Admiration first struck me, then amazement, followed gradually by humility and awe, and then by praise, and our pensiveness.

A bright fire of holy lust began to burn in my breast that was filled with thankfulness to the glory of God to the honour of Him Who so wonderfully wrought this wonder of anatomy.

I did not even know myself how I really felt. The Creator shows Himself most clearly to mankind in man himself.

It seems that one could notice in these works of wonder, in this masterpiece of forming Nature, a bright trace of our Creator even here, quite convincingly clear and at the same time visible.

Aha!, I cried. Let this be written at this scene: Here atheists can no longer remain atheists!

Author Barthold Hinrich Brockes (1680–1747) was a Hamburg patrician and scholar devoted to the Enlightenment.

The quote comes from his main work, *Irdisches Vergnügen in Gott (Earthly Joy in God)*, Volume 6, Hamburg, 1739: p. 298

Wilhelm Kriz has been a professor of anatomy at the University of Heidelberg since 1974 and is the chairman of the Institute for Anatomy and Cellular Biology I; he is also the director of this institute. He studied medicine at the University of Giessen and at the Free University of Berlin; he did his doctorate in 1963. In 1971, he completed his credentials (Habilitation) for a professorship at the University of Münster where he served as an instructor, scientific lecturer and professor before receiving an appointment in Heidelberg. Until now, he has published approx. 150 scientific articles and three medical books. His research has focussed on the functional structure of the kidneys, development of these organs and their loss of function from chronic kidney failure. In 1990, the University of Göttingen awarded Kriz the Jakob-Henle Medal and the German Dialysis Society honoured him with the Bernd-Tersteegen Prize in 1998.

Gunther von Hagens

Anatomy and Plastination

1. The History of Anatomy

Anatomy and Hunting; Ritual Anatomy

Anatomy refers to the science of investigating the body's internal structures. There have always been specialists on the body's interior; hunters were among these specialists in man's early history. Animals killed during the hunt had to be gutted, and the meat had to be removed from the bones; a certain understanding of anatomy was an advantage in this regard. "Kitchen anatomy" therefore concerned the anatomy of animals. Initial interest in human anatomy presumably arose among cannibals, whose motives were primarily ritual in nature. They believed that by consuming their enemies they could absorb their strength. In the earliest advanced civilisations, procedures were developed for immortalising the bodies of the dead—at least when the deceased had been persons of importance. Preserving entire corpses in this way was known in many cultures. The most famous instance is that of the mummies of ancient Egyptian pharaohs and other dignitaries, whose gutted bodies had been treated with fragrant resins and sodium bicarbonate, and then dried; this was to allow the deceased to live on after death. At its high point in South America, mummification even led to the establishment of entire cities of the dead. Ritual anatomy did not achieve any great anatomical insights, however, because the focus of preservation efforts was the mortal shell of the person, the skin in particular. The organs themselves, whose failure was responsible for the individual's death, fell prey to decay.

The major impetus for acquiring detailed anatomical knowledge has always come from medicine. At first, this knowledge lay in the hands of shamans and priests; shortly before the beginning of the Common Era (A.D.), the profession of physician came into being, a vocation for which training was largely of a philosophical nature.

First Anatomical Studies in Greece and Egypt.

At around 500 BC, the Greeks founded medical schools such as those in Crotona (lower Italy) and Cyrene (Africa), where they explored the anatomy of animals, examining even such tiny structures as the organ of equilibrium located in the temples. Aristotle (384–327 BC) was the first known anatomist, even though he is better known today for his philosophical writings. A student of Plato and a teacher to Alexander the Great, Aristotle drew a distinction between nerves and tendons, and described how major arteries branched out into smaller blood vessels.

Shortly after 400 BC, the Greek philosopher Plato came to the conclusion that there must be a fundamental difference between body and soul. He saw the body as only a temporary housing for the soul. This school of thought, known as the dualism of body and soul, provided the necessary foundation for preserving human specimens. The conviction that the soul exists independently of the body made it permissible to open up the body once the soul had departed after death. It was in this spirit that Herophilos and Erasistratos undertook the first dissections of human bodies in Alexandria, where, following the death of Alexander the Great, King Ptolemy I had established a medical school in 320 BC. Dissections were performed on the bodies of executed prisoners—probably in public.

Although first expressed by Plato, the philosophical premise of the dualism of body and soul later finds its way into the Bible, where Paul says the following about the new body to come after the resurrection: "But someone will ask, 'How are the dead raised? With what kind of body will they come?' … But God will give them a body as he sees fit…" (Cor. I, 15:35–38)

Anatomy in Europe in the Common Era

When the Romans conquered Egypt in 30 BC, the medical school of Alexandria declined in importance. The teachings of Galen of Pergamum (131–201 AD), a doctor whose conclusions were based on the study of animals, would now dominate the field. Having studied in Alexandria, Galen settled in Rome and produced some 150 medical writings. It is assumed that he never dissected human bodies, but instead studied monkeys and other animals — his anatomical works were flawed accordingly. Galen was a difficult, high-handed individual, whose arrogance was expressed in his books as follows: "Anyone looking for fame simply has to familiarize himself with all that I have achieved." Galen did, in fact, enjoy an excellent reputation as a doctor — even Emperor Marcus Aurelius refused to go without his services.

Over the course of time, Galen published 200 books and influenced anatomical thought and medicine for the next 1300 years. During this time, dissections of the human body remained an exception to the rule. Only a very few historical sources confirm that doctors dissected human bodies, but these dissections served mainly to preserve the identity of the medical profession at that time. A professor would read from Galen's books while his assis-tants dissected a cadaver, lending the words of the ancient master more significance than was attributed to any anatomical findings revealed by opening the body. Anatomical drawings were correspondingly faulty.

A change in attitude towards the teaching of anatomy first appeared at the end of the Middle Ages, when artists in particular began to investigate the structure of the human body. Today the most well-known artist and scientist of that time is Leonardo da Vinci (1452–1519), who privately performed anatomical dissections of human corpses. These formed the basis for his famous, highly detailed anatomical sketches. For the first time, he provided realistic, correctly proportioned illustrations of the body's interior, even though the details of his drawings were often incorrect. Leonardo da Vinci's work made a significant contribution to society's acceptance of studying human bodies.

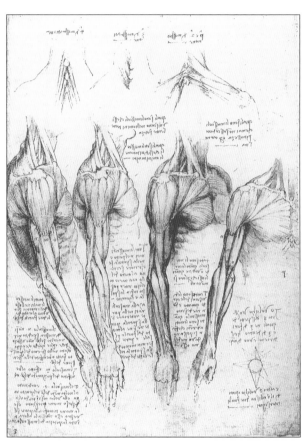

Fig. 2: Anatomical studies of Leonardo da Vinci, 1510.

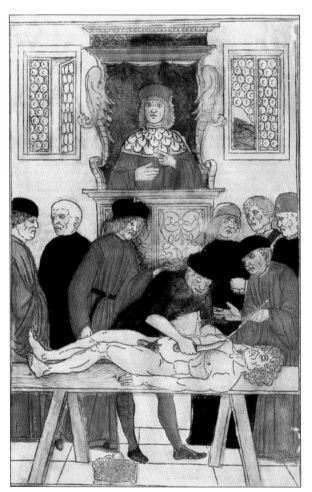

Fig. 1: Fasciolo de Medicina, drawing of an anatomy lecture, 1493. The professor read from the books of Galen, while his assistants performed the dissection

Fig. 3: Towards the end of the Middle Ages, artists began studying the structure of the human body. This illustration presumably shows Michelangelo dissecting a corpse

A short time later, the famous anatomist Andreas Vesalius (1514–1564) had the courage to criticise publicly the practice of limiting anatomical dissections to animals. In his monumental work *De fabrica humani corporis*, Vesalius describes the anatomy of the human body according to what he had observed at recently introduced public dissections at the "Theatre of Anatomy." He is considered the founder of the science of anatomy. The drawings by his illustrator Kalkar were more exact than anything that had been previously produced. The sketches also introduced a new aesthetic quality, showing dissected bodies in nearly life-like poses, standing in nature and surrounded by everyday items. According to available evidence, Andreas Vesalius was also the first person to assemble real bones into an upright structure. He called this a skeleton after ho skeletos, which means "dried up" in Greek. This was revolutionary, as no one had ever before dared to do anything similar with cadavers; he more or less pulled the dead out of their graves and put them back into society. A skeleton assembled by Vesalius can still be found at the Institute of Anatomy of the University of Basel.

Anatomy as it was shown in the drawings of that time was initially a very individual type of anatomy. The specimen and all of its unique anatomical features were copied in as great a detail as possible. Certain artistic means were employed to demonstrate the authenticity and individuality of the illustration; shadows caused by the light coming in through a window, for example, made it clear what time of day that particular specimen was dissected. A fly on the drawing symbolised the momentary nature of the illustrator's art, as in a photograph.

That all changed with Bernhard Albinus (1697–1747), whose illustrator Wandelaer not only enriched contemporary understanding of anatomy with his drawings of animals; he also compiled the many variations that he found into a standard, thereby clearing the way for the statistically average anatomy. Organs were no longer sketched individually or as they were found in the body; instead, they were drawn together with their associated functional structures, thus emphasising systems of organs. A kidney, for example, was not just drawn along with the adrenal gland in the surrounding

Fig. 5: In dissecting corpses in public, Andreas Vesal established what was called the "Theatre of Anatomy."

fatty tissues; the ureters and bladder were included as well. The brain was no longer shown solely from the perspective of the open skull; it was now sketched along with the spine and the peripheral nerves. This provided the foundation for developing schematic diagrams of the anatomy — an abstraction that arose from a more functional understanding of the body.

Fig. 4: Andreas Vesal (1514–1564), founder of the science of anatomy.

The father of cross-sectional anatomy was Russian anatomist Nikolas Pirogov (1810–1881). In his *Anatomia topographica, sectionibus per corpus humanum*, he published two hundred and thirteen cross-sectional illustrations of the human body, including one of a pregnant woman. The cadavers were frozen during the Russian winter in St. Petersburg. The stone printing plates used for his work exist to this day.

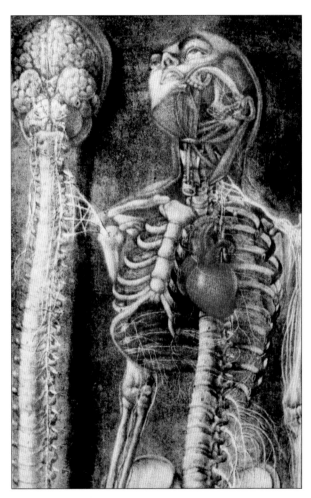

Fig. 6: Bernhard Siegfried Albinus. As anatomy became better understood, organs were sketched more and more frequently in systems representing specific functions

The introduction of the microscope allowed 17th century anatomists to study the microstructure of the body; as a result, many anatomists lost interest in macroscopic anatomy, which was increasingly considered to have no more research potential. This trend was magnified in the West during the 1950's, when the electron microscope came into use in the field of anatomy; the same has also been true over the past 20 years due to anatomical research in the fields of cell and molecular biology. As a result of their research in cell biology, western anatomists have lost nearly all interest in anatomical studies on cadavers.

Anatomy and Art

In the 16th century, the human body was the focus of an entire era in the history of art. At precisely that moment in history when the sculptures and paintings of the Renaissance had elevated the beauty of the human body to an aesthetic ideal, and natural beauty stood at the heart of our understanding of art, artists also discovered the beauty of

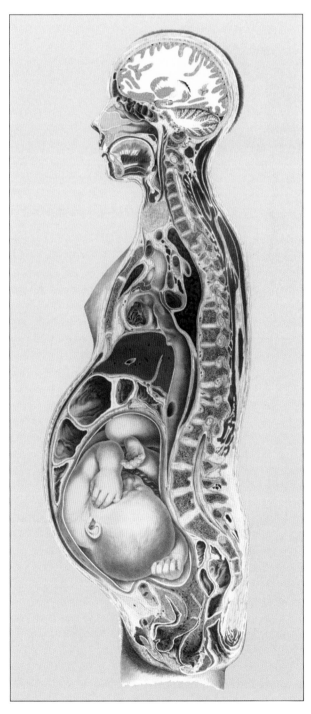

Fig. 7: Cross-sectional drawing of the body of a pregnant woman by Russian anatomist Nikolas Pirogov, 1855

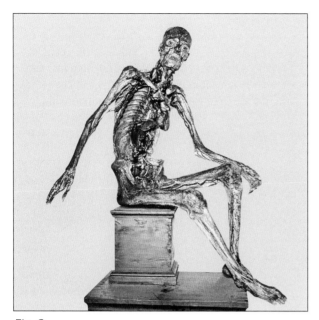

Fig. 8

*Fig. 8 and 9: Metal injections have preserved these rough-
ly 200 year-old whole-body anatomical specimens, which
can still be seen in Florence and Modena.*

the body's interior. In their longing for perfection, painters and sculptors wanted to see the actual muscles upon
which they modeled their works of art. First, they observed anatomists, but it was not long before they took the
scalpel into their own hands. In Italy and the Netherlands,
guilds of doctors, apothecaries and artists even banded
together.

Only when the skeletal systems and musculatures of entire bodies had been studied in detail could the famous
paintings and sculptures of the day come into being. During this era, when artistic talent and anatomical knowledge were combined, the most artistic works in the history of anatomy were created. Surviving anatomical
illustrations, which are now considered part of man's cultural heritage, were clearly not drawn from memory — real
specimens served as models. Due to the lack of appropriate preservation techniques, however, cadavers decom-
posed shortly after they had been dissected.

Only a very few of them could be preserved, and these can
still be seen today at the Italian Museum of Anatomy. Bodies were first dried and their surfaces were treated with
oils; in some cases, specimens were injected with metal
alloys as a means of highlighting arteries.

The dissected bodies were displayed in aesthetically pleasing, life-like poses that are expressive in a way that brings
out the individual character of their anatomy. Some of the
bodies are even shown in a manner that makes them seem
to exude charm and humor. What is so fascinating about
surviving pictures is that, in addition to providing a detailed depiction of the specimen, they also surround the
specimen with ancient landscapes. The resulting surreal atmosphere created by these illustrations is astonishing;
take, for instance, a drawing in which a rhinoceros makes
its way into the scene, its proverbial thick skin forming
a contrast to the dissected, skinless human being. KÖR-
PERWELTEN is presented here as natural art. The beauty of the medieval specimens manifests itself in their perfection, in the harmonious contours of the specimens, in
the pleasing, perfect balance of their components and the
clarity of anatomical detail. By performing precise studies
of anatomical relation-ships and sharing the results of
these studies, anatomy artists established anatomy as a
science. They sought the source of truth in the original
and made seeing for themselves, i.e. the "aut-opsy," the
foundation of their scientific endeavours. As the science
of anatomy developed further, the significance of the artist as such was increasingly relegated to the background.
Anatomy was gradually reduced to medical courses on
dissection and dissection in the service of pathology; as
a result, it gradually became the sole privilege of doctors.
Finally, the invention of photography made artists largely dispensable.

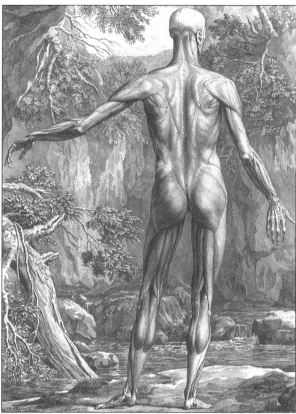
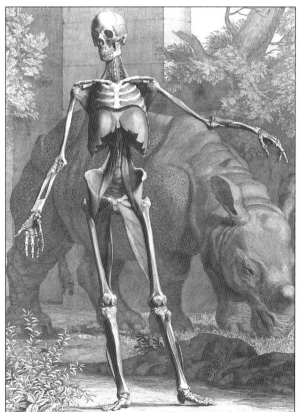
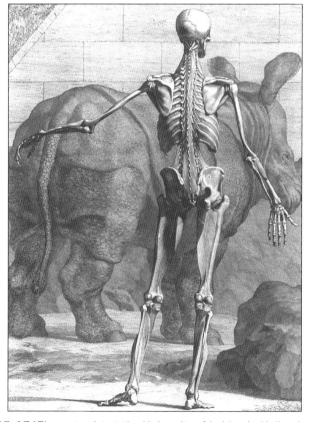

Figs. 10–13: Depictions of Bernhard Siegfried Albinus (1697–1747), anatomist at the University of Leiden in Holland, 1747

Fig. 14: Dissected bodies were shown in life-like poses, their gestures accentuating the individuality of their anatomy.

Today an artist's place in the science of anatomy is mostly limited to occasional modifications to existing anatomical illustrations and to sketching anatomical findings yielded by surgery. If artists wished to study a real cadaver, they would now have to go begging to anatomists; being granted this privilege, however, is generally an exception rather than the rule. It, therefore, comes as no surprise that the aesthetic quality of anatomical drawings made of the human body during the Renaissance has remained unrivaled to this day.

Anatomy and the Papacy

The unmitigated vanity of today's medical profession has laid sole responsibility for the over 1000-year stagnation of anatomical studies at the feet of the Church. *De sepulturis*, the papal bull issued by Pope Bonifacius VIII in 1300, is gladly interpreted as evidence of the animosity towards anatomical science on the part of the Church. The purpose of this decree was quite different, however: crusaders had begun the practice of dismembering the corp-

ses of their fallen comrades, boiling their bones and sending them back home. The reason for this was that they could thus be buried on consecrated ground in their native lands; the time-consuming custom weakened the troops' fighting ability, however, and this was the reason that the papal bull was intended to put a stop to it. Overzealous clerics interpreted it as a general ban on dissection.

A notable example of how well-disposed the Church was towards anatomy is that the body of Pope Alexander V was dissected in the year 1410. Popes Sixtus IV and Clement VII expressly permitted the dissection of human cadavers in Padua and Bologna. The Museum of Anatomy in Bologna owes its existence to support from Pope Benedict XIV, who had always been very open-minded regarding modern science. Even when he was still the archbishop of Bologna, Benedict had indicated the importance of anatomy and stressed the necessity of dissecting cadavers. The Holy See expressly permitted corpses to be opened during epidemics of bubonic plague.

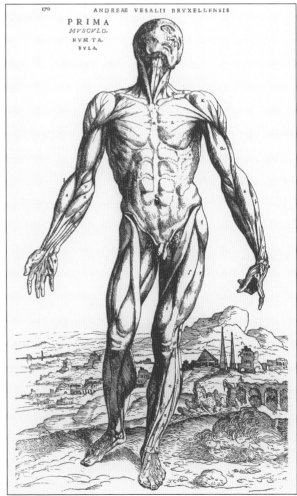

Fig. 15: Andreas Vesalius, Muscle Man, fabric, 1543.

Fig. 16: In 1860 a wood carver named Frantisek Rint artistically adorned the charnel house of the All Saints Church in Kunta Hora, Czech Republic, with the bones of 40,000 people.

Without the Christian belief of the dualism of body and soul mentioned earlier, anatomical dissection would never have originated and become established in Italy, a country ruled by the papacy. Similarly, without this belief, the Catholic tradition of preserving ritual relics would never have developed. Even today, relics can be found in many Catholic churches, and many old cemeteries have what are known as ossuaries—charnel houses with stacks of bones and skulls reaching to the ceiling.

The History of Procuring Cadavers

Anatomists of the Renaissance dissected the corpses of executed prisoners, disputing the right of criminals to their own bodies. This was the case in England, where Henry VIII (1491–1547) commanded that the bodies of criminals hanging from the gallows be handed over to anatomists. Dabbling in anatomy became so popular, in fact, that dissections began to be carried out in public theatres of anatomy so that anyone having an interest could satisfy his or her curiosity. It was not long before bodies became so scarce that people began robbing cemeteries. Parish councils received frequent complaints; in one such complaint, it was reported that thieves had stolen seven adult cadavers and three children's bodies on the night from Thursday, January 12 to Friday, January 13, 1786. In this case, it was claimed that young anatomists had, in attempts to hide the remains from the neighbours, burned the bones and used the fat from the dead as heating fuel in the winter. Robbing graves became an established pro-

fession; its representatives were known as "resurrection men." Because of the public interest in educating medical students, a blind eye was turned to this practice, until 1828 when two Scots named Burke and Hare began strangling people in order to deliver the bodies directly to anatomists. The public was so horrified that the English parliament immediately passed the Anatomy Act in 1832, a law that would secure the supply of bodies to anatomists, thereby depriving grave robbers of their economic base. Since that time, England has had an official anatomy examiner bearing the title "Her Majesty's Inspector of Anatomy." In Germany, there was also an effort made by the state to offset shortages of cadavers for anatomical purposes. In Prussia, for instance, circulars from 1889 saw to it that unclaimed cadavers were delivered to anatomical institutes. Bodies found, for which no survivors could be identified, formed the basis for the supply of corpses at anatomical institutes up until the 1960's. Bodies were transferred to institutes of anatomy by such public institutions as the Social Welfare Office.

In the 1960's, German anatomical institutes switched over to the practice of seeking bequeathments, in which individuals stated that, upon their deaths, their bodies should be donated to the nearest anatomical institute. Since then, the supply of cadavers has so greatly outpaced demand that most institutes of this type no longer need to accept unclaimed corpses.

How cadavers are procured for anatomical purposes varies greatly from one country to the next, and depends on the cultural and religious context. In the United States, for instance, where this is a state issue just as it is in Germany, institutes of anatomy either operate their own body-donation programmes or they obtain bodies from independent, state-run organisations (State Anatomy Boards), which are responsible for supplying cadavers to interested institutes. Such organisations also run special donation programmes for obtaining bodies. In addition to this, federal law holds that unclaimed cadavers are to be sent to State Anatomy Boards, where, for example in Maryland, they are chemically preserved and turned over to any interested institutions for a small fee (to cover costs).

History of Preserving Cadavers

Man's need to be immortalised is as old as the human race. Cave paintings, Egyptian pyramids, art collections, endowments and monuments all testify to this. It, therefore, comes as no surprise that there has always been a desire in all civilisations to protect one's own body and those of relatives from decomposition, or at least to slow the pro-

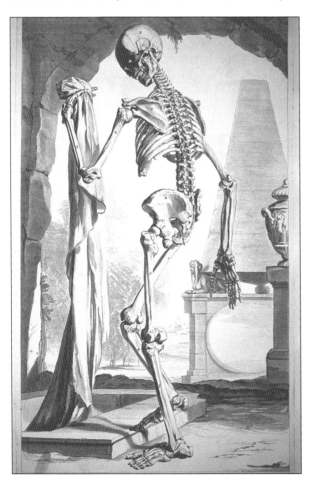

Fig. 17: Because of ignorance regarding the process of decomposition, it was a long-held belief that the body lived on in some diminished state.

cess down and to prevent the body from becoming a transitory object immediately following death. In the past, however, permanent preservation was reserved for only a few wealthy individuals. Yet it was not simple death rituals that led to the development of methods for preserving cadavers; fear of apparent death also played a role. Up until the 18th century, the processes of death and dying were not well known, and people were very unclear and unsure as to when the actual moment of death occurred. It was believed that the body lived on in some diminished state, especially for however long the flesh was still on it. Comments such as "Corpses are ravenous and devour their own garments!" or "Corpses can hear!" were not uncommon in documents of the time. If the ground over a grave sank or if the gases that result from decay caused it to rise (mass graves were common at the time, and a significant amount of gas was produced as a result), the tombstone would rise and sink, thereby sending out what appeared to be encoded messages from the dead. It was not until people understood the circulatory system and the functions of the brain that the moment of death could be defined as a unique event in time. Finally, the development of appropriate preservation methods was extremely important for the advance of medicine, as the study of human anatomy had previously been greatly impeded by the process of decay.

Artificial preservation methods undertaken by man are not the only means of preserving corpses. Natural preservation can also take place, and requires that the cadaver dry out in a relatively bacteria-free environment over a long period of time, as happens to a body when kept in an air-tight sarcophagus or in a crypt ventilated with dry air. The same is true for bodies buried in moors where they are preserved by the humic acid found there. Many natural mummies, including Ötzi (the oldest and most well known European mummy) prove that the degree to which they have been preserved is no worse than in the case of the mummies of the Pharaohs, for which such great pains had been taken.

Cultic Preservation of Bodies

The idea has persisted throughout nearly every epoch, culture, and religion that death does not mean the end of our individual existence. When death is seen as a transition of the soul to a spiritual world, as is the case with Jews, Christians, Buddhists and other religious societies, then the body is considered to be of secondary importance; rituals accompanying death are kept relatively simple.

It was different with early cultures that were often convinced of a somatic life after death. Here the deceased were buried with a rich array of burial objects, commensurate with their social status. Moreover, the question arose on how to preserve the bodies of the dead from decomposition. Es-

Fig. 18: "The little Inca prince," ca. 500-year-old ice mummy. National Museum in Santiago de Chile

Fig. 19: Tollund man, one of the best-preserved bog bodies from the pre-Christian era.

pecially the Egyptians developed embalming and mummification methods over several thousand years, the results of which can even today be admired in museums throughout the world.

Why it was the Egyptians who developed such methods can presumably be explained by the following. Because of the annual flooding of the Nile Valley, the people were forced to bury their dead beyond the reach of the floodwaters, in other words, in the dry, hot sand or rocks of the surrounding desert regions. Here the conditions were ideal for natural mummification: warm, dry sand that could dehydrate the body while at the same time stabilising it in its outward form. The steady draughts prevailing in these desert regions additionally favoured the drying-out process. Finally, finding natural mummies by the Egyptians themselves must have contributed to making the idea of a somatic afterlife a central part of their religious world view.

The art of embalming in Egypt reached its zenith in the period from 1700 to 1100 BC. It confined itself, however, to the "mortal shell" of the corpses. The organs, whose failure was the cause of death, such as the lungs, liver, kidneys, and brain, could not be sufficiently preserved. Their fate was as follows: First, the brain was removed through the nose with the aid of a hook. After opening the abdominal cavity through a slit along the left side of the body, the viscera were taken out except for the heart; they were then washed in palm oil and preserved in an alcohol solution in canopic jars. They nevertheless quickly fell prey to decomposition because the essences (natron, resins) only had a superficial effect. The body cavity was also washed and filled with powdered myrrh, resins and perfumes. The slit was then sewn back together. Next, the body was placed in a solution of potassium nitrate or saltpeter for 70 days.

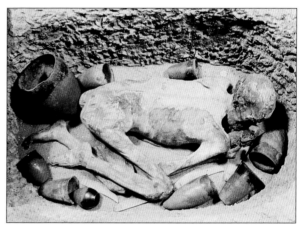

Fig. 20: "Ginger" — the oldest, fully preserved dry mummy in the world. Ca. 3200 years ago, she was buried in the hot desert sands of Egypt. British Museum, London.

Finally, it was again washed, rubbed with oils or resin and wrapped repeatedly in complicated layers of linen bandages. It was thus possible to preserve permanently only the skin and the bones, which could hardly rot under such dry conditions, anyway.

Methods of preservation similar to those of the ancient Egyptians are also utilised by the natives on the Canary Islands, in Africa (Guinea, Congo, Sudan and the Ivory Coast),

Fig. 21: Egyptian mummy. Vatican Museum, Rome.

in Asia (inter alia, India, Sri Lanka and Tibet), in Oceania (inter alia, Melanesia and Polynesia), America (in many Indian tribes of North and South America) and in Europe. In fact, they are partially still in use even today, for example by headhunters in the Amazon region, in Assam, Burma, Malaysia and New Guinea, to produce shrunken heads as trophies.

The complex processes of mummifying corpses developed from methods used to preserve food, for example, drying (dried fruits and meats), curing with smoke, salts, acids and protective solutions (pickling fluids, honey, sugar or alcohol). Two famous examples of using methods for preserving food to protect corpses were: 1) the body of Alexander the Great, which was kept in honey for the return to Macedonia after his untimely death; and 2) the body of Horatio Nelson, which spent the return journey from the victorious battle of Trafalgar, which had ended fatally for the admiral, in brandy.

Modern Embalming

Until the 17th century, corpses were preserved with the embalming methods developed by the Egyptians. The embalming methods commonly used today differ from the old ones both in the substances employed for preservation as well as the technology. Here we can primarily mention the

introduction of new chemicals for preservation, especially formaldehyde, and the development of embalming through arterial injection. The latter was first made pos-

Fig. 22: Canopic jars. They were used to hold the viscera of Egyptian mummies.

Fig. 23: Shrunken head of a Jivaro. Trophies of human heads were supposed to convey the power and strength of an enemy to the victor.

sible when William Harvey published his revolutionary ideas on the circulatory system. During his research, Harvey had injected dyestuffs into the blood vessels of cadavers. This new principle of arterial injection was first used successfully by Frederick Ruysche (1665–1717), who taught anatomy in Amsterdam. Unfortunately, Ruysche neglected to record exact information about the chemicals that he used. Detailed descriptions on arterial embalming were first written by the famous Scottish anatomist, William Hunter (1718–1783). He employed a solution consisting of turpentine and resinous oils, mixed with dyes, which he chose to inject in the femoral artery. In 1868, chemist August Wilhelm von Hofmann discovered formaldehyde that was later integrated into preservation techniques. Some years before, Laskowski (1886) had already introduced his Genevan embalming fluid, glycerin (discovered by Scheele in 1779), to protect specimens from dehydration and phenol (introduced as a disinfectant by Lister in 1867) to preserve them.

The importance that these discoveries had for practical preservation is shown by a survey that was published by Grönroos in 1898. Of the 44 anatomical institutes in Europe surveyed by the study, all of them utilised arterial injection for embalming. Embalming fluids that had gained Europe-wide acceptance were those that used solutions with formaldehyde (embalming and hardening), phenol (to inhibit the formation of fungi) and glycerin (moisture-retentive as it is a humectant). By the beginning of the 20th century, all of the substances had already been introduced, which have remained relatively unchanged until today and have been most frequently used to preserve cadav-ers. These include formaldehyde, phenol, glycerin, ethanol and water. A typical example is the preservation fluid used in the Institute of Anatomy at the University of Heidelberg: formaldehyde 3 %, lysoformin (contains formaldehyde, glutaraldehyde and a wetting solution) 1.5 %, phenol 6%, glycerin 15 %, alcohol 30 % and water 45 %.

2. Plastinated Specimens and Plastination

What are Plastinated Specimens?

Approx. 70 % of our bodies consists of fluids. They are indispensable both for living and for decomposing. With Plastination, fluids in our tissue are replaced by reactive plastics, such as silicone rubber, epoxy resin or polyester resin, in a special vacuum process. Body cells and the natural surface relief remain identical with their condition prior to preservation down to the microscopic level. The specimens are dry and odourless and are thus "graspable" in the most literal sense of the word. Thanks to these properties, plastinated specimens are of extremely high value both in edu-

cating medical students and in enlightening interested laypersons.

With the invention of Plastination, it has become possible for the first time to preserve natural anatomical specimens in a durable, realistic and aesthetic manner for instructional and research purposes as well as for general education. Natural specimens are especially valuable for medical studies and also for laypersons as the complicated structure of the locomotive system and organs as well as their relative positions and relationships to one another cannot be fully comprehended in their three-dimensional complexity when only books are used. Regardless of the quality of the pictures, they cannot replace the original. Artificial anatomical models can also make only limited contributions to understanding anatomy as they are schematised at best, are not capable of showing fine details and cannot convey the individuality of the human body. One model is the same as the next one. Anatomical variations, however, are significant from one individual to another. For this reason, a thorough, practical anatomical education for medical students using dead, human bodies has been laid down by law in most of today's advanced societies.

Beyond their didactic qualities, plastinated specimens also radiate a certain fascination, based primarily on their authenticity. Plastination stops decomposition and dehydration so completely that the insides of bodies cease to be objects of revulsion. Observers are not bothered by any kind of offensive odours.

Plastination creates beautiful specimens as a sensuous experience that are frozen at a point between death and decay. Thanks to this realistic quality, Plastination represents the most attractive form of exhibiting durable human specimens. This becomes particularly evident in the transparent body slices that provide a window into structures that are indispensable to life even in areas which would normally be viewed with a magnifying glass. To achieve the unlimited durability of a specimen, an inordinately large amount of time-consuming dissection work is now justified, which was heretofore not justifiable. One thousand and more hours of dedicated work are necessary to create one whole-body specimen dissected to show minute details. Plastinated specimens far exceed the expressive power of untreated specimens, for example, when — thanks to dyed plastics — grey brain matter is more obviously distinguishable from the white matter than would be possible with an unplastinated brain.

New Types of Specimens through Plastination

Plastination permits us to produce completely new types of specimens because it makes otherwise soft body parts such as muscles or the skin rigid, for example, in 3-milli-meter-thick body slices. Plastination also makes it possible to produce "exploded-view" specimens, "open-door" specimens and "open-drawer" specimens. With "exploded-view" specimens, body parts are shifted in all directions.

These specimens are particularly instructive when the body parts are "exploded" in only one direction, for example, in the longitudinal. Instructional "open-door" specimens also succeed in that hinges are attached in such a way that an open view into the innermost realms of the body is provided. Finally, parts of the body can be shifted forward like open drawers, thereby giving a clear insight into the body.

These interstitial specimens that permit the observer to shift back the individual parts of the body to their original position in the mind's eye and reduce the body to its original shape and size contrast with traditional "removal dissections"

practiced at universities. Here, each succeeding layer is removed from the bodies. The major disadvantage of this procedure is that by the end of the course, students have often forgotten which parts were removed at the beginning.

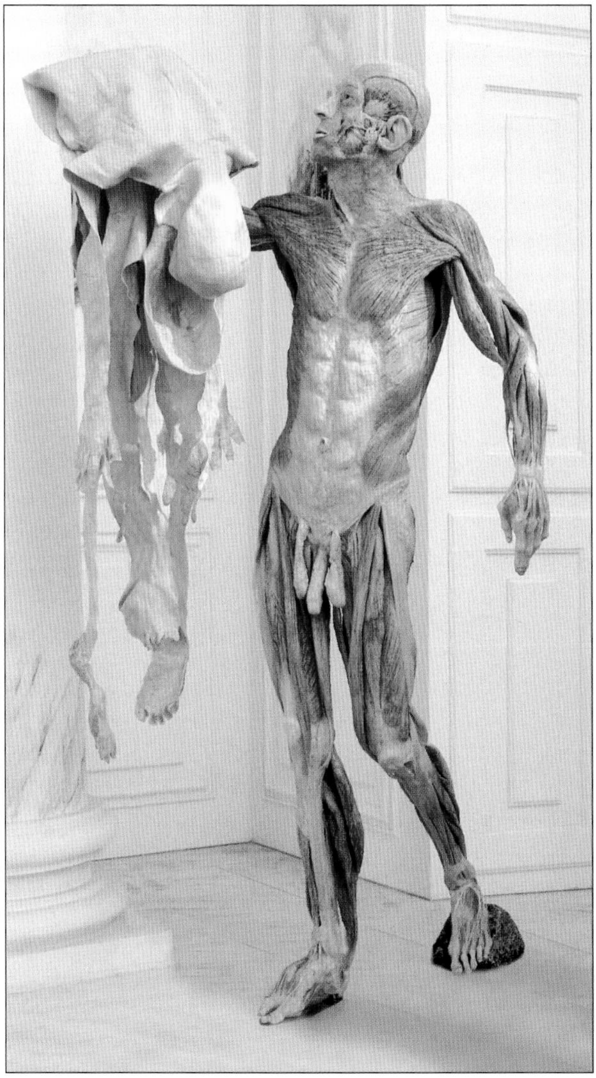

The specimens shown in this book were dissected and plastinated at the Institute for Plastination under my supervision. They are the result of five years of work as of this point in time.

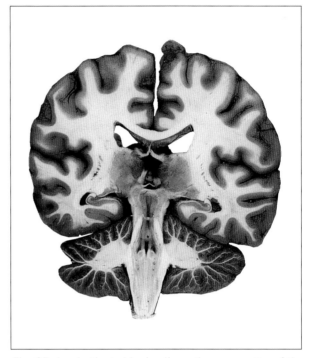

Fig. 25: In plastinated brain slices, the grey matter of the cerebral cortex and the nuclei are clearly distinguishable from the white matter.

The Technology of Plastination

In principle, Plastination is relatively simple. As shown in the chart on p. 25, plastinated specimens are created through two essential exchange phases: In the first phase, bodily fluids are replaced by acetone through diffusion. In the second phase, the acetone still in the body is replaced by reactive plastics. It is then removed from the plastic bath to be cured into a fully plastinated specimen.

The decisive trick, with which liquid plastic can be infused into the last cells, is forced vacuum impregnation. Just as babies use a partial vacuum to suck the milk out of their mothers' breasts, acetone is sucked from the specimen in the vacuum. In this way, the vacuum created in the specimen keeps a steady supply of plastic flowing into the tissue. Gradually the specimen fills up with plastic. Seen physically, the process takes advantage of the difference in pressure between the volatile acetone and a plastic solution with a high boiling

Fig. 24: A whole-body specimen in a life-like pose.

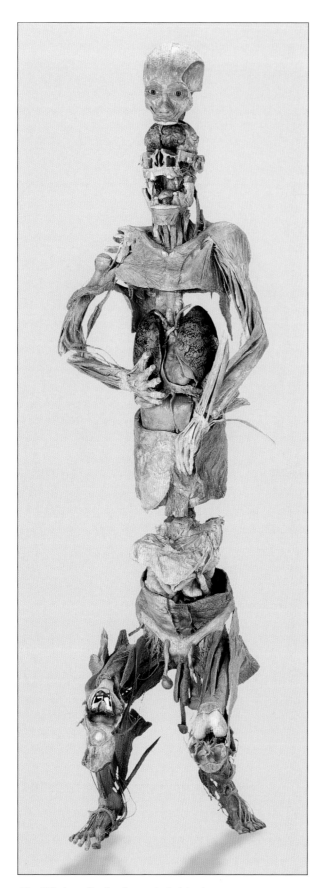

Fig. 26: Longitudinally exploded body.

point. Thin body slices take only a few days for this; conversely, with whole-body specimens, this can take weeks. Only when the vacuum falls below one-hundredth of normal atmospheric levels (<5 mm Hg) and only individual acetone bubbles squeeze out of the specimen is it removed from the plastic bath and cured.

The advantages of this "forced impregnation with plastic in a vacuum," which is the main step in Plastination, are primarily the following:

1. Impregnation can be done with a number of liquid, polymerisable plastics

2. By regulating the vacuum, the speed of impregnation can be adapted to the type of specimen, its thickness and the viscosity of the plastics used.

3. Impregnation can be used to minimize shrinkage at low temperatures, e.g., at −25° C.

In this way, the Plastination process permits numerous possibilities for variation. It also means that the process can be very complex in individual details on the one hand; how ever, its strengths come just from these complexities on the other hand. If optimum results are desired, the choice of plastics and the type of Plastination technology can be adapted to the respective specimen. Here are some examples:

Fig. 27: Forced impregnation. Acetone is squeezed out of the specimen and is constantly sucked away.

The Plastination Process

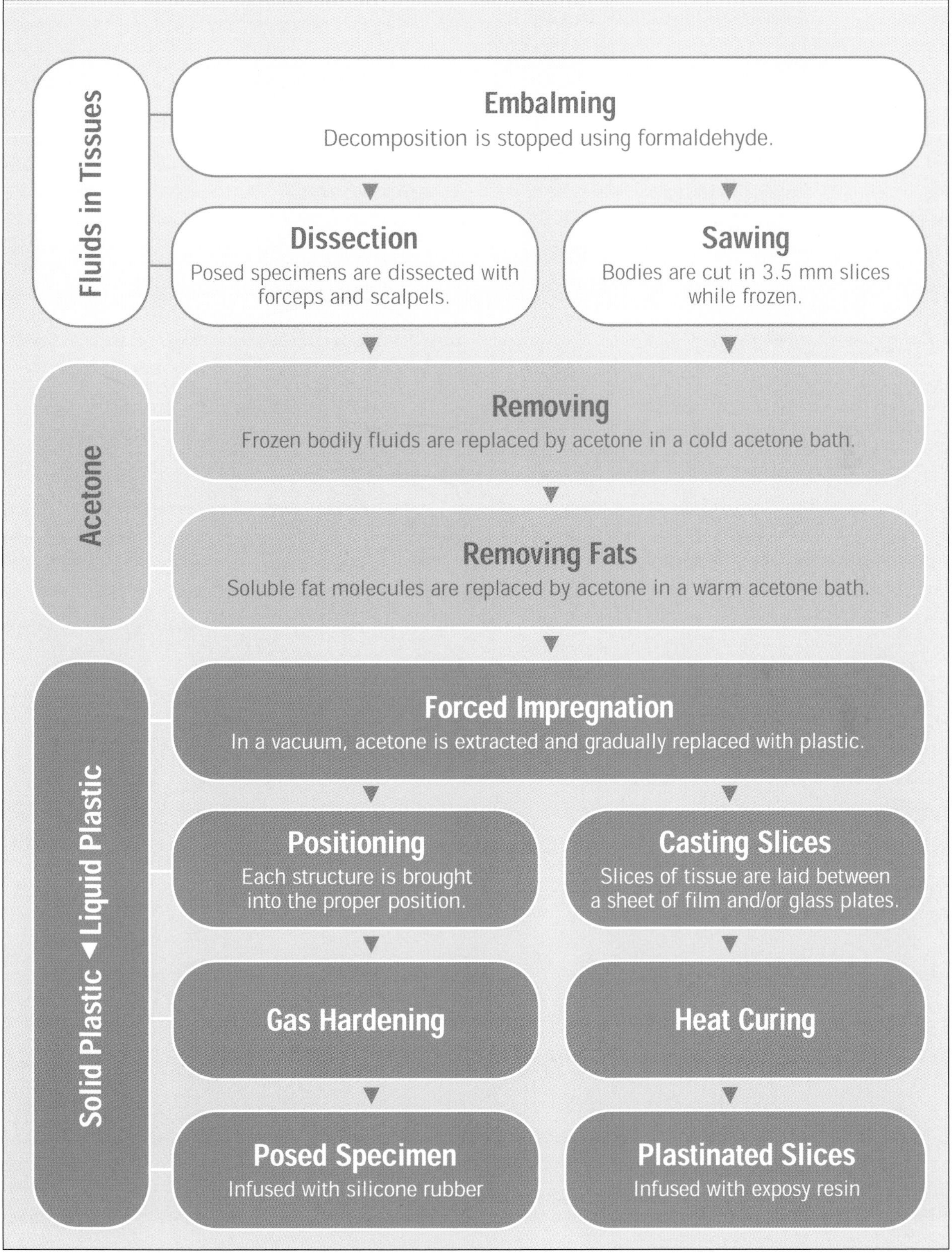

Fluids in Tissues

Embalming
Decomposition is stopped using formaldehyde.

Dissection
Posed specimens are dissected with forceps and scalpels.

Sawing
Bodies are cut in 3.5 mm slices while frozen.

Acetone

Removing
Frozen bodily fluids are replaced by acetone in a cold acetone bath.

Removing Fats
Soluble fat molecules are replaced by acetone in a warm acetone bath.

Solid Plastic ◄ Liquid Plastic

Forced Impregnation
In a vacuum, acetone is extracted and gradually replaced with plastic.

Positioning
Each structure is brought into the proper position.

Casting Slices
Slices of tissue are laid between a sheet of film and/or glass plates.

Gas Hardening

Heat Curing

Posed Specimen
Infused with silicone rubber

Plastinated Slices
Infused with exposy resin

Most specimens, especially bones and intestines, must first be defatted in acetone at room temperature. Conversely, brains would shrink substantially in size if subjected to such a treatment. The same applies for specimens still covered with skin, such as embryos and fish, which therefore require additional infusion with plastic. Freezing specimens may also cause their volume to expand, and when this occurs too slowly, ice crystals can form. Emulsifying plastics cause swelling so that newcomers to the process often wonder why a brain plastinated with these materials no longer fits into its skull. Transparent series of slices should be 5 mm thick through the abdomen while slices of the head should be 3.5 mm thick. All of this depends still on a number of different factors, such as age, distribution of fat, venous congestion and others.

The demand for research is still enormous despite all of the progress until now. A particular focus is on retaining the colour of tissue, optimum presentation of blood vessels as well as improving the plastination of slices and treating specimens that are difficult to preserve, such as jellyfish. An International Society for Plastination, a professional journal and biennial conferences are the main forums for discussing advances in Plastination.

Plastics used in Plastination

Developments in Plastination have always been closely bound up with development of suitable plastics, as the mechanical and optical properties of the plastics employed largely determine the character of the specimens. The plastics normally used are silicone rubber, epoxy resins and polyester resins.

After curing, silicone rubber is elastic and thus lends elasticity to the specimens. It only refracts light very weakly, which accounts for the natural look of specimens infused with silicone. For this reason, silicone rubber is used to plastinate

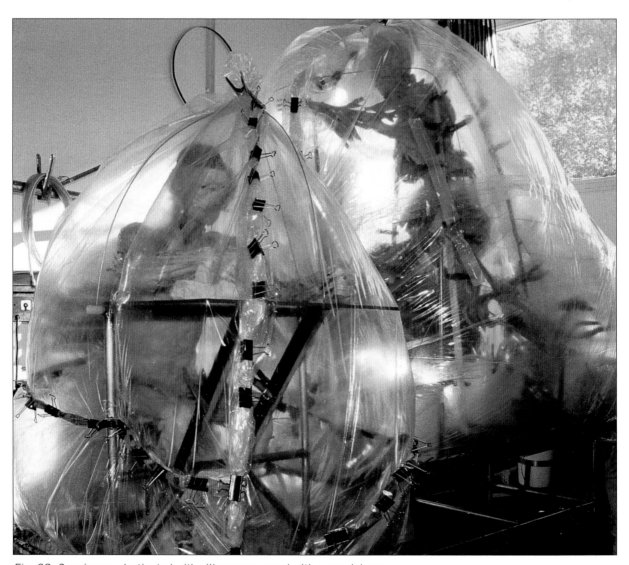

Fig. 28: Specimens plastinated with silicone are cured with a special gas.

Fig. 29: A body that has been frozen at −70° C and infused with polyurethane is sawn into 3mm-thick slices.

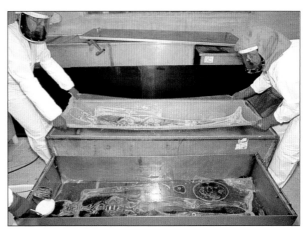

Fig. 30: Body slices dehydrated with acetone are then placed in a polymer solution.

whole organs (in contrast to slices); here plastination of whole-body specimens is a more recent development. A very thin-bodied silicone provides the best results with whole organ packages. Gas-curing is used to harden the specimens after all of the anatomical structures have been properly positioned. Plastination with silicone rubber is the simplest of all the techniques used in this process and thus has the most users worldwide.

The highly refractive properties of epoxy resins allow the slices of saturated tissue to appear transparent when the surface is smooth. Because polymerized epoxy resin is also extremely hard, epoxy resin blends were chosen as the polymer of choice for plastinating cross-sectional specimens. The resins are heat-cured.

The use of epoxy resins for Plastination is highly suitable for solving clinical problems, because plastinating bodies that have been cut into a series of slices makes it possible to perform precise, three-dimensional analyses of the specimens. In the past, this has allowed scientists to investigate such complex issues as the blood supply in the kneecaps and wrist bones, and the paths taken by the tiny muscles and nerves around the prostate gland that are critical for sexual potency.

A highly refractive polyester resin cured by ultraviolet light is only used for slices of the brain. Polymerisable emulsions that turn white during the curing process are used for thick, natural-looking specimens.

Scientists just getting started with Plastination work with one to two types of polymer systems; exper-ienced scientists will use up to ten. Polymers utilised for Plastination must have low viscosity, should withstand yellowing and be compatible with the tissues being plastinated; also, the time available for processing these polymers should be as long as possible, or, even better, unlimited. For this reason, only special polymer blends developed specifically for Plastination are used.

The Idea behind Plastination

I developed the Plastination techniques at the University of Heidelberg Institute of Anatomy in 1977, patented it between 1977 and 1982, and have been continually improving the process ever since. When, as an anatomy assistant, I saw my first specimen embedded in a polymer block, I wondered why the polymer had been poured around the outside of the specimen because having the polymer within the specimen would stabilise it from the in-

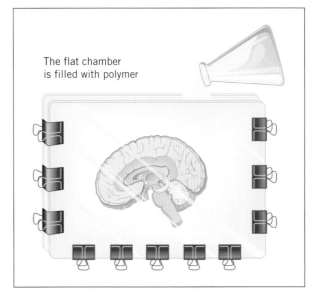

The flat chamber is filled with polymer

Fig. 31: Cross-sectional plastination. Tissue slices that have been saturated with polymer are placed in a flat container where additional polymer is poured over them.

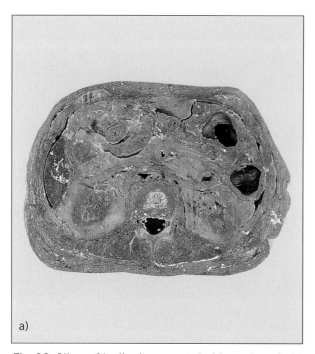
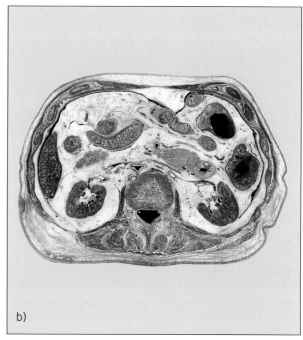

Fig. 32: Slices of bodies impregnated with a polymerisable emulsion a) before curing and b) after curing. Emulsification during the curing process lightens the colour of the specimen.

side out. I could not get this question out of my mind. A few weeks later, I was to prepare a series of slices of human kidneys for a research project. The usual process of embedding the kidneys in paraffin and then cutting them into thin slices seemed like too much wasted effort to me, as I only needed every fiftieth slice. Then one day, I was in the butcher shop in the university town where I was studying, and as I watched the sales woman slice ham, it dawned on me that I ought to be using a meat slicer for cutting kidneys. And so a "rotary blade cutter," as I called it in the project-appropriation request, became my first Plastination investment. I embedded the kidney slices in liquid Plexiglas and used a vacuum to extract the air bubbles that had formed when stirring in the curing agent. As I watched these bubbles, it hit me: it should be possible to infuse a kidney slice with plastic by saturating it with acetone and placing it under a vacuum; the vacuum would then extract the acetone in the form of bubbles, just as it had extracted air before. When I actually tried this, plenty of acetone bubbles emerged, but after an hour the kidney was pitch black and had shrunk. At this point most people would have dismissed the experiment as a failure, and the only reason I went ahead and repeated it a week later using silicone rubber was because my basic knowledge of physical chemistry told me that the blackening effect was due to the index of refraction of the Plexiglas, and that the shrinkage could be attributed to having permeated the specimen too quickly. The next time, I carried out this process more slowly, using three successive silicone baths as a means of preventing a single bath (along with its contents) from curing too quickly. After curing the

specimen in a laboratory kiln, I had the first presentable sample of Plastination. That was on January 10, 1977, the day that I decided to make Plastination the focus of my life. The roots of this decision go back to January of 1968, following my arrest for unsuccessfully attempting to defect from East Germany. While I was being detained in a Bratislava jail, a Czech official gave me the opportunity to escape. I stood before an open window, but could not make up my mind to flee. I was convinced that the East German secret police would not incarcerate me—that conviction cost me two years in an East German prison for "deserting the Republic." That is the reason that in 1977, I made a clear decision in favour of uncertainty, because uncertainty always represents an opportunity.

The first round of plastinated specimens looked anything but promising. Their surfaces were smeared with polymer, transparent tissue slices were full of air bubbles, and it often happened that specimens met their end in polymer baths that had cured prematurely. Only a series of further developments over the past 20 years have made it possible for me to transform plastination from a largely impractical idea to an internationally recognised preservation technique. Significant innovations and developments included the following:

1. The ability to delay curing of the impregnation bath while simul-tan-eously speeding up the curing process once a speci-men has been completely infused with polymer. Specimens saturated with silicone rubber in a vacuum, for instance, are not cured until placed in a gas

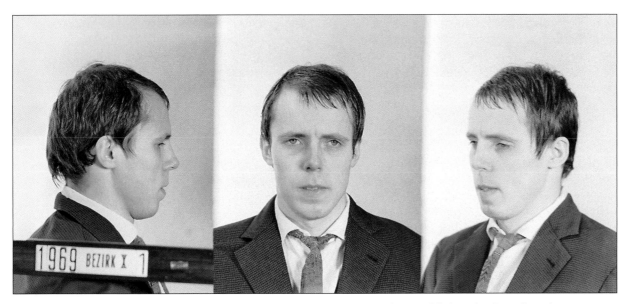

Fig. 33: Prison photo of Gunther von Hagens, taken in 1969 by the East German Ministry for State Security.

atmosphere. This even makes it possible for large specimens such as entire bodies to be saturated over the course of several months without running the risk that the impregnation bath will cure too early. After the specimens are taken out of the bath, they are further dissected and positioned — only then are they subjected to curing.

2. The development of plastinating slices, in which tissue sections are infused with polymer in flat glass containers or between plastic sheets.

3. The use of highly refractive polyester resin copolymers for plastinating slices of the brain. These copolymers create an excellent color distinction between the cerebral cortex, medulla oblongata and the nuclei.

4. Development of a new class of polymers that do not emulsify until the curing process has begun, thereby yielding firm, yet natural-looking specimens.

5. The development of perfusion plastination. The first steps in this process are to drain and rinse all of the blood from an organ, position it and allow first acetone and then silicone to flow through it. The specimen is then cured by means of a gas perfusion technique that sends the curing agent through the organ's vascular system. Entire systems of organs can be plastinated in this way, yet because their vascular system is hollow (only the cells themselves are permeated with polymer), they remain light-weight and flexible.

The term "Plastination" is a word of my own invention. In my initial patents of 1977/78, I referred to the procedure as "Polymer Impregnation of Perishable, Biological Speci-

mens", but I did not think that it was very catchy; it was also completely inappropriate for popularizing the technology, particularly abroad. Because the term "plasticize" was already used in the field of polymer chemistry to mean something

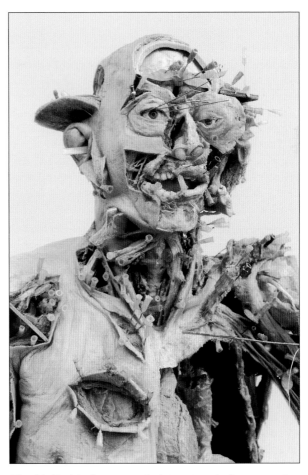

Fig. 34: Positioning anatomical structures before gas curing.

else, I came up with the following little jingle during a visit to a Viennese pub in 1979: "Plastination teaches the nation, because BIODUR (a trade name for polymers used in Plastination) retains the structure." In the 19th edition of the Brockhaus Encyclopedia (1992), on the other hand, the term plastination is shown to be derived from the Greek (from plassein = to mold, form).

The Inventive Process

Society praises its living conformists and honors its deceased rebels. As a result, people are caught up in a conflict between individuality and group consensus. If an individual con-forms to the group, he will be popu-lar. If he goes his own way, he will lose the group's approval and quickly come to be considered an oddball. The lure of this status is enhanced by ever increasing specialisation, which offers a previously unknown degree of choice and potential for personal development, thereby permitting individuality to a degree never seen before. The more individualism a society allows, the more inventors it will produce. Inventions have always been created by individuals — particularly when these have been individualists. Groups do not invent; their existence is dependent upon conformist thinking. Inventions under socialism tended therefore to be rare.

An invention must be new for it to be patentable; it must represent an advance in technology and must be acknowledged as surprisingly good even by experts in the field. In the language of patent law, "surprisingly good" is expressed by the words "inventive merit." As such, it is distinct from simple modifications to existing inventions. The door to invention has never been open to as many people as it is today. A computer, for example, is the only investment software developers need to begin inventing. The essential invention behind Plastination, i.e., introducing polymers into every cell in a tissue sample, was not expensive.

During my twenty years of working on Plastination, I have produced a whole series of individual inventions. Again and again, people have asked me how I come up with these ideas and what steps I take.

The inventive process that I utilise corresponds to the usual four stages of invention: recognizing the problem, analysing it, working out solutions and applying those solutions.

(1) Recognizing the problem: I question everything as a matter of principle. Anything that is good can be improved because better is superior to good. Recognising that infusing a specimen with polymers must be superior to embedding it in a polymer block (as had been done up to that point) was the central problem that led me to develop the Plastination process.

(2) Analysing the problem: Not only do I try to recognize the problem at hand; I also try to imagine what sorts of additional questions might arise from the problem. This includes studying handbooks, textbooks, patent literature and company brochures, and regularly visiting trade fairs.

(3) Solving the problem: As a matter of principle, I am never completely satisfied with a solution. Instead, I always have several irons in the fire, letting three to five potential solutions compete simultaneously with each other for a relatively long period of time. It is also important that I not settle on any one solution too early on. When following up on an approach to a solution, my gut feeling tells me that the solution in question will be the one that will work, even if I know that it is nonsense from a purely objective standpoint. I always have to go back and rethink the problem and factor in my own mistakes. When discussing suggested solutions with experts, I am often inclined to believe that the more emotionally a given potential solution is rejected, the more revolutionary and essentially feasible it must be.

(4) Applying the solution: This is where studying company brochures and visiting trade fairs again becomes important. Constantly updating my technical expertise in the field and constantly thinking through ways of applying solutions is indispensable. As a result, I think about Plastination nearly all the time: before I get up in the morning, when I am looking at my schedule for the day, when I am in the shower, driving my car, or doing my shopping. That is how a pudding mould becomes a cranium, a meat slicer becomes a cutter for making anatomical slices of the brain, a pancake turner becomes a turner for brain slices, an aquarium pump becomes a vaporizer for the gas-curing process, and clamps to hold price tags in store windows are "recycled" to hold the plates of the shallow containers used to used to infuse slices with polymer. Adapting and recycling estab-lished technologies in this way is the stuff that enriches the inventive spirit.

I often try out impossible, utterly ridiculous options; decisive insights frequently arise from trying out nonsense. Hence, I sometimes allow mistakes to happen or even make them consciously. Odd experiments, mistakes and coincidences are a productive part of the inventive process. A key development in Plastination, for instance, was the use of a gas-curing technique for silicone rubber. This invention came about while attempting to extend as much as possible the time available for preparing a specimen. I hoped to achieve this by placing infused specimens in a curing bath; the curing agents that I was using, however, partially dissolved the polymer, causing it to leach back out again.

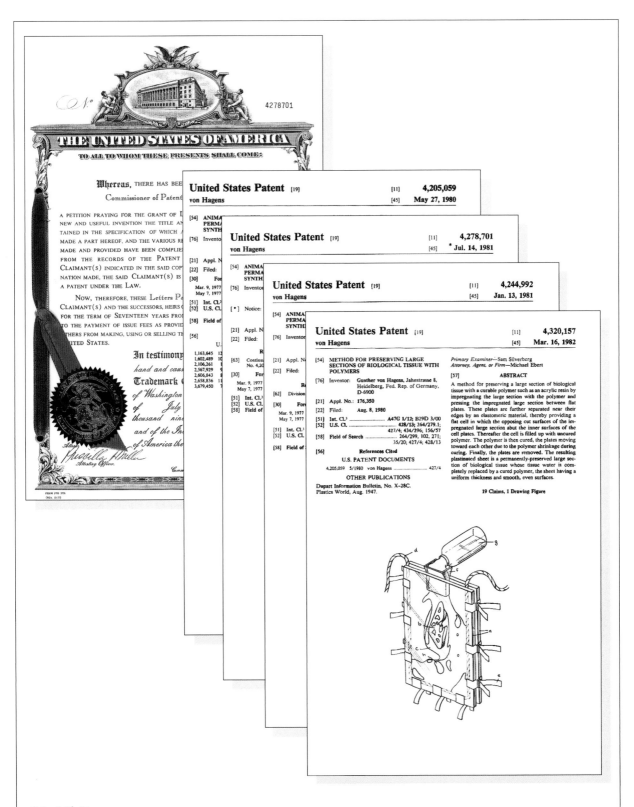

Patent Rights

The Plastination process is protected by a series of patents, particularly in the United States. Plastinating specimens for non-commercial purposes such as medical instruction or museum exhibits, however, is not subject to any such limitations.

As the polymer leached out of a specimen, it created countless polymer bumps on its surface, nearly covering it com-pletely. I knew this before performing an experiment, in which I left a brain in the curing bath overnight. Because the container that I was using no longer held sufficient curing bath, I had propped it up at an angle so that the brain would be completely submerged. The next morning, I found that the container had fallen over, and only the base of the brain was still in the bath. This section had hardened, and, as expected, was covered with little plastic knobs that would require a great deal of effort to re-move. The real excitement, however, came when, much to my surprise, I discovered that the major portion of the brain, which had been sticking out of the curing bath, had also hardened, but in fact had done so perfectly, without any annoying bumps. This could only have been the result of the evaporated curing bath, i.e., the gaseous vapours of the curing agent. I quickly repeated the experiment, having procured even more volatile hardening agents. Thus the gas-curing process was born, a technique that has significantly influenced further development of Plastination with silicone polymers, and which is now used in 38 countries.

The constant effort to find new ideas, to see what has never been seen before, does, however, affect my personality. My penchant for hats, for instance, is not reflective of an artistic demeanour; it has more to do with my self-image as an inventor. My hat symbolizes my internalized individualism, which is born of the conviction that an unusual outward appearance fosters non-conformist thinking. A look that flies in the face of social conventions has a nurturing effect on my creativity.

Donating Bodies for Plastination

Exhibiting real human specimens is made possible most of all by countless donors. During their lifetimes, these people willed that, upon their deaths, their bodies should be plastinated and thus made available for educating doctors and providing instruction for anyone else with an interest in medicine. They have expressly waived their right to burial. The Institute for Plastination also accepts donations of bodies that have been provided by survivors. Unclaimed bodies are also accepted from government agencies such as the Social Welfare Office. Finally, the Institute also accepts specimens from old anatomical collections when such collections are liquidated. This particular exhibition includes, for example, a plastinated hydrocephalic baby, a phenomenon that, thanks to advances in medicine, no longer occurs in today's highly developed societies. In some cases, these specimens are over 100 years old, and the Institute either purchases them outright or procures them in return for its plastinated specimens.

Because I am the director of both the Institute for Plastination of Dalian University in China as well as the Plastination Center of the State Medical Academy of Kirgizskaja, body-donation programmes have been initiated at these institutions, improving cooperation and exchange of specimens between them and the Institute for Plastination in Heidelberg.

Motivations of Donors

Reasons for donation are as varied as life itself. The desire to donate one's body as a way of aiding a good cause is a common theme. Emotional rejection of decomposition and cremation, a desire to save burial expenses, or simple enthusiasm for Plastination are often given as reasons. Comments such as the following indicate the wide variety of opinions (partially abridged):

- "I would like to make the human body—'the natural work of art'—more accessible to anyone who's interested."

- "Through my many years of work with the Institute for Plastination I have had the opportunity to become very familiar with plastination, and it fascinates me more and more all the time."

- "Since I've been helped over and over again by blood transfusions, it's important to me to help future generations by allowing research to be performed on my body."

- "After my death I would prefer to be like this than to be consumed and metabolized by worms and tiny organisms."

- "If I were displayed as a whole-body specimen, my body might make visitors stop and think."

- "I've abused, neglected and ignored my body. But it still works, renews itself and tests its limits. Gratitude for that is a major reason for me to donate."

- "Maintaining a grave site is just one last way of pulling the wool over other people's eyes."

- "Ever since I heard about the plastination process, the prospect of my own death hasn't bothered me at all."

- "Using plastination as a way of furthering the development of art and culture is what fascinates me most."

- "I've always felt a need to donate my body to science, and the idea of being plastinated fills me with a sense of inner tranquillity and happiness."

- "When this world comes to an end and Christ returns, He

will raise me to new life with a new body, as is written in the Bible."

- "I'm a Bible-believing Christian and I know that man has a soul, and when he dies, the breath of life within him will return to God, and when Christ returns I will be raised to new life in a new body, as is written in the Word of God."

- "As a former Heidelberg student, I feel very attached to the city of my alma mater. I see your programme as a way for me to return to Heidelberg."

- "You've 'cut through' a taboo, as it were, and for that I'm particularly grateful to you. And there's one thing I'm now sure of: when I've breathed my last, my body will perform an important function for mankind. Mind and spirit will gaze upon it with envy… I even dreamed that I had been cut into fine slices and was admiring myself. It was a lovely dream."

- "Plastination has added a new dimension of memory to anatomical thought. It will be my pleasure to contribute to its progress!"

- "Because the medical arts have saved me from death several times, I feel a need to show at least a small token of my appreciation to medicine by donating my body."

Transforming a Cadaver into a Plastinated Specimen

Terms are usually defined according to such criteria as form, quality, function or an administrative act. Because a purely descriptive definition of a cadaver slated for burial is not clearly distinct from that of a mummy, relic, specimen, skeleton or plastinated specimen, we must draw upon additional qualities such as intent, administration and qualitative change. Intent can be seen in bodies that have been donated for Plastination to promote education and research; the administrative act consists of accepting bodies for Plastination, transferring documents and assuring anonymity; the qualitative change is the first Plastination step, i.e., preserving the body for Plastination (with formalin or by freezing). Transforming a body into a plastinated specimen (either an entire body or a part of the body) is accomplished by curing a polymer inside the specimen. Ensuring anonymity is important for distancing the body from its plastinated counterpart, as it is the only sure way of ending the sense of reverence surrounding that body, i.e., the sense of personal and emotional attachment to the deceased. Anonymity also makes sense, because it fits in with anatomical traditions, thereby distinguishing plastinated specimens from relics and mummies of persons known by name. Conversely, the only time that Plastination should be non-anonymous

is in exceptional cases where there is ample justification. It goes without saying that every human specimen continues to possess human qualities. That also means that a plastinated specimen must be used for educational purposes, as dictated by the testamentary disposition of the donor.

Plastination, Art and Knowledge

Dissection and Plastination are done by hand. In 1860, anatomist Joseph Hyrtl said, "Dismemberment is the heart and soul of anatomy. It is a craft, however, that requires skill if it is to be success-ful. The art of dismemberment must be learned. Beyond that, it also requires an innate talent for technical work. Anyone not possessing this talent will not make much progress towards solving the mysteries of the grave."

The most difficult aspect of this is plastinating entire bodies. Whole-body plastination is an intellectual achievement requiring the ability to see the finished specimen in the mind's eye just as a sculptor envisions the completed statue while he is carving it. If the specimen has soft, flexible tissues such as muscles when it leaves the silicone rubber bath, it will need to be positioned, a process guided by both aesthetic and educational considerations. The chess player's nervous system, for instance, is highlighted specifically. The plastin-ated pregnant woman is protecting both her genitals as well as the fetus in her uterus. Specimens that have been plastinated without such gestures often appear doll-like by comparison.

Experience at exhibitions has shown that the aesthetic aspects of posed specimens make such an impression that visitors consider a number of these to be works of art. There is no dispelling that conclusion either, because "art is in the eye of the beholder." No anatomical works of art have been created; they become works of art through the judgment of the visitors to exhibitions.

From my perspective, however, plastinated specimens are not works of art, because they have been created for the sole purpose of sharing insights into human anatomy. Art, unlike the products of skilled trades and the sciences, is not created for a purpose. Unless the term 'artist' is used in the inflated sense in which Beuys uses the word, a plastinator is at most a skilled labourer in the field of art, but not an artist as such. It would be completely misguided to refer to posed specimens as works of art, because (modern) art is a term subject to interpretation; as a result, everyone projects his or her own personal understanding of art and morality onto the motivation underlying my efforts.

In order to avoid misunderstandings and to depersonalise discourse, I have introduced the term KÖRPERWELTEN, by

Fig. 36: A plastinated body in a realistic pose.

and instructive. Displacing these fragments and opening doors cut in the body provide new perspectives for viewing the body. The novel forms that arise from such techniques, such as a body that was expanded lengthwise, are necessary results of displacing fragments; they do not, however, reflect a dominant, recurring theme of the dissection process.

Even though plastinated specimens are not intended to meet any artistic demands, and even though I do not create the specimens in pursuit of any artistic goals, they may well satisfy certain artistic criteria. Like works of art, attractively posed specimens have a certain aesthetic effect and emotional content, which is attested to by, among other things, the fact that half of the visitors to the KÖRPER-WELTEN exhibition in Mannheim went precisely because of the aesthetic appeal that the specimens held for them (this according to a scientific survey taken by Dr. Lantermann of the University of Kassel's Institute of Psychology). These are qualities not generally possessed by objects that are of purely scientific interest.

Posed specimens provide an optical bridge to self-awareness. Immanuel Kant said that man's powers of awareness are two-fold. By that he was referring to emotional and rational awareness; whereas the former is conveyed more by aesthetics and feelings, the latter is imparted by intellect and instruction. Emotions and intellect are both involved when making visual sense of Plastination exhibits, particularly when these are whole-body specimens. Feelings, i.e., emotional awareness, have a direct effect without our really being conscious of it. This type of insight leaves many visitors feeling fascinated and moved. The aesthetic pose, which is occasionally criticised, is what helps dispel revulsion; because it is so powerful, it also promotes emotional awareness.

In an exhibition for lay persons, who are not attending an anatomy lecture but who have instead come to the museum just to "have a look," it is especially important that objects be directly understandable without lengthy explanations. The whole-body specimens achieve this most successfully. The intellectual awareness of the visitor is aroused by components of whole-body specimens, such as organs, muscles and bones. Achieving awareness in this way is a greater and more satisfying accomplishment than is the case when studying individual organs or body parts. Seeing a skeleton likewise leads to a greater understanding of the body than does seeing an individual bone.

The realism of the specimens contributes greatly to the fascination and power of the exhibition. Particularly in today's media-oriented world, a world in which we increasingly obtain our information indirectly, people have retained a keen sense for the fact that a copy has always been intellectually "regurgitated," and as such is always an interpretation.

which I mean the "aesthetic and instructive presentation of the body's interior." "Presentation" in this case can be understood in two ways: both in the sense of an artistic rendering and in the sense of the work performed by a skilled labourer in the field of art. The instructive component of this presentation likewise has two meanings: on the one hand, it refers to making us aware of our physical nature, of nature within us; on the other hand, it can be understood as a concrete act of sharing anatomical information. Only in this sense do I consider myself to be an artist — an anatomy artist.

KÖRPERWELTEN falls within the tradition of the Renaissance when art was a product of ability; Plastination has brought anatomy art a step further by making it possible to take soft tissues such as muscles or fat and fix them permanently into any given pose. This gives rise to completely new types of specimens, including slices of bodies only 3 mm thick, which are as transparent and colourful as stained glass. The ability to position soft tissues permanently also makes it possible to fragment the body in ways that are both aesthetic

Fig. 37: Whole-body plastinates. Displaying these specimens in realistic, life-like poses carries on the tradition begun by the founding fathers of anatomy.

In this respect the KÖRPERWELTEN exhibition satisfies a tremendous human need for unadulterated authenticity.

Living Anatomy

The anatomy of a corpse is not very interesting in and of itself. It is significant only because through it we can study the anatomy of living human beings to a certain degree. Whereas the human skeleton has been standing upright ever since Vesal's work during the Renaissance, the wet, dripping corpses of anatomical institutes have had to remain on the dissecting table. Lying here, with either their front or back hidden from the researcher's view, is how an intact body has traditionally been presented.

As a student I always found it difficult to follow the advice of our anatomy professor and associate the pleasant bodies on display at the swimming pool with the utilitarian study of surface anatomy. The difference between the stiff corpse lying on the dissecting table and the interplay of muscles in swimming, running and sitting people was just too great.

"Living anatomy" was always a popular subject with students, although rather neglected by classical anatomy. In this course, students would feel each other and then project and paint muscles and organs on each other's skin. Neither a hobby anatomist nor a beginning anatomy student

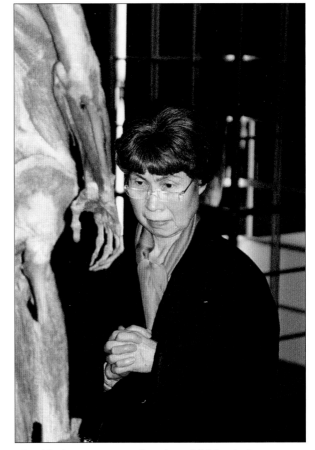

Fig. 38: A woman attending the exhibition in Japan.

Fig. 39: Mixed reactions at the exhibition in Japan.

The Face Within

Whole-body plastinations join the ranks of skeletons and mummies as a new means of determining our post-mortem existence for ourselves. In addition to an external face associated with our personalities, we all possess a face within. This internal face is a great deal more variable and unique than our external faces. Even slices of a head, torso or arm no more than 3 mm thick are individual representatives of their donors, and can be distinguished by their shape, size, colour and tissue composition. The aesthetics of the human body, celebrated during the Renaissance, visibly lives on in the body's interior — even at a microscopic level. Donors demonstrate their natural anatomical individuality, regardless of whether the body has been plastinated in its entirety or whether it is displayed as a series of slices. The manner and quality of both the dissection and the Plastination work will determine which outward appearance the face within will acquire.

A posthumous change in identity is really nothing new. In Japan, the deceased have been given new names since time immemorial. Plastination, however, also represents a shift in value from a useless corpse to a plastinated specimen, which is useful, aesthetically instructive and produced by nature.

Austrian philosopher Ludwig Wittgenstein once said, "The human body is the best picture of the human soul." As a doctor, that statement is only too understandable. The external face, the human countenance, has always been considered the mirror to the soul.

The soul, on the other hand, also has an effect on the body. Happiness and worry have visible effects on the face within — just look at anorexia or stomach ulcers. Does that mean that an entire plastinated body is also an embodiment, a reflection of the soul? Thinking along these lines does not, however, bring us any further in our search for the individual soul. The closest that I have come to the location of the soul is when I am plastinating a brain. The function of brain cells and the memories stored within them collapse when the person dies. That makes it likely that death also erases our ability to remember. Yet without memory there is no awareness of the self, and without awareness of the self, there is no individual soul. The decisive question is therefore whether there is not some individual capacity for memory associated with the brain. If so, does that fly away as part of the soul, leaving the brain behind as an empty container?

is interested in the anatomy of the dead because a real patient is living, moving, and posing. Hence, it is only natural that plastinated whole-body specimens should be positioned upright and realistically — and thus imparting the information that they are intended to convey — in the living environment from which they came.

Plastination allows us to solidify soft tissue and as a result has made it possible to stand entire bodies in upright positions. Doing so carries on the tradition begun by the founding fathers of anatomy. As the Tokyo exhibition was nearing — the first major public Plastination exhibition — our colleagues at the National Science Museum in Tokyo clearly recognised the unique qualities of the posed whole-body specimens, and discussed this with us for weeks. The issue under debate was the horizontal display of whole-body specimens, but the decision that came out of the discussions favoured living anatomy and the new dimension that it adds to the way we view the body as a whole. In the foyer of the Heidelberg Institute of Anatomy is a sign that reads, "Hic gaudet mors succurrere vitae," which means, "Here Death is happy to rush to the aid of the living." And he should do it standing upright. This realistic pose creates anatomical individuality. A whole-body specimen is attractive when its pose is compatible with dissected anatomy and its function within a living being.

Plastination is the most modern, lasting and vivid means of preserving specimens of the human body for educational purposes. The process is therefore especially well suited for honouring the desire of donors to make a posthumous contribution to the education of future generations. Like marble statues, they outlast the lifetimes of their crea-tors. Life is short, but Plastination will last (and will edu-cate) for a long time.«

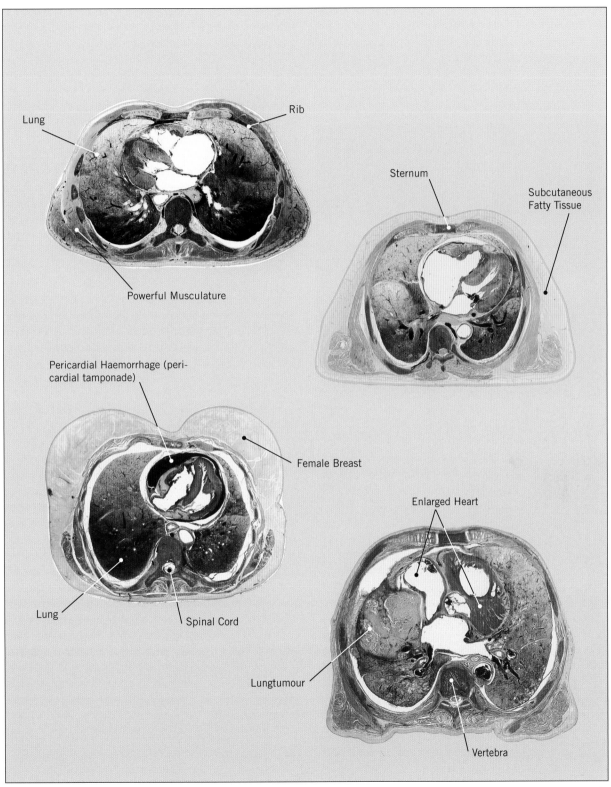

Fig. 40: The face within: These chest slices were all taken from different donors. Even though they were all cut at the same height, they look completely different depending on, among other things, individual body size, distribution of fat and blood, organ size, age and disease.

A Word of Appreciation

I would like to thank those people who have donated their bodies to Plastination, which in turn have made the existence of the Institute for Plastination and the development of public exhibitions of plastinates possible. I would also like to express my gratitude to my co-workers in the Plastination Institutes in Heidelberg / Germany, Bishkek / Kyrgyzstan and Dalian / China for their dedication and commitment.

I would like to thank my distinguished teacher, Prof. Wilhelm Kriz, for supporting me with unswerving foresightedness during my university years and for allowing me the room to develop that is so vital for success.

Finally, I would like to thank all of my critics for their qualified and also their unqualified criticism, which has gone a long way in helping me continually to assess and to reassess my work.

Fig. 41: Specimen of French anatomist Honoré Fragonard (1732–1799). A metal alloy with a low melting point was injected into the blood vessels; remaining tissue was dried and treated with varnish. The specimen may still be seen today at the "Ecole Nationale Vétérinaire d'Alfort" in Alfort near Paris.

Gunther von Hagens, the creator of plastination, began his medical studies at the University of Jena in 1965. He was arrested after he had distributed leaflets protesting against the invasion of Czechoslovakia by Warsaw Pact troops and soon thereafter had tried to flee from East Germany. Finally, in 1970, only after the West German government had bought his freedom as well as that of other political prisoners was he able to continue his studies at the University of Lübeck, which he completed there in 1973. In 1974, he received his license to practice medicine before moving to the University of Heidelberg, where he completed his doctorate in the Department of Anesthetics and Emergency Medicine in 1975. He subsequently worked at the Institutes of Anatomy and Pathology. It was in Heidelberg starting in 1977 that he invented the basic technologies for forced infusion of anatomical specimens with reactive plastics especially developed for this purpose. It was also in Heidelberg that he founded BIODUR™ in 1980 to market the respective polymers and equipment; finally, he founded the Institute for Plastination in 1993. Since 1996 he has been visiting professor at the School of Medicine in Dalian in China and Director of the Plastination Centre at the State Medical Academy in Bishkek/Kirgizstan where he was awarded the title of an honorary professor.

Definitions

In discussions on the ethical justification of utilising human specimens, varying ways of understanding certain terms have frequently been the cause of misunderstandings. This list of definitions should aid in preventing such misunderstandings in future.

Anatomy art:
Aesthetically instructive presentation of bodily interiors.

Anatomical cadaver:
Preserved corpse that is anatomically dissected and is buried upon completion of dissection.

Corpse:
A deceased human body, which will decompose and for which a funeral will be prepared. In contrast to an anatomical specimen, it is the object of personal grief or human sympathy.

Dignity:
Personal right to humane treatment guaranteed in the German constitution. It is subject to moral standards, which may vary in accordance with social progress and development.

Dissection:
Removing anatomical structures and/or making them visible.

Ethics:
Principles and norms that are generally valid in leading one's life, derived from an individual's responsibility towards others.

Funeral:
Burial or cremation of a corpse.

Gestalt plastinate:
Aesthetic, instructive whole-body specimen positioned in a life-like pose.

Inner face:
Anatomical individuality of bodily interiors, which have been made visible through plastination.

Morals:
System of ethical norms and standards of behaviour based on tradition, social conventions and religion that sets the rules for interpersonal conduct for a given time frame.

Mummy:
Preserved human body, whose human form is essentially complete in the assembly of its parts and whose death goes back several generations; it is no longer an object of human grief.

Plastinate:
Specimen of a human or animal, whose cells have been infused and hardened with reactive plastics.

Plastination craftsmanship:
Skilled craftsmanship in producing high-quality, aesthetic and instructive plastinated specimens.

Privilege of viewing bodies:
Privilege of physicians, medical students and other representatives of the medical professions to view the insides of bodies. This privilege evolved with the development of medical science. The freedom to make use of this privilege by interested lay-persons gained through the Enlightenment at the beginning of the modern era was lost when the anatomical theatres of the Renaissance were transformed into dissection halls for students and autopsy halls for pathologists.

Relics:
Human remains, preferably individual bones, but also personal objects of deceased religious authorities, e.g., saints.

Reverence:
A feeling of profound awe and tactful respect shown towards the dead.

Robbing the dead:
Stealing the personal effects of deceased persons.

Specimen:
Demonstration exhibit for research and instructional purposes, existing either as a decomposable, fresh specimen or as a preserved permanent specimen.

Whole-body plastinate:
Deceased human body, whose human form is essentially complete in the assembly of its parts and whose identity remains anony-mous; it is no longer an object of human grief and has been plastinated.

Whole-body specimen:
Deceased human body, whose human form is essentially complete in the assembly of its parts and has been preserved; it is no longer an object of human grief and its identity remains anonymous. It will be converted into one or more permanent anatomical specimens.

Angelina Whalley

The Human Body — Anatomy and Function

Just like all of the plants and animals that exist today, man is the offspring of primordial, single-cell organisms — the result of more than 3.5 billion years of continuing evolution. And just like all higher organisms, every human individual develops from one single cell, a fertilised egg. When grown to maturity, we consist of approximately 60 billion cells of immense variety. Nevertheless, they form a unity of a manageable number of various organic systems that cooperate in an orderly fashion in order to perform all of our complex bodily functions.

Using plastinated specimens that have been permanently and durably preserved, I will now explain the structures of the human body and their functions according to the following outline:

- The Locomotive System

- The Nervous System

- The Respiratory System

- The Cardiovascular System

- The Digestive System and Abdominal Organs

- The Kidneys and Urinary Tract

- The Reproductive Organs

- Prenatal Development is treated in a separate chapter

- Whole-Body Specimens of particular interest are presented.

- Finally, I will present the configurations of blood vessels.

The pictures in the following chapters show nearly all of the exhibits in the KÖRPERWELTEN exhibition. Moreover, some additional specimens are shown, which are not displayed in the exhibition.

Angelina Whalley has been the managing director of the Institute for Plastination in Heidelberg since January 1997. She began her medical studies at the Free University in Berlin and then transferred to the University of Heidelberg, where she completed her doctorate with an experimental dissertation on kidney physiology at the Physiological Institute in 1986; she also obtained her licence to practice medicine in the same year. She did scientific research at the Institute of Anatomy for three years, inter alia in the plastination laboratory, as well as two years at the Institute of Pathology of the University of Heidelberg. Together with Gunther von Hagens, René Maschke and Wilhelm Kriz, she published *Schnittanatomie des Menschlichen Gehirns* (Steinkopf, Darmstadt 1990), and she worked out definitions for the terms used in Walter Hoffmann-Axtheim's *Lexikon der Zahnmedizin* (Quintissenz, Berlin 1993) from general pathology. Since 1993, she has also been a director of BIODUR™ Products, a company that markets plastics and auxiliaries for plastination. As a plastination artist, Angelina Whalley has done the conceptual planning for all of the previous exhibitions of plastinated specimens.

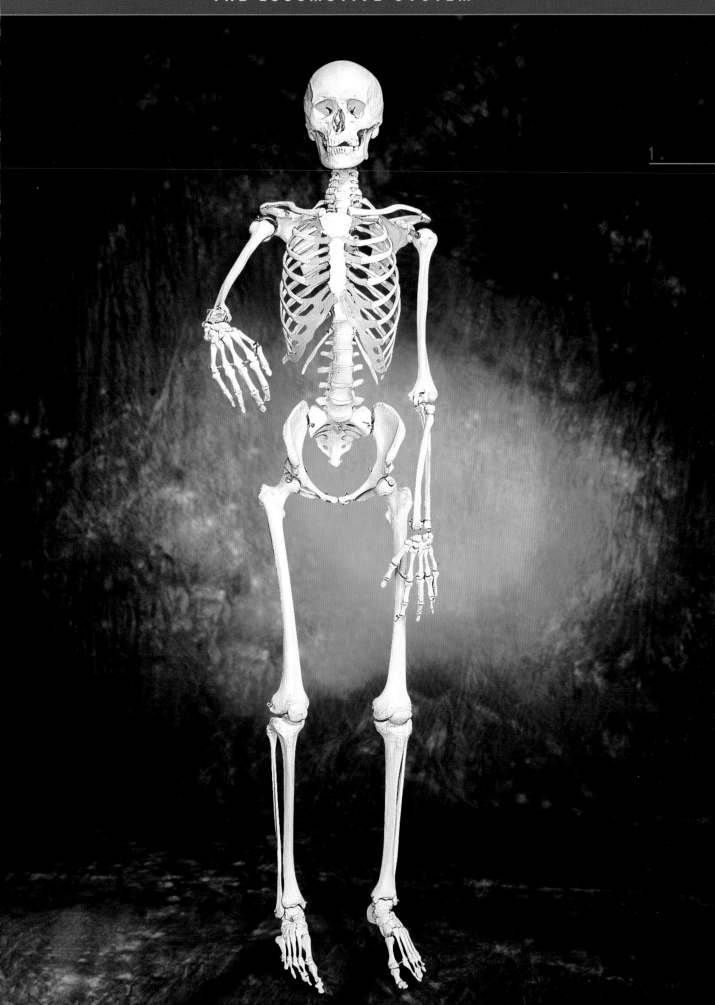

1. The Locomotive System

The human body is made up of various systems of organs that interact in a coordinated way to permit vital functions to continue. Movement is an essential function of the body. It is made possible by the locomotive system, which consists of bones, muscles and joints.

The Skeleton

The sum total of all of the bones, the skeleton, represents the body's internal framework. With more than 200 bones and 100 moveable joints, it provides the body with stabil-

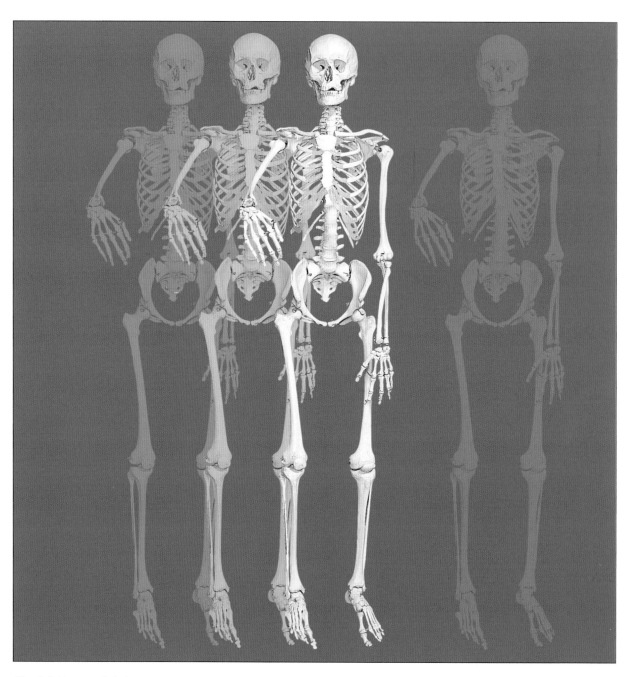

Fig. 1.1 Human skeleton

ity, support and mobility. It offers points of origin and anchorage for the skeletal muscles and thus aids in forming mechanical levers that convert muscular action into movement. In addition to the support function, the skeleton also performs a number of other vital tasks. One is to protect the internal organs against external mechanical damage; another is to produce corpuscles in its red bone marrow. It also makes vital mineral salts available to the body's metabolism as needed.

The skeleton generally consists of the skull, the vertical, S-shaped, curved spinal column as well as the ribs connected to it, and two sets of limbs. The arms are attached to the torso via the shoulder or pectoral girdle by means of the shoulder blade (scapula) and the collarbone (clavicle). The legs are connected to the torso via the pelvic girdle. The form of the individual bones corresponds to their respective functions.

The framework of bones has an enormous capacity for withstanding mechanical stress and is nevertheless surprisingly light. Although the skeleton of an adult only weighs approx. 10 kilograms, it is stronger than reinforced concrete. By

comparison, steel rods of the same size would probably weigh 4 to 5 times as much. This extraordinary capacity can be explained by the structure of bones as shown by a sagittally-sawn thighbone (Fig. 1.2). Nearly every bone has a hard, compact outer zone (cortical substance) and a core of spongy bone or trebicula (cancellous bone). The latter is configured according to physical demands and forms lines of tension depending on the force of pressure and contraction. This structure lends bones substantial stability while at the same time remaining lightweight. It has a high content of mineral salts (especially calcium and phosphate), which provide bones with the necessary hardness and strength. Conversely, the collagen fibrils (= tension-proof protein) of its protein content furnish them with a certain elasticity.

The smallest bones of the skeletal system are the three ossicles of the inner ear used in hearing (Fig. 1.3). Corresponding to their appearance, they are called the hammer (malleus), anvil (incus) and stirrup (stapes). Together with the eardrums, they form an essential part of the middle ear. Their function is to convey vibrations through the oval window to the snail-shaped cochlea in the inner ear.

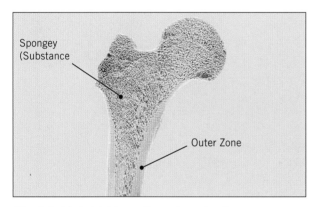

Fig. 1.2 Adult thighbone (femur), sagittally sawn

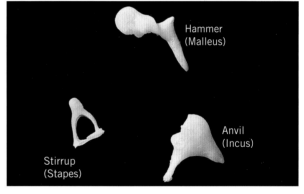

Fig. 1.3 Auditory ossicles

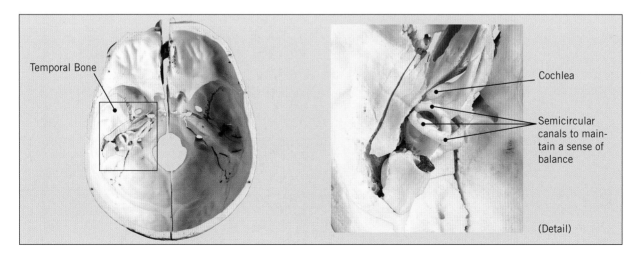

Fig. 1.4 The inner ear is embedded in the temporal bone at the base of the skull

The semicircular canals are located next to the cochlea; they aid in maintaining the sense of balance. To present the cochlea and the semicircular canals as on the specimen shown above, the surrounding bone first has to be carefully ground down until it is very thin to reveal the tube-like structures.

Bone is very dynamic tissue that is constantly being broken down or built up to be able to adapt to rapidly changing circumstances. It reinforces itself in places where it is subjected to frequent or unduly high strain as in certain jobs or sports. Moreover, due to its outstanding capacity to re-

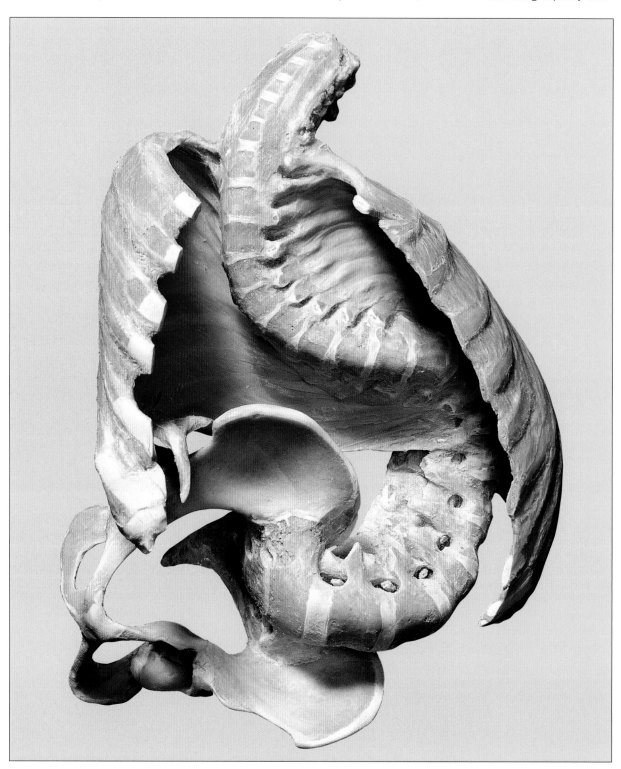

Fig. 1.5 Torso with severe deformation of the spinal column and thoracic wall caused by a hereditary disorder of bone formation and development.

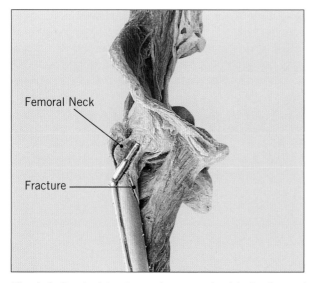

Fig. 1.6. Surgical treatment (osteosynthesis) of a femoral neck fracture

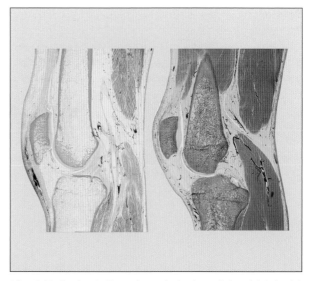

Fig. 1.7. Sagittal slices through the knee joint, (right) with normal bone structure, (left) with osteoporosis

generate, it can repair itself when it is broken. To mend properly, there has to be absolutely immobile contact between the bone fragments. For this reason, with bone fractures, stainless-steel screws, wire and plates are frequently used to join the fragments firmly (= osteosynthesis; Fig. 1.6).

Not infrequently, bone fractures due to osteoporosis occur especially with the elderly. By osteoporosis, we mean a decrease in the solid bone substance and / or density. The collagen fibrils are less numerous and the outer or compact zone is diminished (Fig. 1.7).

Osteoporosis is a natural part of the aging process. However, it can also occur in conjunction with other diseases at an earlier age. Deformations of bones can be caused by various illnesses, e.g., hereditary diseases, metabolism disorders, improper mending of bone fractures, or even incorrect distribution of stress or poor posture. The deformation of the spinal column and the thoracic wall as shown in Fig. 1.5 were caused by a hereditary disorder of bone formation and development (osteogenesis imperfecta). As a consequence, the internal organs have to adapt to the deformation of the chest cavity. Such a severe deformation of the thoracic wall is not infrequently accompanied by respiratory problems.

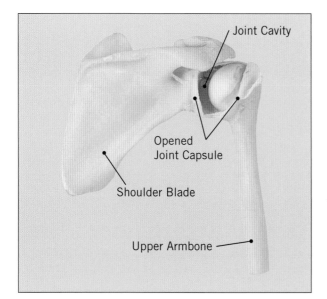

Fig. 1.8. The shoulder joint (seen here from behind)

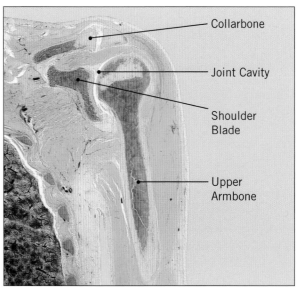

Fig. 1.9 Frontal slice of a shoulder joint

Joints

One basis for the mobility of the body is formed by joints, which link the bones to one another. The shape of the joints corresponds to the respective type and scope of movement required. The types of joints vary with respect to the number of bones included in the joint, their shape, their cartilage covering, and finally the type and number of movements permitted by the respective joints. Their names are derived from their similarity to technical, articulated connections, such as hinge joints, saddle joints, condylar joints, ball and socket joints, and pivot or rotational joints. There are also joints that are firmly fused together with one another and that do not permit any movement at all.

The surfaces of the joints of the respective "bone partners" are covered with cartilage to reduce abrasion. Larger joints are also "lubricated" by a mucous fluid. A capsule outwardly encloses a joint while ligaments stabilise it. They prevent the bones in the joint from being pulled apart by the force of muscle contractions and the surfaces of the joints from rubbing against each other.

Should the cartilage be lost through wear or disease of the joints, it can lead to severe pain whenever the joint is subjected to weight or movement. Cartilage then loses its elasticity, becomes brittle, begins to splinter, and finally deteriorates. This process of deteriorating cartilage is called arthrosis. At advanced stages, the bones themselves are ground down, which in turn react with protruding growths. Especially the large joints of the lower extremities, such as the knee joints (Fig. 1.18), are frequently affected by arthrosis as they are subjected to excessive mechanical strain by having to support the entire weight of the body.

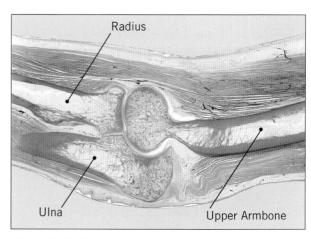

Fig. 1.10 Sagittal slice of an elbow joint

The shoulder joints (Figs. 1.8 and 1.9) link the upper extremities with the torso by means of the upper armbones (humeri) and the shoulder blades (scapulas). As ball and socket joints, these are the joints with the greatest freedom of movement.

Three bones form the elbow joint (Figs. 1.10–1.12), namely the upper armbone, the ulna and the radius. From here, the movements of the lower arms are controlled, e.g., bending and stretching as well as turning the hand palm-upwards.

The human hand (Fig. 1.13) is capable both of unusually precise motor functions and powerful gripping movements. Its 27 bones, which are moved by 37 skeletal muscles, permit a large variety of movement patterns.

The hip joints (Figs. 1.14 and 1.16) link the lower extremities to the torso by means of the pelvic girdle. The pelvic girdle consists of a tight connection between the two hip-

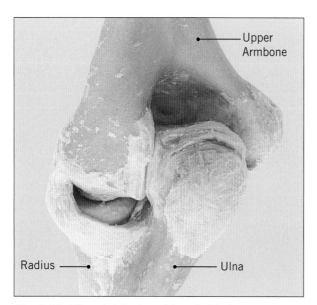

Fig. 1.11. Elbow joint, viewed from behind

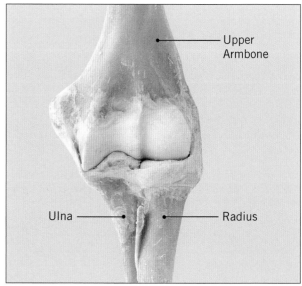

Fig. 1.12 Elbow joint, viewed from the front

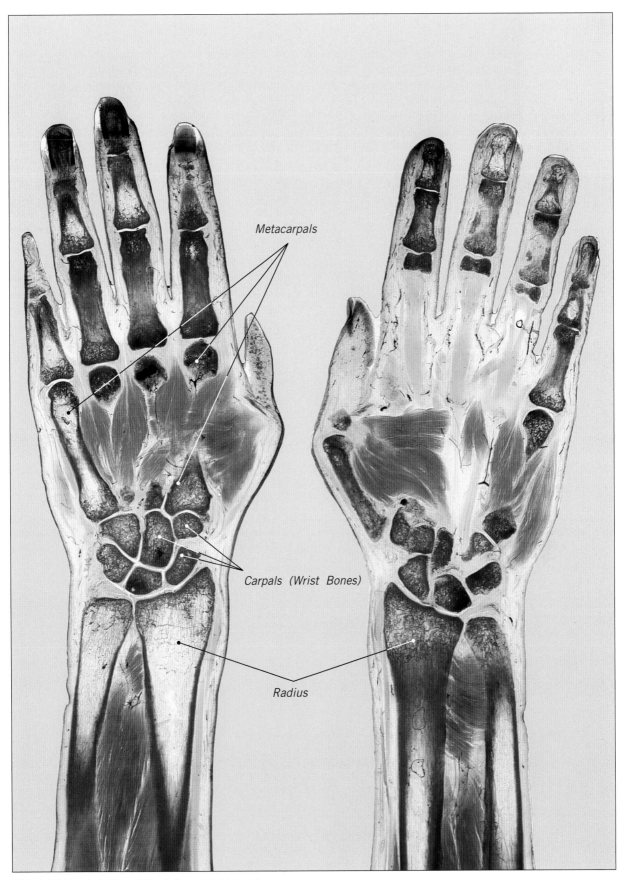

Metacarpals

Carpals (Wrist Bones)

Radius

Fig. 1.13 Frontal slice of the left and right hands

bones (front and side) and the sacrum (posterior). Together, they form a cushioning ring, known as the pelvis, by means of which the burden of the body's weight is conveyed to the legs. The sockets of the acetabula are set into the pelvic girdle on both the right and left sides; they surround the head of the femur or thighbone by more than half. Like the shoulder joint, the hip joint is also a ball and socket joint; however, freedom of movement is restricted in favour of greater solidity and stability.

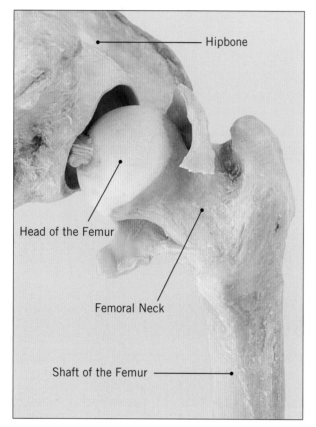

Fig. 1.14 Hip joint

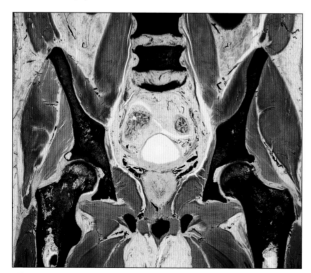

Fig. 1.16 Frontal slice through the hip joint

With severe signs of wear (arthrosis), fractures of the femoral neck or other disorders that limit the functions of the hip joint could make an artificial hip transplant necessary. With its ball-shape and angle of inclination in the hip joint itself, an artificial hip is modelled on a natural hip joint. The head of this prosthesis is made of highly polished stainless steel; it is attached to a long stem, which is embedded and cemented into place in the bone-marrow canal inside the femur (Fig. 1.15).

The knee joint (Fig. 1.17) links the femur, the longest bone in the human body, with the supporting bones of the lower leg, known as the tibia or shinbones. The disc-shaped kneecap is embedded in the sheath of the tendon of the femoral quadriceps muscles at the front of the thigh. It is also a part of the knee joint. As the knee joint bears the greatest weight of the body, it requires a particularly high degree of stability. This is provided by four main

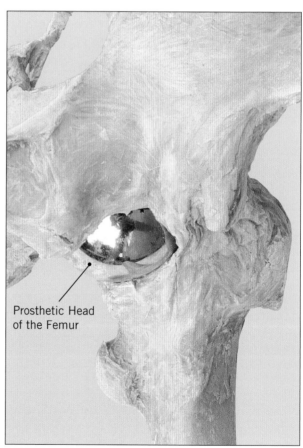

Fig. 1.15 Hip joint with prosthesis

ligaments (the inner and outer collateral ligaments and the front and rear cross ligaments) and 13 muscles acting on the joint. Two crescent-shaped cartilage discs (menisci) ensure that the relatively incongruous parts of the joint fit together better.

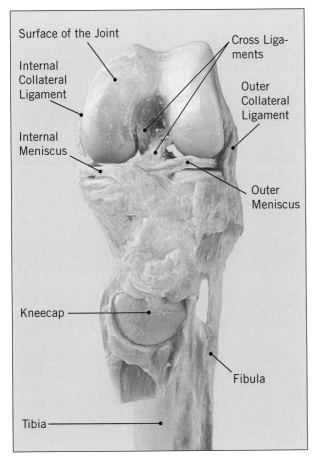

Surface of the Joint

Internal Collateral Ligament

Cross Ligaments

Outer Collateral Ligament

Internal Meniscus

Outer Meniscus

Kneecap

Fibula

Tibia

Fig. 1.17 Knee joint

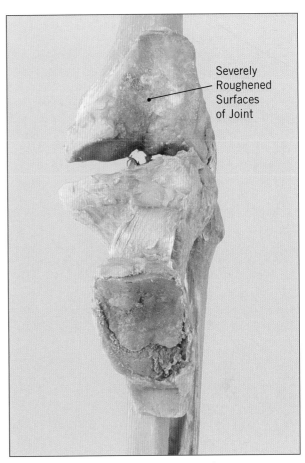

Severely Roughened Surfaces of Joint

Fig. 1.18 Knee joint with severe arthrosis

Based on its form, the knee joint is a hinge joint that permits both bending and stretching movements; when it is bent, small turning movements are possible. This enhances the flexibility of the body while at the same time increasing the vulnerability of the knee joint.

The feet and toes (Figs. 1.20 and 1.21) represent vital elements for walking upright. They bear the weight of the body as well as equalizing it when walking or running and aid in maintaining equilibrium. Each foot has 26 bones, more than

100 ligaments and 33 muscles, of which several originate at the lower leg. The foot has two ankle joints; the upper one permits the back of the foot to be pointed up or down while the lower one allows the foot to be set an angle either inwards or outwards.

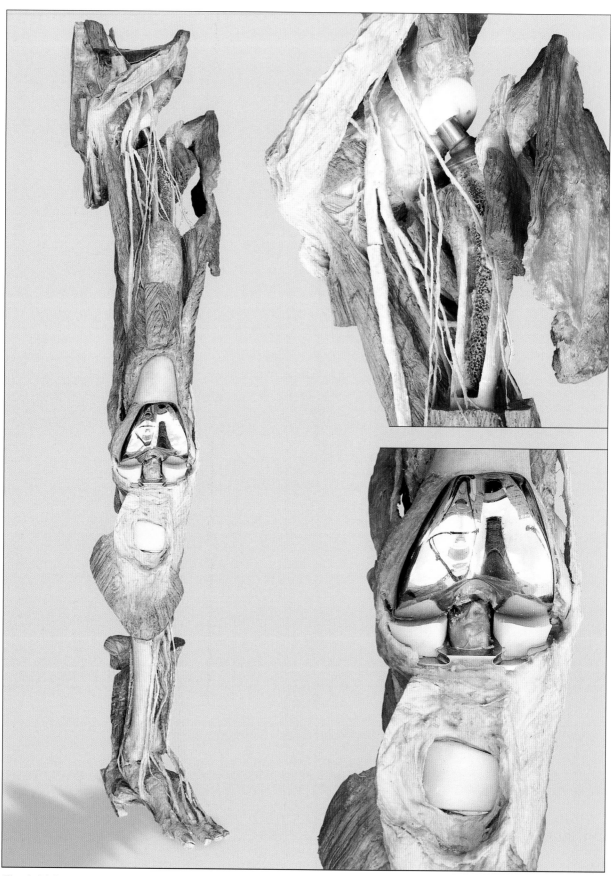

Fig. 1.19 Lower extremity with knee-joint prosthesis

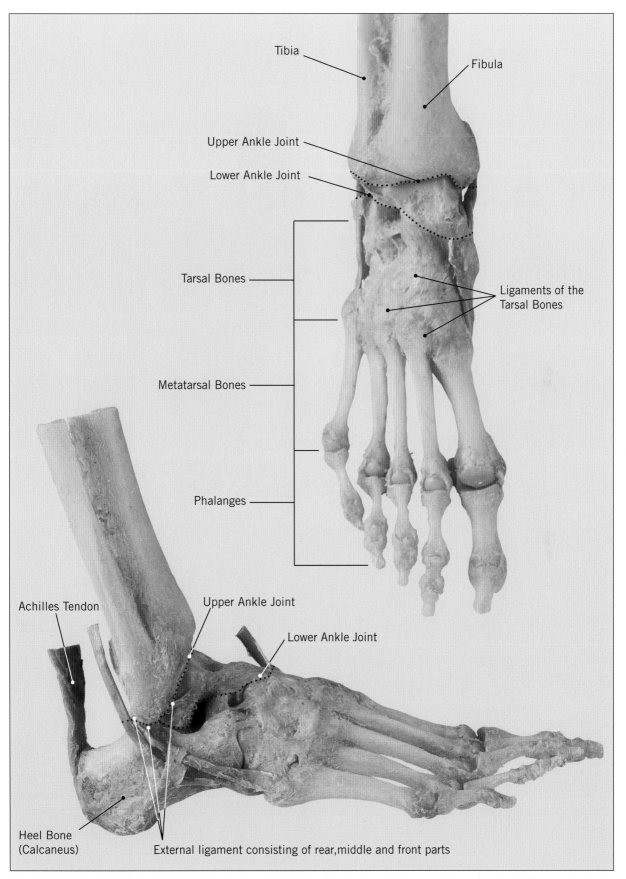

Tibia

Fibula

Upper Ankle Joint

Lower Ankle Joint

Tarsal Bones

Ligaments of the
Tarsal Bones

Metatarsal Bones

Phalanges

Achilles Tendon

Upper Ankle Joint

Lower Ankle Joint

Heel Bone
(Calcaneus)

External ligament consisting of rear,middle and front parts

Fig. 1.20 Dissection of foot showing ligamentous structure. Dense, taut ligaments emanating from fibrous membrane covering bones (periosteum) extend across joint cavities and hold the bones of joints together.

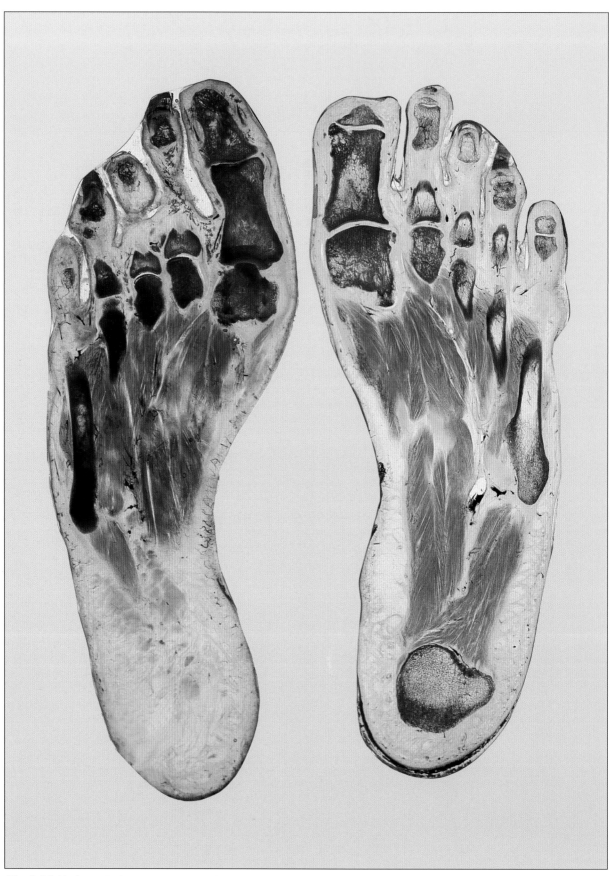

Fig. 1.21 Horizontal slices through the left and right feet

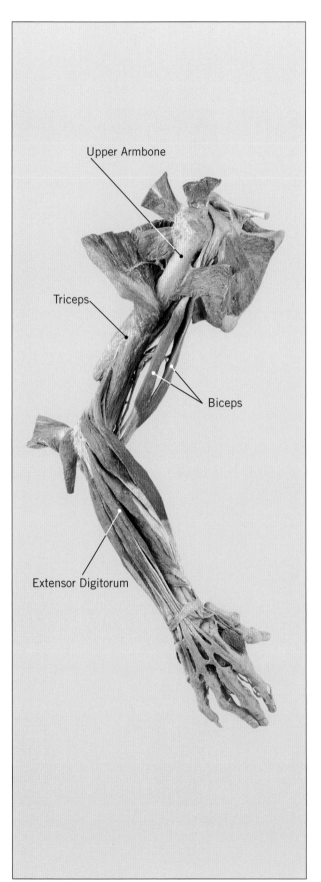

Upper Armbone

Triceps

Biceps

Extensor Digitorum

Fig. 1.22 Upper extremity

The Muscular System

A muscle is a biological flexor. It functions in that its fibres contract to become shorter. There are two types of muscles:

(a) Skeletal muscles perform the voluntary movements of the body and ensure that the body can remain upright. In microscopic slices, the skeletal muscle fibres display a striped pattern. For this reason, the skeletal muscles are also referred to as striated muscles.

(b) Microscopic slices of smooth muscles are not striated. Their muscle fibres are used to form the walls of blood vessels and hollow organs, such as the stomach or intestines, and thus move involuntarily, that is, they are not controlled by the human consciousness.

The heart muscles are very unusual. They are striated but are involuntarily controlled.

The skeletal muscles play a major part in forming the surface relief of human bodies. Together they account for about 40 % of the body weight of men and 23 % of women. There are over 620 voluntary muscles, each with its own function, supply of nerves and its own points of origin and attachment. They can thus be distinguished from one another by size and appearance. A typical muscle has a venter or "belly," which tapers to both sides and runs into a band-like tendon that is anchored to the bone.

Even the slightest bodily movements are generally not performed by one isolated muscle. Instead, various muscle groups are involved in a complex interplay, often with conflicting results. Muscles that contract in the same direction are referred to as synergists while those pulling in the opposite direction are called antagonists. The biceps of the upper arm, for example, has the brachial muscles as synergists when bending the elbow joint (flexing) and the triceps as antagonists to extend the elbow joint. Synergists and antagonists are functional groups that act in perfect harmony. When the one contracts, the other inhibits excessive movement. This makes flowing, modulated movements possible.

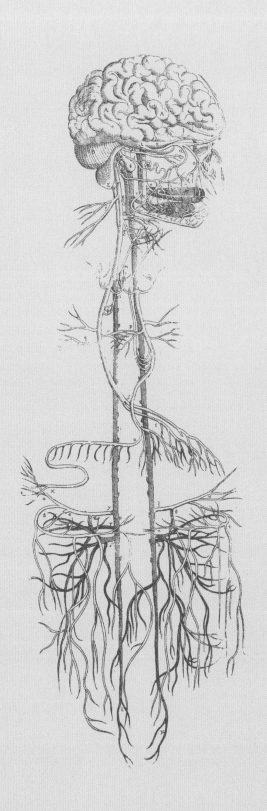

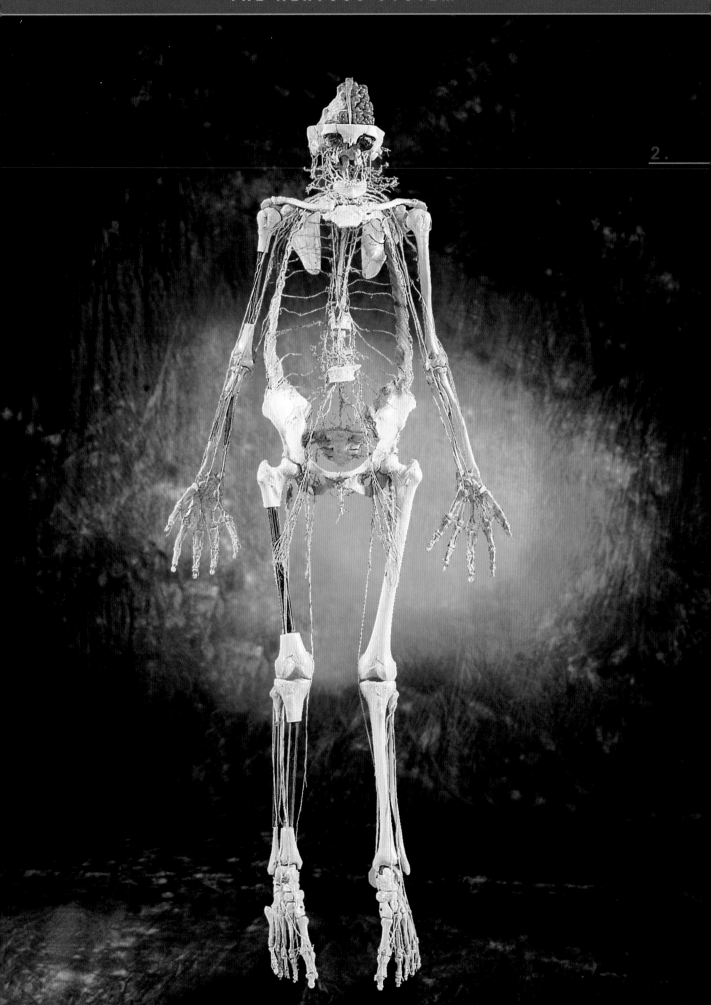

2. The Nervous System

Without a central communication system with connections that encompass an entire country from one end to the other, a modern nation would soon become ungovernable. It is the same with the human body and its nervous system. An extraordinarily fine network of nerve fibres stretches from the head to the toes to monitor and regulate bodily functions. They emerge directly from the brain or the spinal cord and branch out to the periphery in ever-finer nerve endings (Fig. 2.1). Most of them are bundled together like rope and form more or less thick strands. The thickest peripheral nerve is the sciatic nerve, which is approx. 1.5 cm in diameter. Other nerves can be as thin as 0.02 cm.

The brain and the spinal cord belong to the central nervous system; the remaining nerve structures comprise the peripheral nervous system. One part of this is the autonomic nervous system that is divided into the sympathetic nervous system and the parasympathetic nervous system. It is responsible for regulating such vital bodily functions as breathing, digestion and the heartbeat and is not controlled by either the will or the consciousness. As a consequence, regulation of the functioning of vital organs is ensured even when sleeping, and we do not have to think constantly about breathing or to give our stomach orders to begin digestion while eating. The sympathetic and parasympathetic nervous systems behave like antagonists: should, for example, the sympathetic nerve impulses dominate, our heart would beat faster, our blood pressure would rise, intestinal action would diminish and the pupils would dilate. Parasympathetic nerve impulses would bring about exactly the opposite effects.

Nerve cells are the most basic units of the nervous system. They are specialised in transmitting tiny electrical signals, whose number and timing convey information from one part of the body to another. These nerve impulses are processed at a speed of up to 400 kilometres per hour.

The brain (Fig. 2.5) is the body's central nerve centre that controls all thoughts and nearly every movement; it also processes sensory impressions and enables us to feel, remember and to speak. It lies in the cranial cavity protected from external mechanical influences just like a walnut in its shell (Fig. 2.7). It also enclosed by three meninges or membranes, namely [from the outer layer], the dura mater (hard membrane), the arachnoid and the pia mater (soft membrane). All three membranes extend to the spinal canal and there envelop the spinal cord.

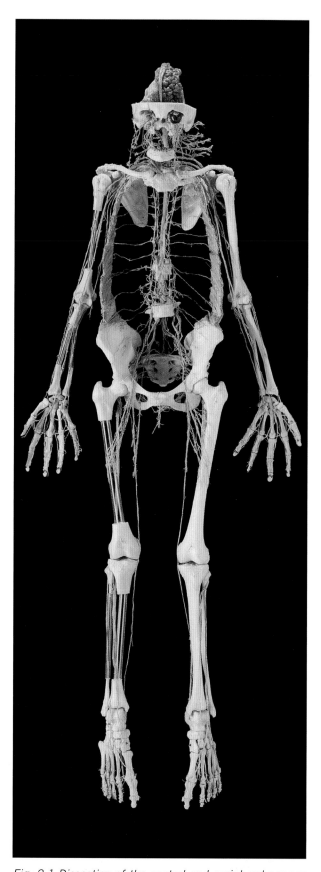

Fig. 2.1 Dissection of the central and peripheral nervous systems

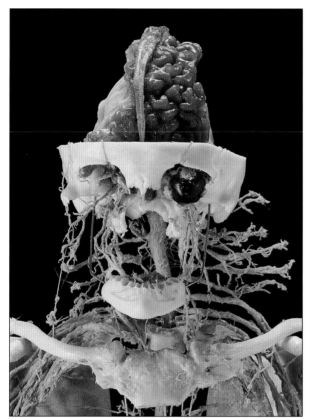

Fig. 2.2

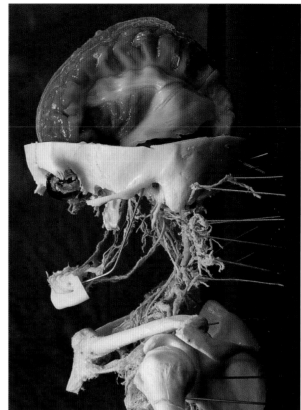

Fig. 2.3

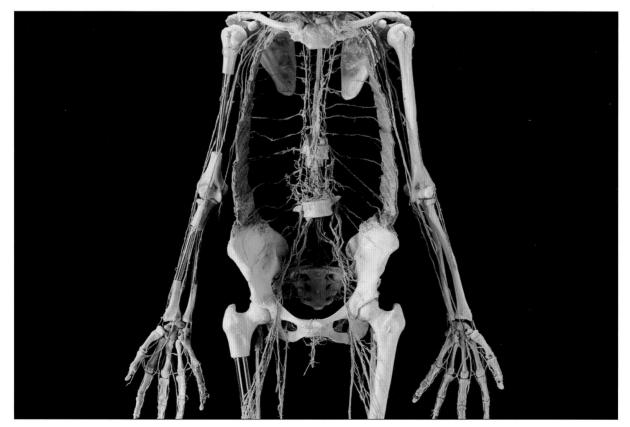

Fig. 2.4

The cerebrum takes up most of the space in the cranial cavity. It is the seat of our consciousness and of our higher mental functions, such as thought, reason, emotion and memory. From the outer layer inwards, it consists of gray cortical matter, some white layers of marrow and several core regions of gray matter, known as basal ganglia. Along its convexity, it is divided into left and right hemispheres by a longitudinal fissure. These cerebral hemispheres are joined at the corpus callosum (Fig. 2.8). As a result of its massive expansion in the course of evolutionary history, the furrowed surface of the cerebrum displays numerous convolutions (gyri) and recesses (sulci). Consequently, only about one-third of the surface is visible; the remaining two-thirds remain concealed within the grooves. If it were laid out flat, the cerebral cortex would measure nearly 1.5 m^2. On the surface of the brain slices in Fig. 2.9, the grey matter of the cerebral cortex and basal ganglia (thalamus, hyopothalamus , nucleus caudatis, nucleus lentiformis, etc.) can easily be distinguished from the white matter. While the grey matter is composed of nerve cells, the white matter consists of nerve fibres.

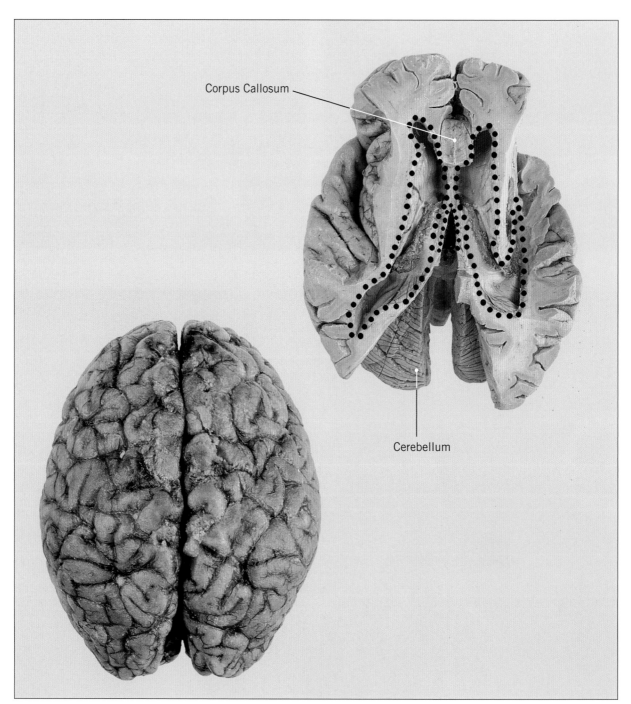

Corpus Callosum

Cerebellum

Fig. 2.5 Human brain, viewed from above

Fig. 2.6 Brain dissection with a view of the ventricle system (marked area)

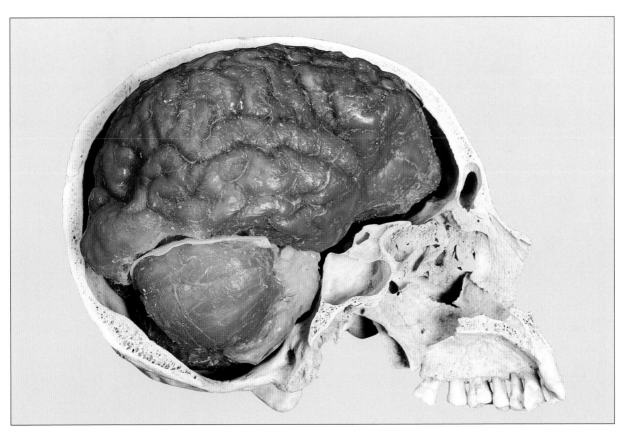

Fig. 2.7 Human brain in half skull

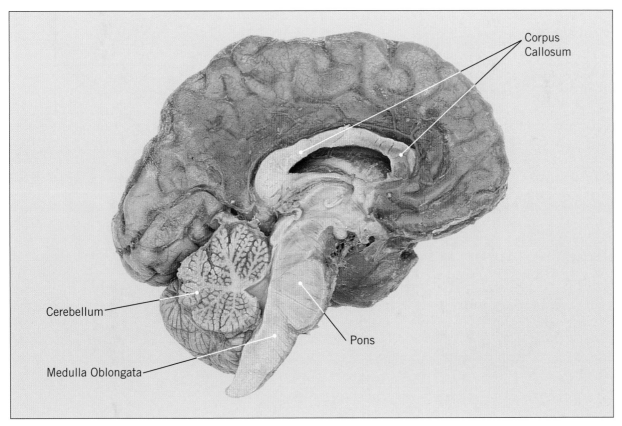

Corpus
Callosum

Cerebellum

Pons

Medulla Oblongata

Fig. 2.8 Left hemisphere of brain

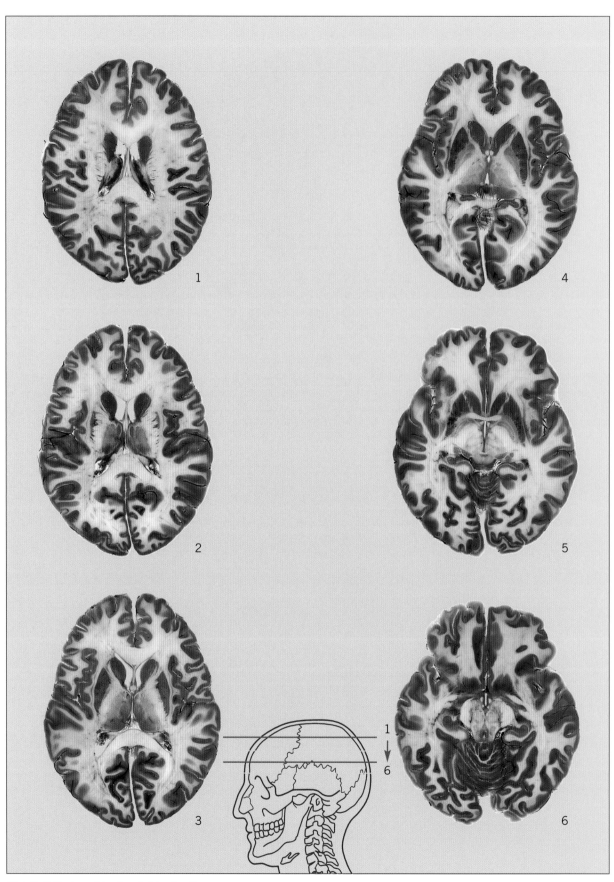

Fig. 2. 9 Series of horizontal brain slices

Underneath the cerebrum are located the more primitive, biogenetically older brain structures, i.e., the brain stem and the cerebellum. Here many basic functions of the body are controlled. The upper part of the brain stem, the midbrain, curves up into the cerebrum. It contains a number of centres for coordinating movements as well as for visual and auditory sensations.

The pons, which is connected to the cerebellum, is situated under the midbrain. The medulla oblongata is in the area leading from the brain to the spinal cord. It contains nerve cells that regulate vital bodily functions, such as the respiratory centre, lower circulatory centres as well as reflex centres for swallowing, coughing, sneezing, vomiting, etc. Moreover, it is crossed by pyramidal fibres and thus serves as a dispatch centre for messages from the brain to peripheral regions of the body and vice versa. The cerebellum is located behind the brain stem. It is primarily responsible for controlling equilibrium and for coordinating the movements of the locomotive system with one another.

The brain of an adult weighs approx. 1300 grams. It thus only accounts for about 2 % of total body weight but requires 20 % of the blood supply. We lose consciousness if the supply of blood to the brain is interrupted for only 10 seconds. Severe damage to brain tissue can be caused by prolonged disorders or disruptions of blood flow (for example, resulting from an obstruction of a cerebral artery due to a blood clot or a massive haemorrhage). This syndrome is referred to as a stroke. A stroke caused by haemorrhaging usually occurs because of a rupture in an artery damaged and distended by high blood pressure (aneurysm). Haemorrhaging can be restricted to the space between the soft membranes or pia mater (subarachnoid haemorrhage) (Fig. 2.10); with more severe haemorrhaging, it can seep into the brain matter (Figs. 2.11 and 2.12). Depending on what regions of the brain are afflicted by the stroke, certain dysfunctions may occur, such as loss of speech or paralysis on the side of the body opposite the hemisphere affected. Should vital centres be afflicted, a stroke may be fatal (approx. 15 % of all deaths).

Within the brain, there are four cavities (ventricles; see Fig. 2.6) that are connected with one other and in which fluid circulates. Like an internal shock absorber, this fluid offsets the effects of physical forces that could affect or injure the brain or the spinal cord. The cerebrospinal fluid is continuously regenerated and resorbed; in this way, it is completely replaced every 6 to 7 hours.

When normal flow within the ventricle system is obstructed by, for example, tumours, infections or congenital deformations, the fluid collects in the ventricles and causes them to become distended (hydrocephalus).

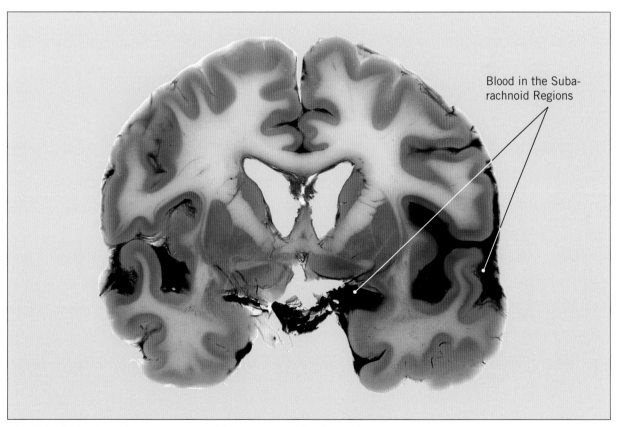

Blood in the Subarachnoid Regions

Fig. 2.10 Brain slice with subarachnoidal haemorrhage following a stroke

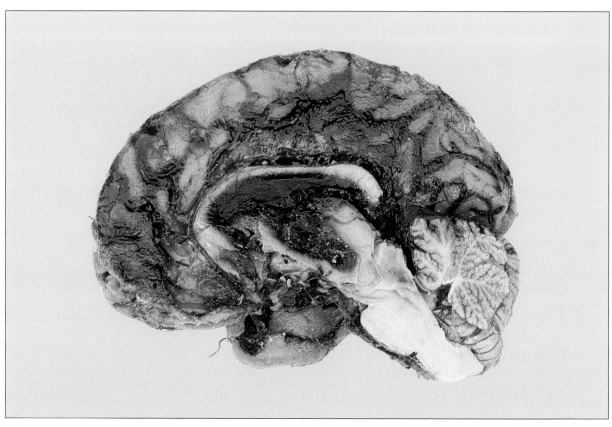

Fig. 2.11 Brain hemisphere with subarachnoid haemorrhage and brain-stem haemorrhage following a stroke

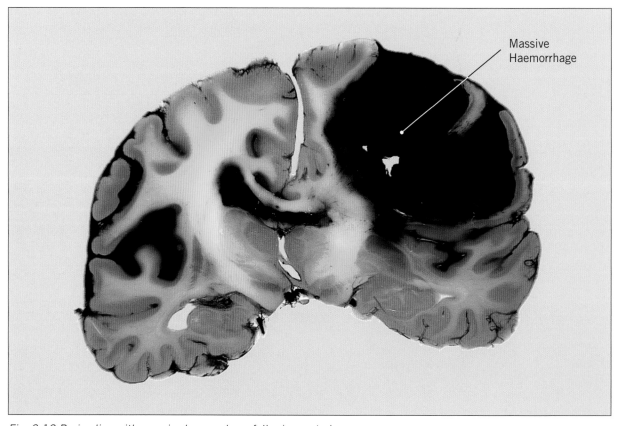

Fig. 2.12 Brain slice with massive haemorrhage following a stroke

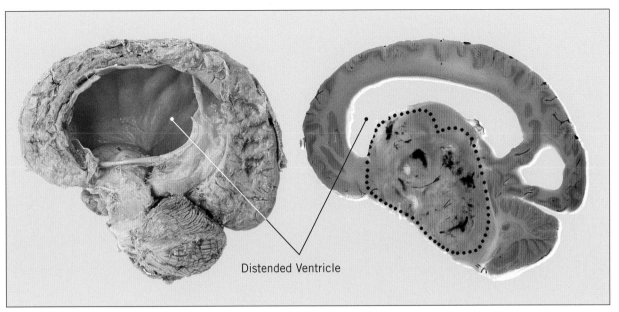

Distended Ventricle

Fig. 2.13 Right hemisphere of brain with hydrocephalus

Fig. 2.14 Brain slice with brain-stem tumour (marked area) and hydrocephalus

The increased pressure inside the brain displaces brain tissue, thereby damaging it (Figs. 2.13 and 2.14). With children whose cranial development has not been completed, this increased pressure is partially compensated by abnormal expansion of the skull (Fig. 8.11, p. 127).

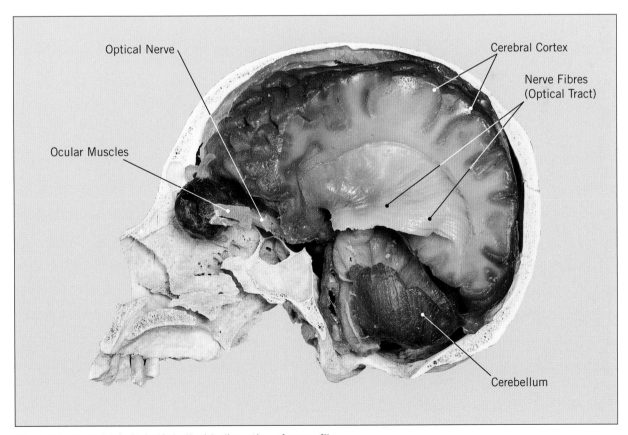

Fig. 2.15 Whole brain in half skull with dissection of nerve fibres

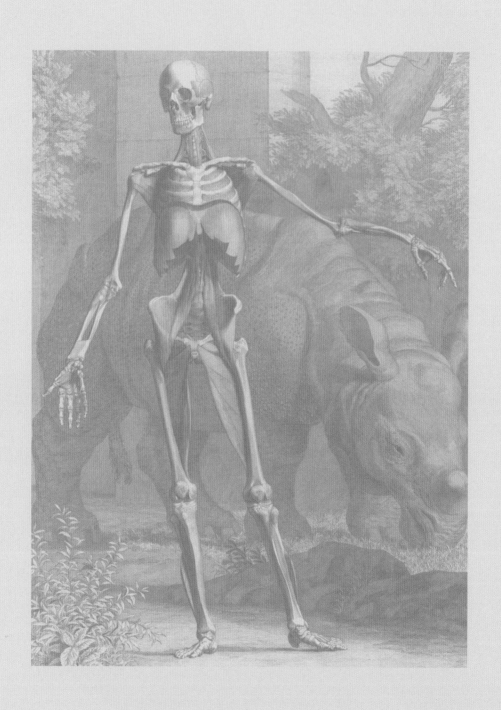

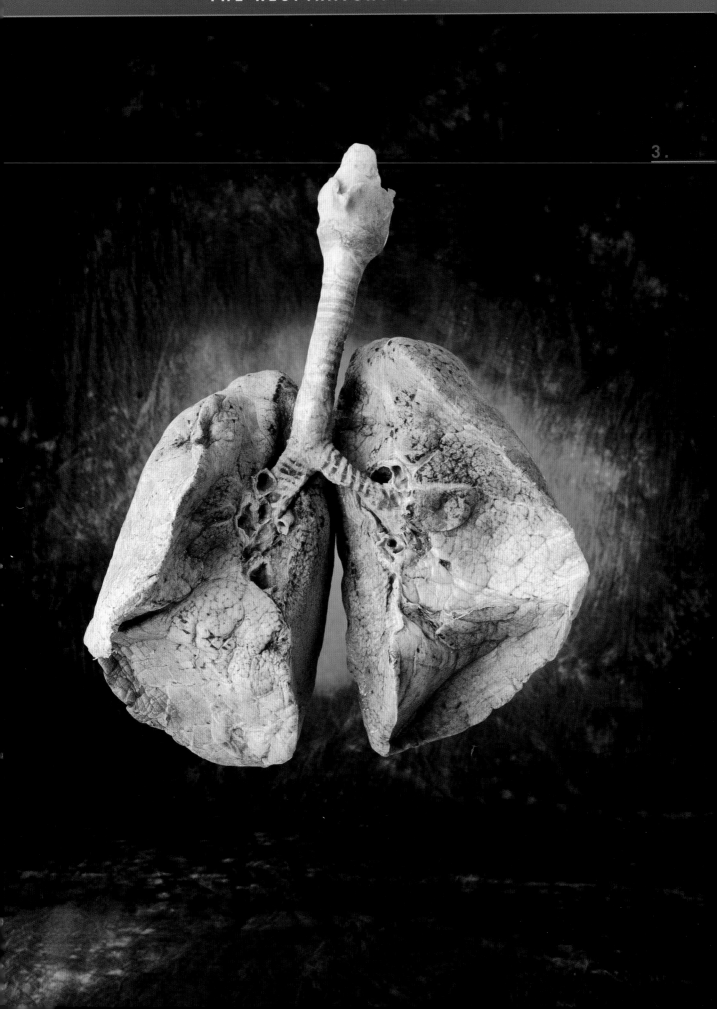

3. The Respiratory System

Life depends on a continuous supply of oxygen that we derive from the air that we breathe. Without oxygen, most of the cells in our bodies would only be able to survive for a few minutes. It is an important element in the biochemical processes of cellular metabolism that convert nutrients into energy to keep the body going.

The lungs are the main respiratory organs; they consist of two conical organs (Fig. 3.1). In a cross-section through the thoracic cavity, it is easy to recognize how the lungs are nestled in, and protected on both sides by, the rib cage in the chest. The heart is in the middle, between the two lungs, and beneath it are the blood vessels entering and exiting (Fig. 3.6).

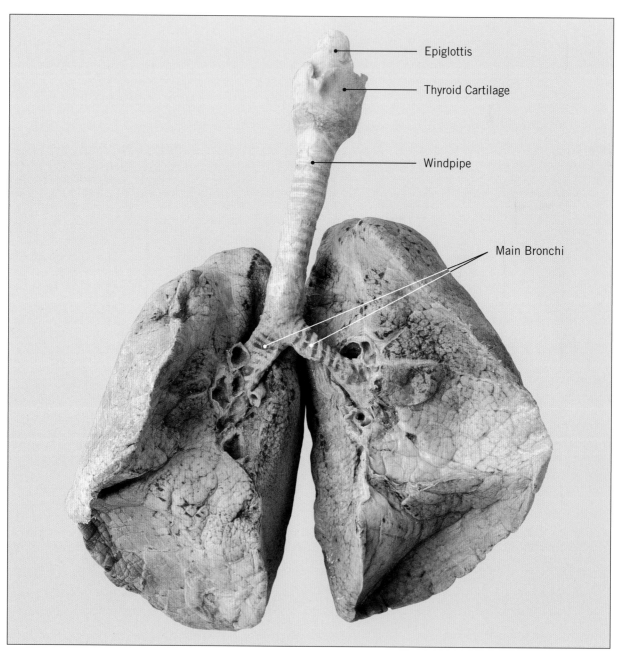

Epiglottis

Thyroid Cartilage

Windpipe

Main Bronchi

Fig. 3.1 Lungs with the main bronchi, windpipe and larynx

Both lungs display horizontal and diagonal fissures that divide them into individual lobes: three on the right side and two on the left. The left lung is also somewhat smaller to make room for the heart (Figs. 3.4 and 3.5).

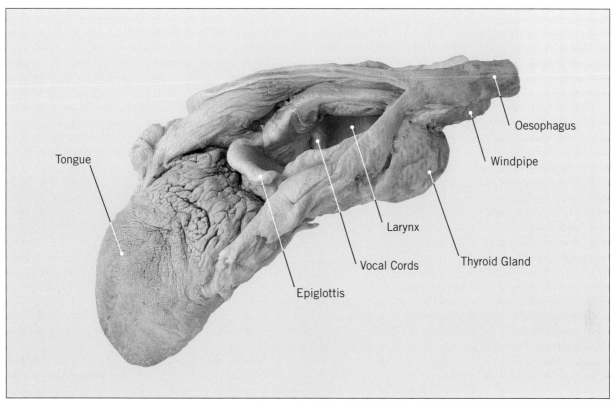

Tongue

Oesophagus

Windpipe

Larynx

Vocal Cords

Thyroid Gland

Epiglottis

Fig. 3.2 Opened larynx. In front of it, thyroid gland of normal size

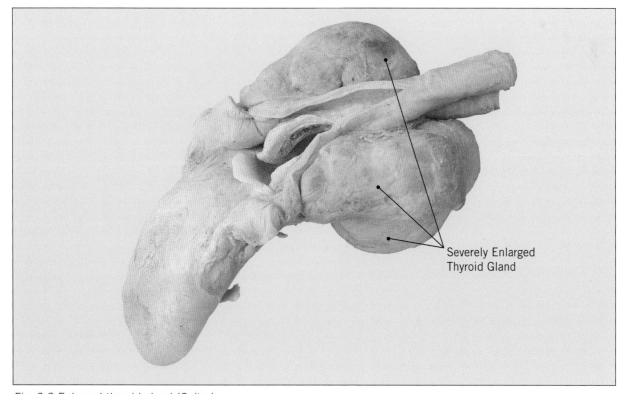

Severely Enlarged
Thyroid Gland

Fig. 3.3 Enlarged thyroid gland (Goitre)

Air is inhaled through the nose or mouth, passes the larynx (Fig. 3.2) and finally reaches the conical lungs via the windpipe. At its lower end, the windpipe separates into two main bronchi that extend into the left and right lungs where they divide into ever-smaller branches (bronchioles) as in trees.

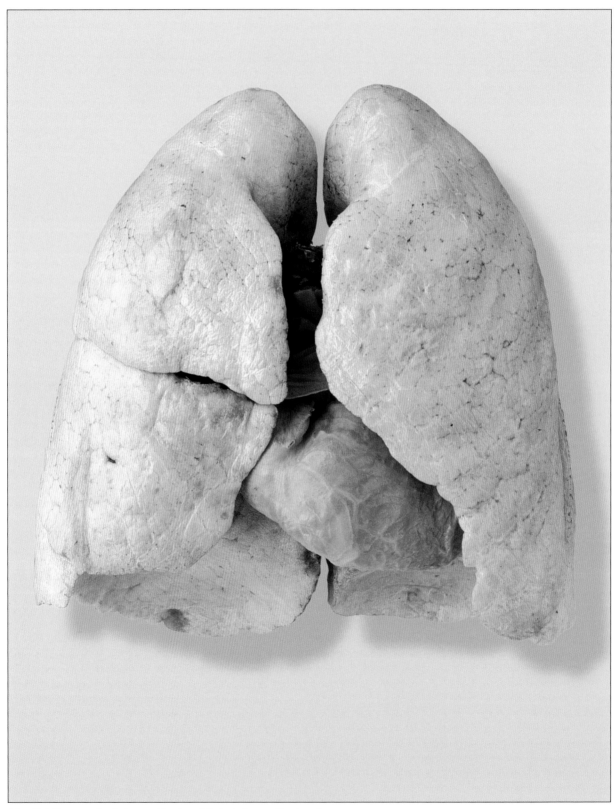

Fig. 3.4 Non-smoker's lungs; the heart is in between the two lungs

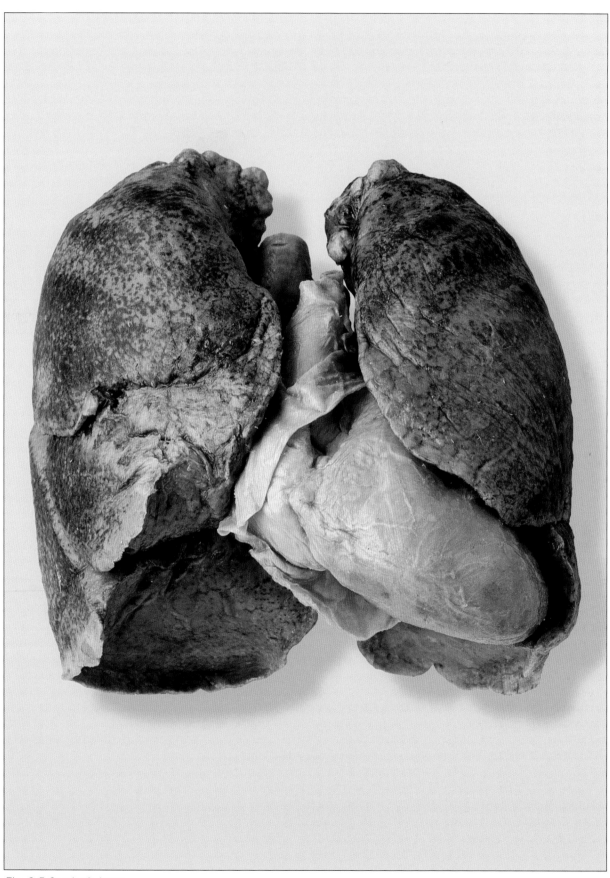

Fig. 3.5 Smoker's lungs

The walls of the windpipe and bronchi contain cartilage to stiffen them so that they stay rigid and open at all times for the passage of air even with more severe fluctuations in air pressure. Finally, the smallest bronchioles open into fine, cul-de-sac-like air cavities (alveoli), each of which has its own network of capillaries. Here is where the transfer of gases takes place: Oxygen in the air inhaled into the lungs diffuses in exchange with the carbon dioxide in the blood in capillaries, which is then removed by red corpuscles. Like bunches of grapes on a vine, alveoli are densely clustered and give the slice of lung tissue a spongy appearance (Fig. 3.8 a). Each lung has between 300 and 450 million alveoli, whose walls if laid out flat would cover an area of approx. 80 to 120 m2 or about the size of a tennis court.

Lung tissue is permeated with fine, elastic fibres as in rubber filaments and has a tendency to contract; it cannot actively expand of itself. When it does nevertheless expand during inhalation, it is a passive action initiated by the both the diaphragm and the intercostals, which are thin sheets of muscle between the ribs. The diaphragm extends as a thin sheet of muscle between the chest and the abdomen, thereby separating the two bodily cavities from one another (Fig. 3.11). When its muscle fibres contract, the diaphragm flattens and the chest cavity expands. As the lungs adhere to the inner walls of the chest all around as a result of existing capillary action, they inevitably have to expand when the chest expands. This in turn makes the pressure inside the lungs less than that outside the body, which causes air to be inhaled through the mouth and nose. During exhalation, the diaphragm relaxes and moves upwards, thereby squeezing the exchanged air back out again.

Breathing can be consciously influenced; however, it is usually accomplished automatically under the control of the autonomic nervous system. During quiet breathing, approx. one-half litre of air is inhaled with each breath; that would mean about six litres per minute. With extreme physical exertion, the amount of air processed through the lungs can temporarily be as much as 120 litres.

Together with the air, countless fine particles of dirt are also breathed in that settle in the lung tissue and are removed by means of constant self-cleaning processes. For this reason, the lungs generally do show tiny, spot-like pigmentations on their surface with increasing age (Fig. 3.1). However, not only particles of dirt, but tars inhaled with cigarette smoke are also deposited in the tissue of the lungs, causing them increasingly to appear black (Fig. 3.5). Smoking 20 cigarettes a day means that 150 ml of tar per year will be deposited in the lungs, the same volume as a coffee cup. Smoking is suicide on the installment plan. As everyone knows, the reason for this is that cigarette smoke can be hazardous to the health and can shorten a smoker's life if it is inhaled in larger amounts over a period of several years. Twenty cigarettes per day would be sufficient to shorten life by an average of five years. Passive smoking can also be hazardous to the health; breathing in the air in a smoke-filled room for an extended period of time is as hazardous as smoking five cigarettes.

Nicotine and the products of condensation in cigarette smoke primarily attack the respiratory and the cardiovascular systems; various other organs are also adversely affected. Cigarette smoke causes chronic infection of the mucous membranes in the respiratory organs (chronic bronchitis) with the typical smoker's cough. As the condition progresses, lung tissue is damaged; the alveolar walls are destroyed, thereby causing more or less large air spaces to develop irreversibly in the lung tissue. As a consequence, the surfaces available for the exchange of gases decrease significantly. This syndrome is known as lung bloating or emphysema. On the surfaces of the slice (Fig. 3.7 a), the affected areas of the lungs look like a piece of Swiss cheese. Emphysema can also develop to a lesser extent under normal circumstances among the elderly as a result of aging.

Lung cancer is still another complication resulting from smoking. The risk of contracting bronchial cancer is 20 times higher for smokers than for non-smokers. Today it represents the No. 1 type of cancer in men. In Fig. 3.7 b, a cross-section is shown through the chest cavity with tumours in the left lung.

Owing to the heavy throughput of blood, the lungs are also frequently the sites of metastases of malignant tumours. In Fig. 3.10, a lung is shown whose surface is almost completely covered with small tumour metastases.

A cross-section through the chest cavity is shown in Fig. 3.9 with extensive tumour growth at the back of the lungs and the dorsal torso walls. The tumour has also displaced large sections of the lungs and has even partially infiltrated into the tissue. In so doing, it has severely destroyed the original tissue, especially in the walls of the chest; the limits of the thoracic vertebrae have been badly obscured and the bone structure has been completely obliterated in some places. Moreover, the tumour has invaded the spinal canal and is pressing on the spinal cord.

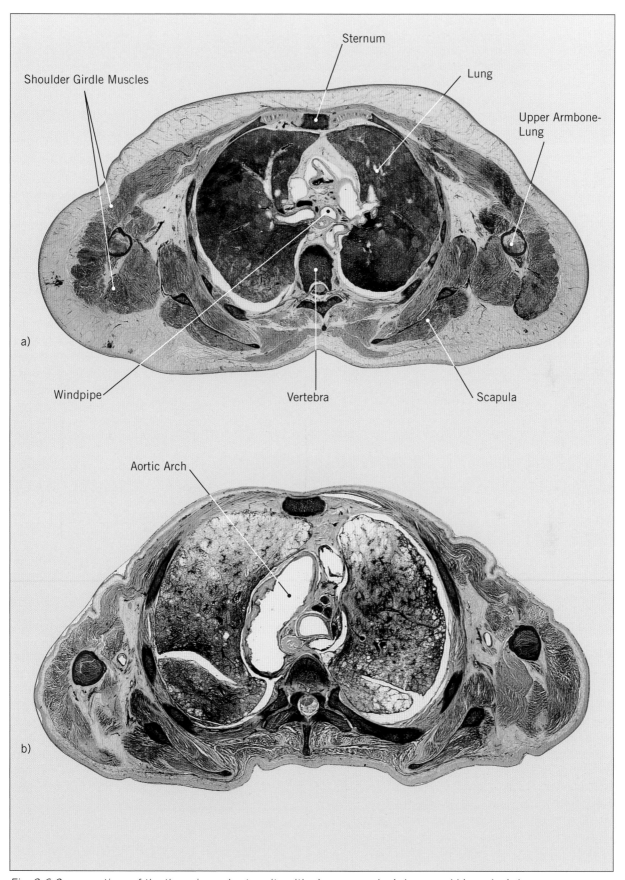

Fig. 3.6 Cross-sections of the thoracic or chest cavity with a) a non-smoker's lungs and b) smoker's lungs

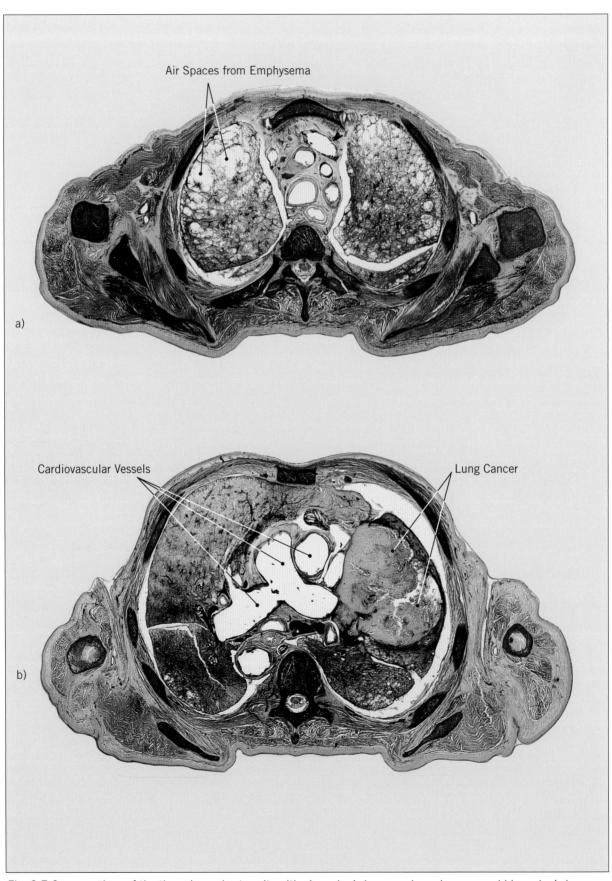

Fig. 3.7 Cross-sections of the thoracic or chest cavity with a) smoker's lungs and emphysema and b) smoker's lungs with lung cancer

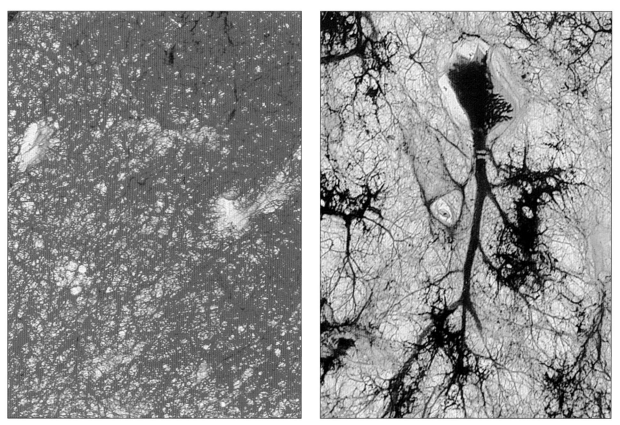

Fig. 3.8 Enlargements of sections of lung tissue taken from a) a non-smoker and b) a smoker

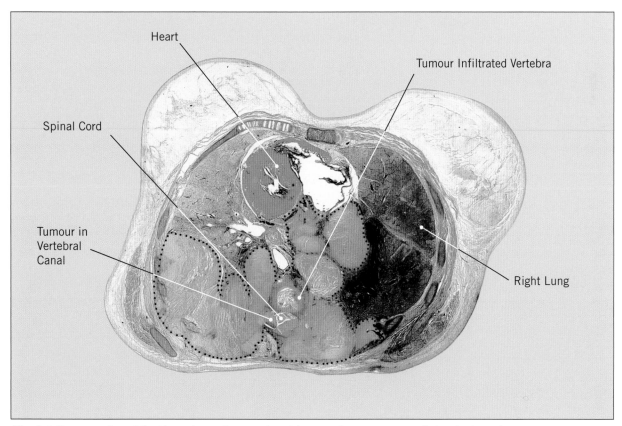

Fig. 3.9 Cross-section of the thoracic or chest cavity with extensive tumour growth (marked area)

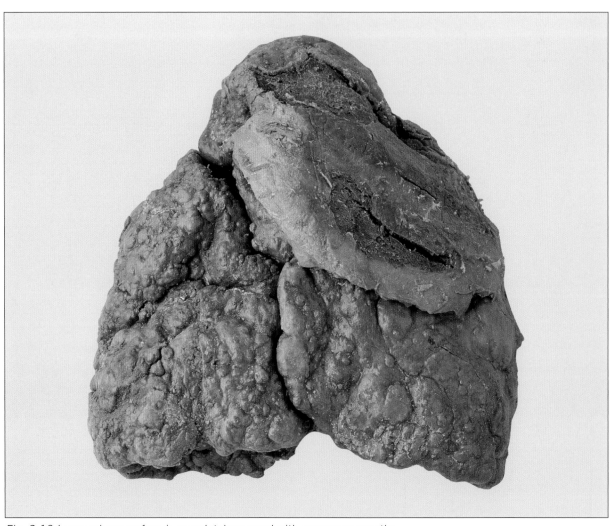

Fig. 3.10 Lungs whose surface is completely covered with cancerous growths

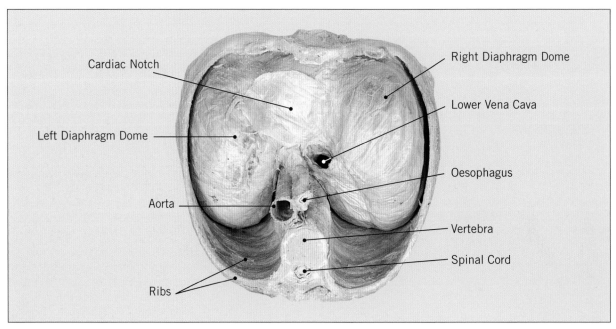

Cardiac Notch

Left Diaphragm Dome

Aorta

Ribs

Right Diaphragm Dome

Lower Vena Cava

Oesophagus

Vertebra

Spinal Cord

Fig. 3.11 Diaphragm, view from above

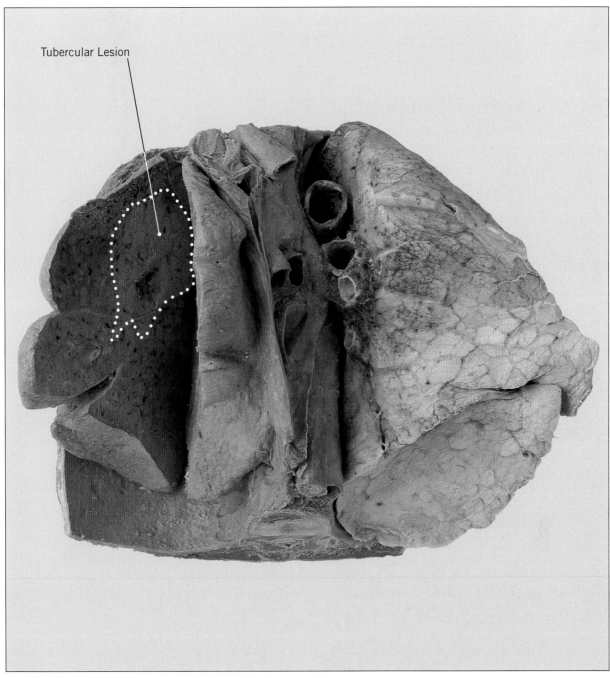

Tubercular Lesion

Fig. 3.12 Lungs with tuberculosis

Inhaled air is not only utilized for exchanging gases; it also serves in forming sounds and articulation. The larynx (Fig. 3.2) is the most important organ for speech formation. It is a hollow organ located between the pharynx and the windpipe. The epiglottis is in the upper part; it is a cartilaginous flap that covers the windpipe during swallowing so that food can be channelled to the oesophagus located behind it. In the middle of the larynx are the vocal cords that are made to vibrate by the air passing through, causing the voice to be heard. By means of several fine muscles in the larynx, the position of the vocal cords can be modified, thereby altering the voice.

Just below the larynx, on the front side of the windpipe, the thyroid gland is situated, whose hormones regulate the metabolic functions and the level of activity in the body. With dysfunctions of the thyroid gland, it can become severely enlarged and can cause the neck to swell (known as a goitre; see Fig. 3.3). A severely enlarged thyroid gland can also constrict the windpipe and thus impair breathing.

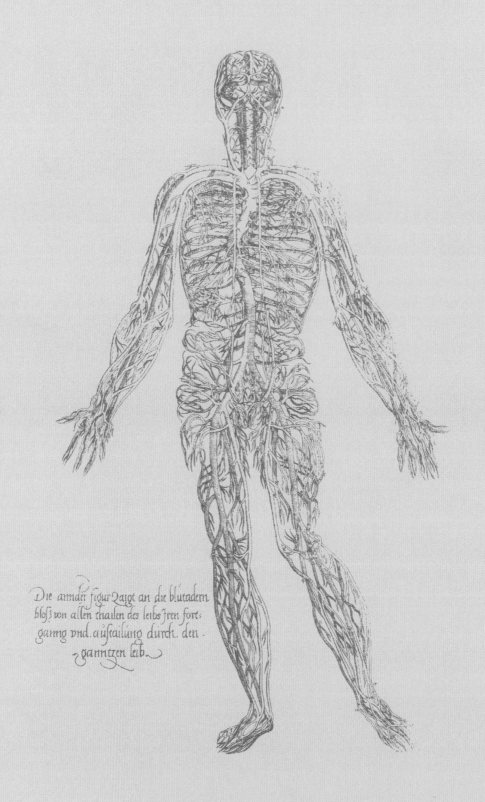

Die annder figur zaigt an die blutadern
bloß von allen thailen des leibs jren fort-
ganng vnd austailung durch den
ganntzen leib.

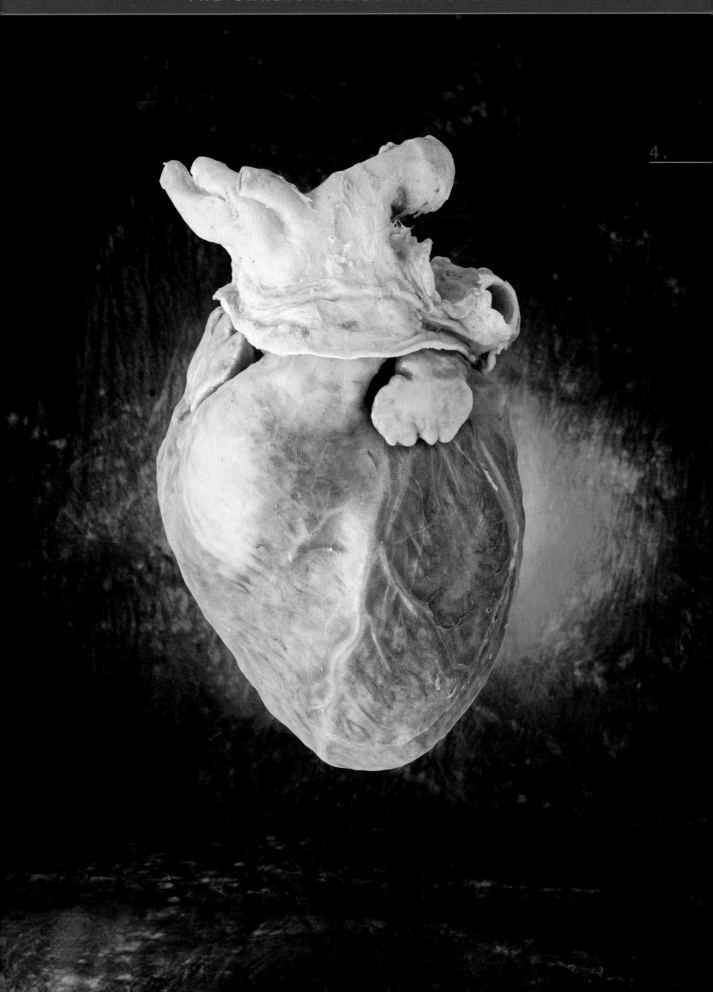

4.

4. The Cardiovascular System

The cardiovascular system is the body's "main transportation service" that not only handles distribution of nutrients, oxygen and hormones to the various regions of the body but is also responsible for removing metabolic waste products. The motor of this "enterprise" is the heart; as transportation routes, there is a dense "roadway" network of blood vessels available.

The Heart

The heart (Fig. 4.1) is a hollow, muscular organ that is enveloped by a membranous sac (pericardium) and is located behind the sternum. Its size is about the same as that of a man's clenched fist. It weighs an average of 300 grams. The heart pumps approx. 70 ml of blood per beat, ca. 70 times per minute when at rest.

That would mean a theoretical number of 100 000 heartbeats every day and approx. 2.5 billion in a lifetime. The actual number, however, would probably be considerably higher as the body is active during most of the day and the heart has to beat more frequently to supply the increased need for blood.

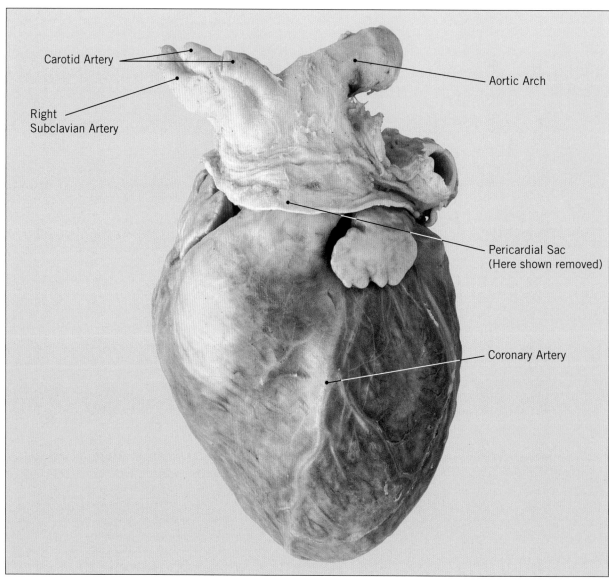

Carotid Artery

Right
Subclavian Artery

Aortic Arch

Pericardial Sac
(Here shown removed)

Coronary Artery

Fig. 4.1 Human heart, view from the front

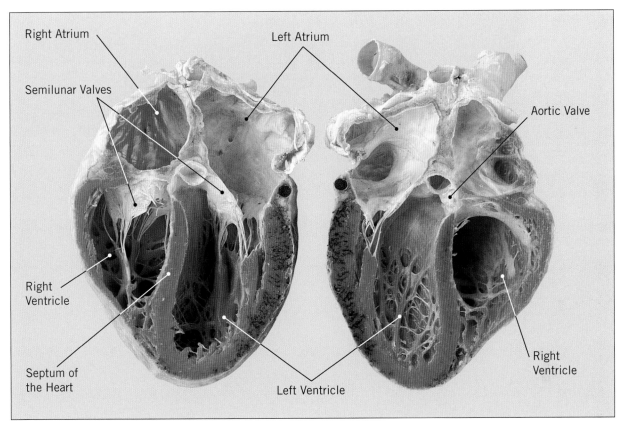

Right Atrium   Left Atrium

Semilunar Valves

Aortic Valve

Right
Ventricle

Septum of
the Heart

Right
Ventricle

Left Ventricle

Fig. 4.2 Human heart, (opened longitudinally)

When a heart is cut open longitudinally (Fig. 4.2), a left and a right half can be seen, separated by a septum or membrane. Each half has atriums with weaker muscles that receive incoming blood and ventricles with stronger muscles to pump the blood out of the heart. The left ventricle has significantly stronger walls than the right ventricle, as it must generate considerable pressure to pump oxygen-enriched blood from the lungs into the greater circulatory system of the body. Conversely, the right ventricle needs relatively little pressure to pump oxygen-poor blood from the body's circulatory system to the lungs.

Triangular-shaped valves stretch between the atria and the ventricles that close during the action of the heartbeat to prevent the blood from flowing in the wrong direction. The aorta emerges from the left ventricle, while the pulmonary artery originates in the right ventricle. The flow of blood into the arteries is regulated by semilunar valves. They only open when the blood in the ventricles has achieved a certain pressure. In the specimen shown in Fig. 4.3, the heart has been cut open in such a way as to permit all four valves to be viewed on one plane from above.

An unimpaired opening and closing mechanism in all of the valves is indispensable for a regular heartbeat. Bacterial or rheumatic infections in one or more valves could deform them in such a way that they could not sufficiently

open or close properly so that blood would flow backwards at each heartbeat. As a consequence, turbulence could develop in the bloodstream that could cause a heart murmur indicating a diseased condition. Because of the altered pressure and volume conditions in the heart, severe disorders of the cardiac valves can weaken it, thereby causing significant dysfunctions in the cardiovascular system. In such cases, the affected valves are replaced by artificial ones (Fig. 4.4).

As in every organ, the heart also has its own blood vessels that provide the blood needed to nourish it. These vessels form the coronary system (Fig. 4.11). When the nourishing bloodstream to a section of the cardiac muscles is suddenly interrupted by an obstruction in a coronary artery (coronary occlusion), it results in a heart attack, i.e., the cells of the affected section of the cardiac muscles die. The larger this section is, the greater is the area damaged by the heart attack (infarct). With smaller infarct areas, the heart can still be capable of pumping enough blood to permit the patient to survive.The necrotic cells will be replaced by a scar formed by connective tissue in a self-healing process over several days or weeks. Old — i.e., healed — infarct areas appear whitish, and the wall of the heart is substantially thinner as can be seen in the example of an infarct in the apex of the heart shown in Fig. 4.7a.

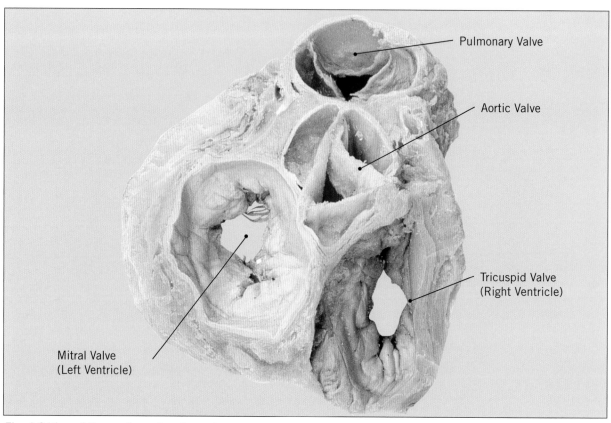

Fig. 4.3 View of the cardiac valves from above

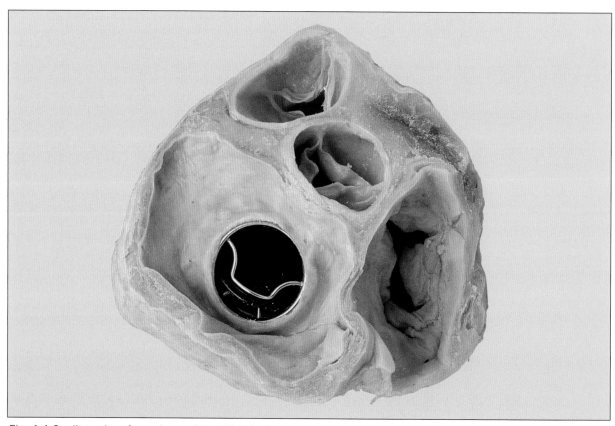

Fig. 4.4 Cardiac valves from above with artificial valve

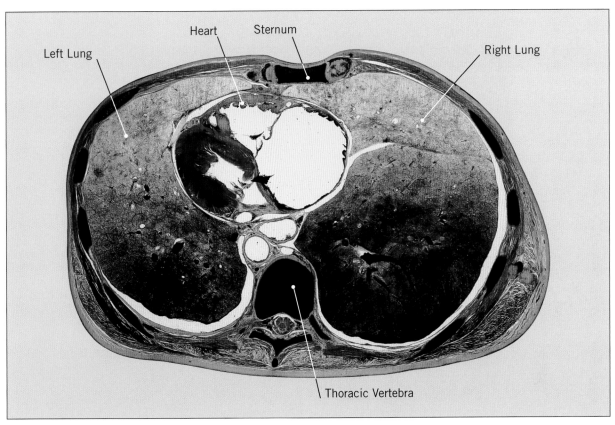

Fig. 4.5 Body slice with heart of normal size

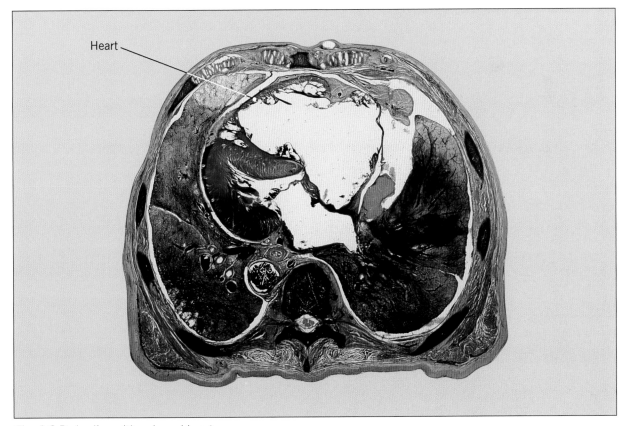

Fig. 4.6 Body slice with enlarged heart

Like skeletal muscles, the heart can also adapt to prolonged overexertion. Consequently, it is not unusual for an athlete's heart to weigh up to 500 grams. However, disorders of the cardiac muscles and other diseases caused by unphysiologically high overexertion of the heart (high blood pressure, weaknesses in the septums of the heart, abnormalities of the cardiac valves) can lead to significant enlargement of the heart. In fact, the heart shown in Fig. 4.8 weighs 800 grams; this massive enlargement was caused by a disorder of the cardiac muscles.

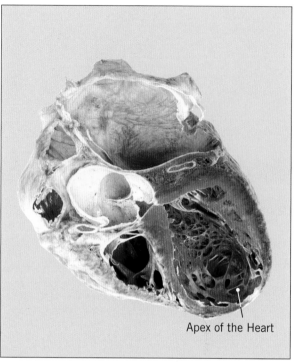

Apex of the Heart

Fig. 4.7 a Human heart with old, healed infarct in the apex of the heart

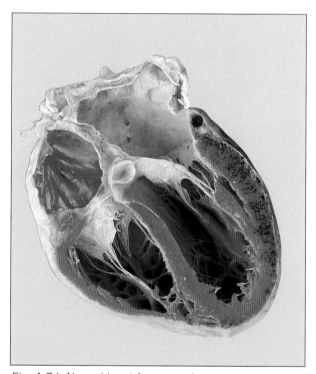

Fig. 4.7 b Normal heart for comparison

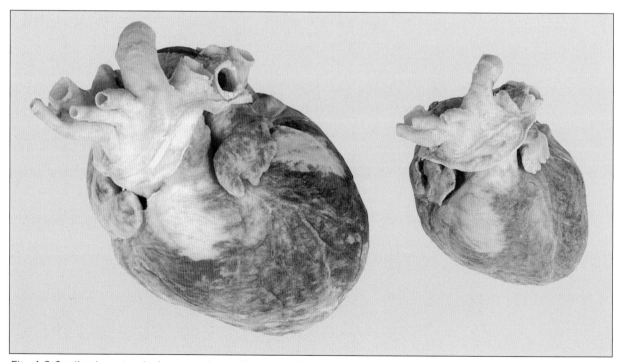

Fig. 4.8 Cardiac hypertrophy in comparison with a normal heart

The Vascular System

The body has an unusually dense network of vessels to transport blood to its various parts. If all of the blood vessels in a body were laid end to end, they would reach a length of over ninety thousand kilometres (nearly 56 000 miles). The large blood vessels in the vascular system represent, so to speak, major highways that distribute the blood to the body. The vessels that lead away from the heart are referred to as arteries. They taper down more and more as they pass into the organs and tissue to form an intricate network of minute, hair-like vessels called capillaries. It is here that the interchange of nutrients, oxygen and other substances takes place between the blood and tissue cells — nourishment and removal of waste products. After a short distance, the capillaries combine to form vessels, called veins, that grow ever larger and convey the blood back to the right side of the heart. From there, the blood is pumped to the lungs to become enriched with oxygen before entering the greater circulatory system via the left side of the heart. In Fig. 4.9, the main branches of the arterial system have been exposed from the heart to the fingertips and the tips of the toes.

Figs. 4.11 shows specimens of the blood vessels in the heart injected with plastic (also called "corrosion specimens"). To produce such specimens, the arteries are first infused with dyed plastics. When the plastic has cured, the tissue surrounding the arteries and the walls of these vessels is removed by chemical (corrosive) action. In this way, the arteries can be made visible down to their most minute and intricate clusters of capillaries.

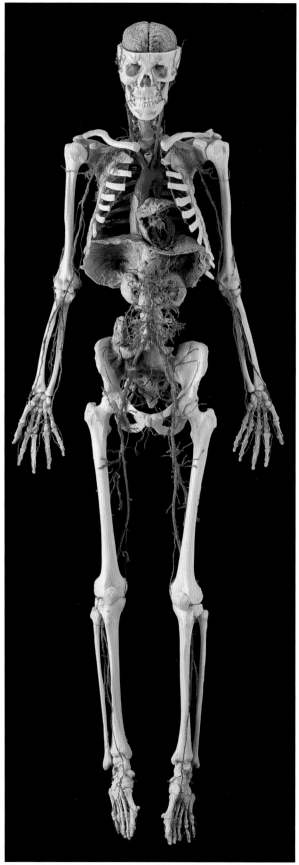

Fig. 4.9 The main branches of the arterial system

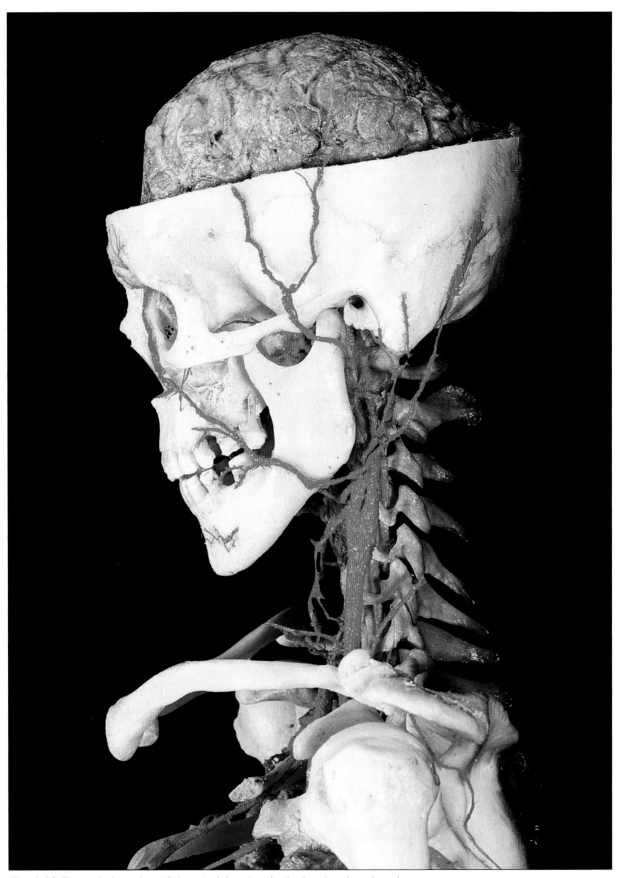

Fig. 4.10 *The main branches of the arterial system in the head and neck regions*

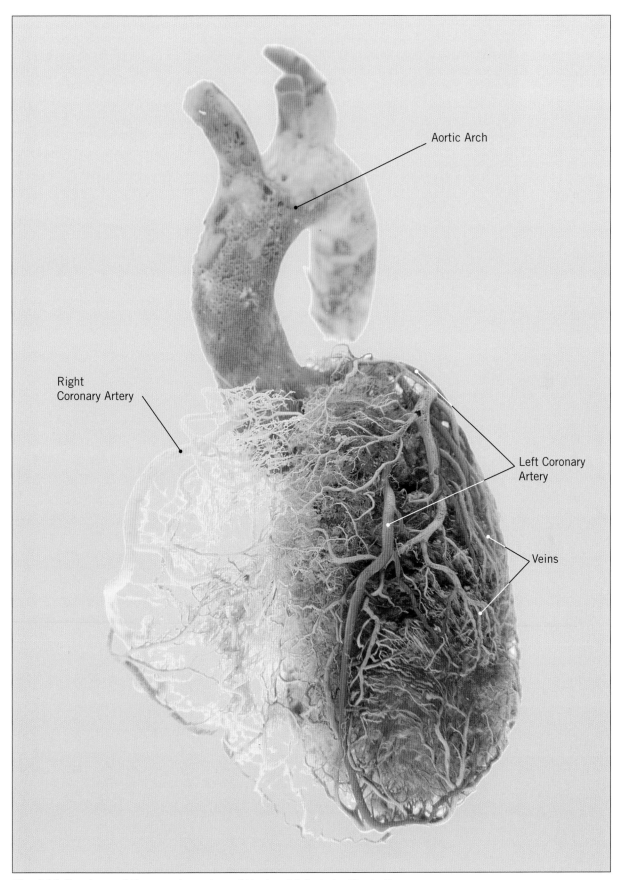

Aortic Arch

Right
Coronary Artery

Left Coronary
Artery

Veins

Fig. 4.11 Specimen of the vascular system of the heart injected with plastic

A prevalent disease of the vascular system is hardening of the arteries (arterial sclerosis). By this is meant changes caused by buildups of fats, proteins and minerals in the walls of these vessels. This causes the arteries to become hard and inelastic. As the disorder progresses, it causes the surfaces inside the arteries to become rough, and this roughness causes blood to clot (thrombi). The clotted blood now narrows or blocks the intravascular bores of the arteries until they are completely clogged (thrombosis). This results in insufficient circulation of blood in the bodily regions dependent on the afflicted arteries. Characteristic syndromes develop especially when arteriosclerotic vessels are located in the heart (heart attacks), in the brain (strokes) or in the legs (pain in the legs when walking; smoker's legs).

Fig. 4.14 shows the smooth inner wall of a normal aorta compared to aortas with varying degrees of arteriosclerotic changes.

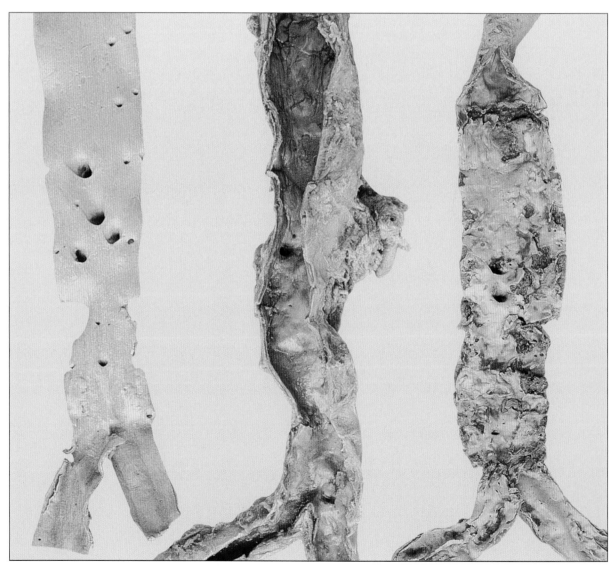

Fig. 4.12 Inner wall of a normal aorta (left), compared to aortas with varying degrees of hardening of the arteries (arterial sclerosis)

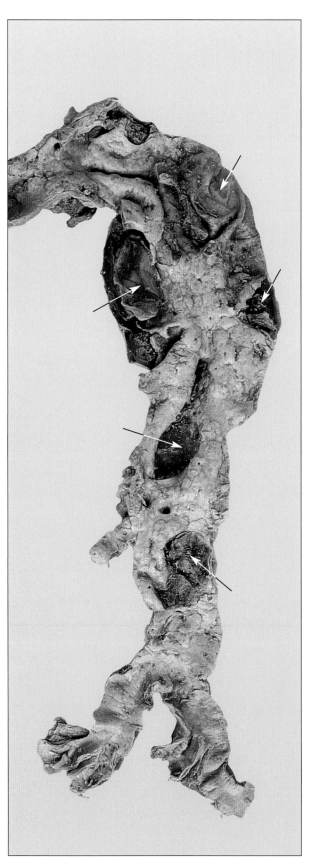

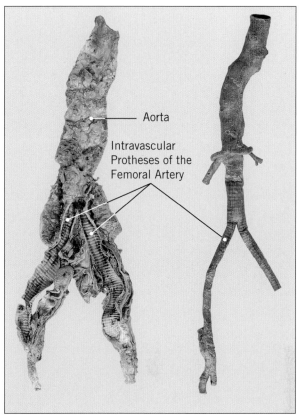

Aorta

Intravascular
Protheses of the
Femoral Artery

Fig. 4.14 Intravascular prosthesis, opened (left), closed (right)

Sclerotic arterial walls also represent weak points in the vascular system. The afflicted walls are prone to yielding to high blood pressure in the arteries, causing them to bulge and to form aneurysms (Fig. 4.13). As the walls of an aneurysm are usually thin and weak, they can rupture under the effects of high blood pressure, thereby causing severe or even fatal haemorrhaging. To preclude this danger in such cases, the affected sections of the arteries are replaced with intravascular prostheses.

Fig. 4.13 Aneurysms in the aorta. They are filled with blood clots.

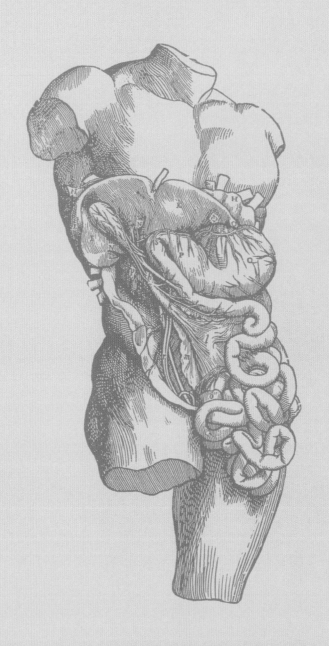

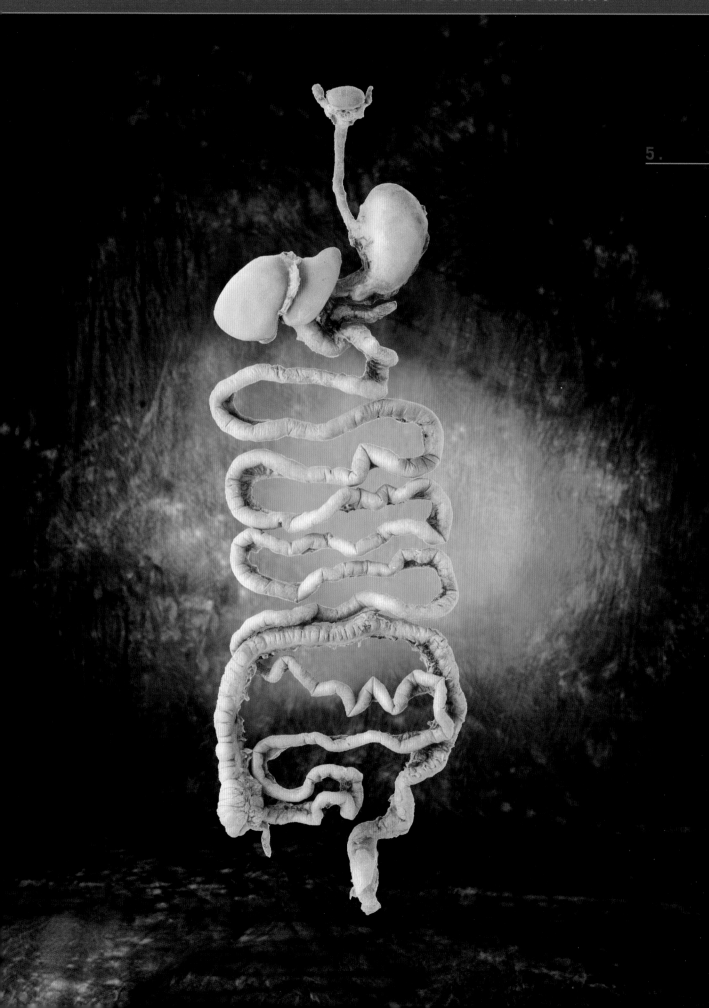

5. The Digestive System and the Abdominal Organs

All of the bodily regions have a constant need for nutrients to provide them with the energy necessary to fulfill their functions properly and to fuel the metabolic processes linked to these functions. Nutrients are absorbed by the digestive system. Its organs break down the nutrients mechanically and chemically into such small pieces that they can be absorbed into the blood and passed on to the individual cells.

In simplified form, the digestive tract (also known as the alimentary canal) can be imagined as a long tube-like system that measures approx. 9 meters from the tongue to the rectum (Fig. 5.1). Food is initially bitten and chewed into very small pieces in the mouth, reaches the stomach via the oesophagus where it is crushed and churned before being partially digested. From there it enters the first section of the small intestine, known as the duodenum, which is C-shaped and encloses the head of the pancreas like a frame. It is here that the ducts that secrete the digestive juices of the liver and pancreas empty into the small intestine to be mixed with the nutrients. After passing the duodenum, they are then transported through the succeeding, approx. 5–6-meter-long small intestine. There the majority of the nutrient molecules are absorbed through the small intestine wall into the bloodstream. Indigestible food particles pass into the large intestine and are finally excreted via the rectum. Nutrients are transported through the individual segments of the digestive tract by rhythmic, wave-like movements of its walls (peristalsis). These peristaltic waves cannot be consciously controlled, but can be activated by food, its aroma, medication, etc.

The stomach is a muscular organ that resembles a pouch; its function is to store ingested food, to initiate digestion both mechanically and chemically and to pass it gradually to the intestines. The size, form and location of the stomach vary considerably and depend on the bodily position, age, how full it is and on eating habits (Fig. 5.3). Its capacity is between 2 and 3 litres. The stomach walls are lined with a wrinkled, irregular mucous membrane (Fig. 5.4). It contains approx. 5 million glands that secrete about 2 litres of gastric juice per day. This primarily consists of hydrochloric acid and proteolytic enzymes to break down the protein in food. Moreover, stomach acids kill any bacteria ingested with the food and as this passes into the intestines, they activate the pancreas to secrete its digestive enzymes. A number of the stomach glands also produce mucous to protect the stomach lining itself from being digested.

If the stomach produces too much hydrochloric acid, it can cause damage to the stomach lining and especially to the lining of the duodenum, which could result in an ulcer if additional bacteria are present. Fig. 5.7 shows an ulcer in the stomach lining and Fig. 5.6 in the duct to the duodenum. In Fig. 5.5, the stomach lining displays numerous dot-shaped signs of bleeding that stick out as black spots in the specimen and are the result of inflammation of the mucous membrane (gastritis).

Actual digestion takes place in the small intestine, i.e., the nutrient molecules are broken down chemically and then absorbed into the bloodstream. Enzymes from the pancreas split protein, starches and sugar, while bile produced in the liver aids in digesting fats.

A relatively large surface is needed to absorb the numerous nutrient molecules from the intestines. For this purpose, the mucous membrane of the small intestine is formed by folds, which extend up to 1 cm into the bore of the intestinal tube. Moreover, the entire lining is covered with 1-mm-high, finger-like villi (up to 40 villi per mm^2). In addition, each cell in the small intestine projects 0.0015-mm-long projections (brush-like microvilli). The surface area of this lining is thus increased to a total of 120 to 150 m^2. The nutrients absorbed here are transported by the blood or lymph to the liver via the portal vein.

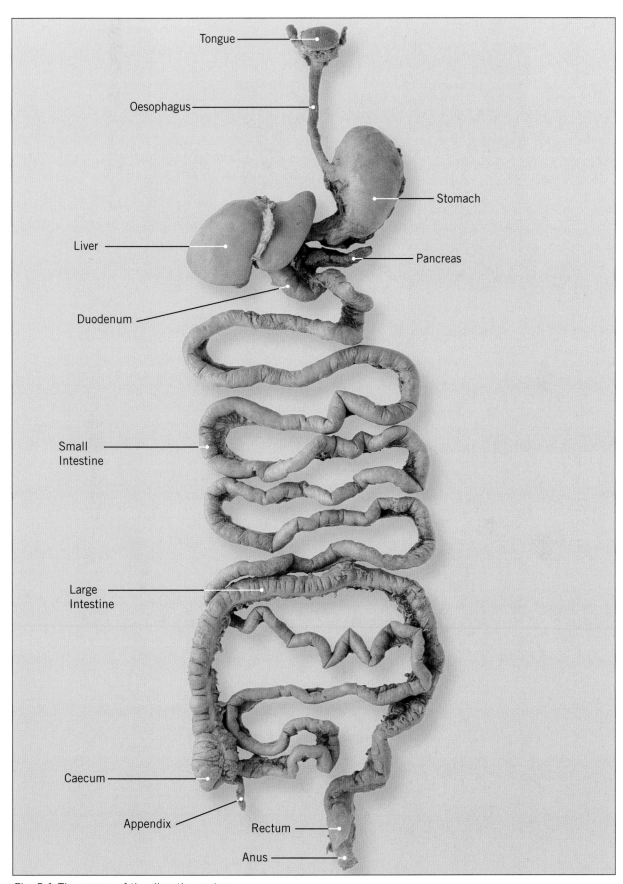

Tongue

Oesophagus

Stomach

Liver

Pancreas

Duodenum

Small
Intestine

Large
Intestine

Caecum

Appendix

Rectum

Anus

Fig. 5.1 The organs of the digestive system

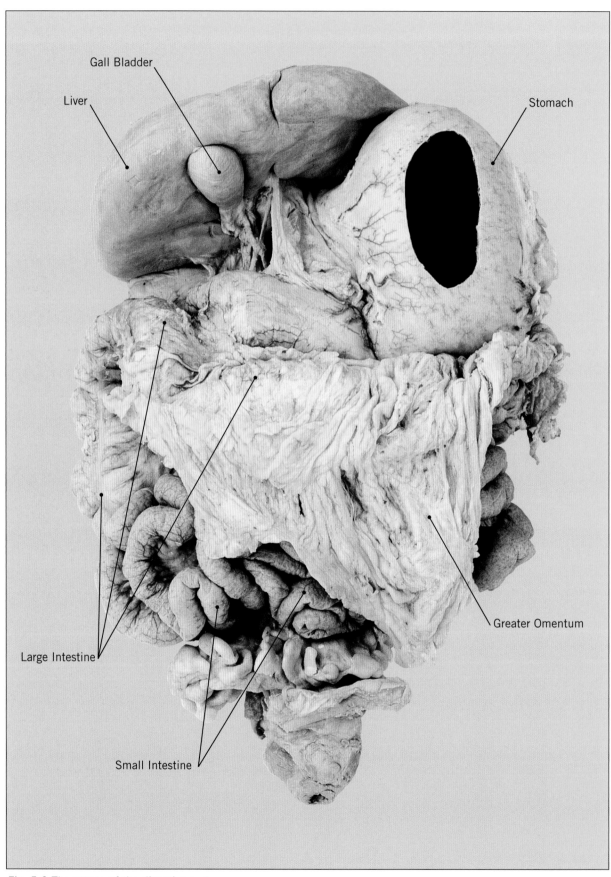

Fig. 5.2 The organs of the digestive system

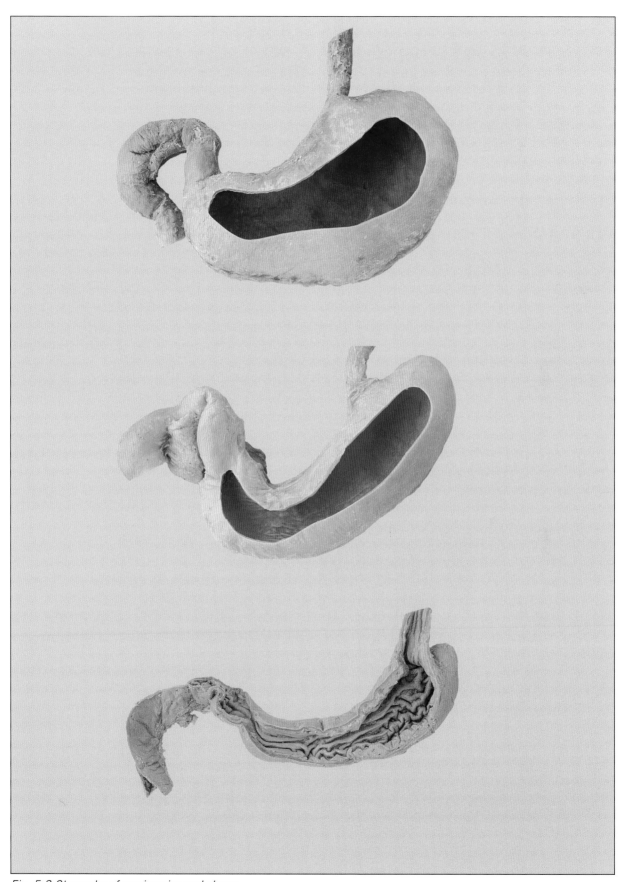

Fig. 5.3 Stomachs of varying size and shape

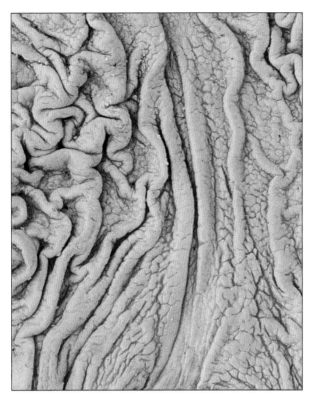
Fig. 5.4 Mucous membrane of stomach lining

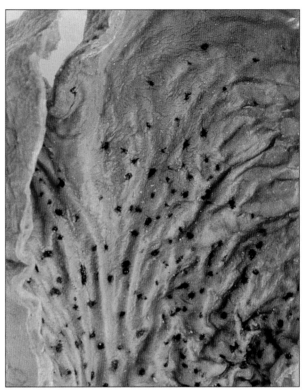
Fig. 5.5 Inflammation of the mucous membrane with dot-like signs of bleeding

Undigested foodstuffs are passed on to the large intestine where they are thickened by absorbing water. Both of the intestines are separated by a flap to prevent the contents of the large intestine from flowing back into the small intestine. The large intestine begins in the lower abdomen with the caecum and continues on to frame the loops of the small intestine before entering the lesser pelvis on the left side

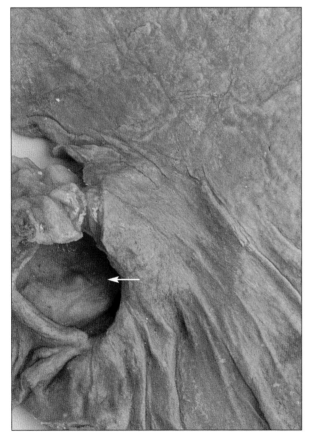
Fig. 5.6 Duodenal ulcer

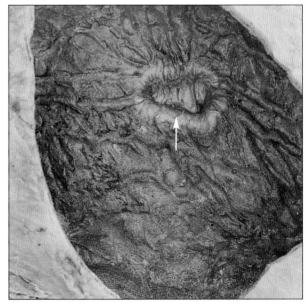
Fig. 5.7 Stomach ulcer

Gall Bladder

Fig. 5.14 Livers of different sizes

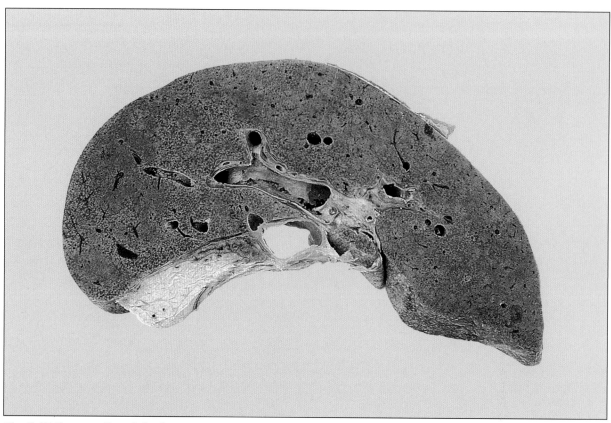

Fig. 5.15 Cross-section of the liver

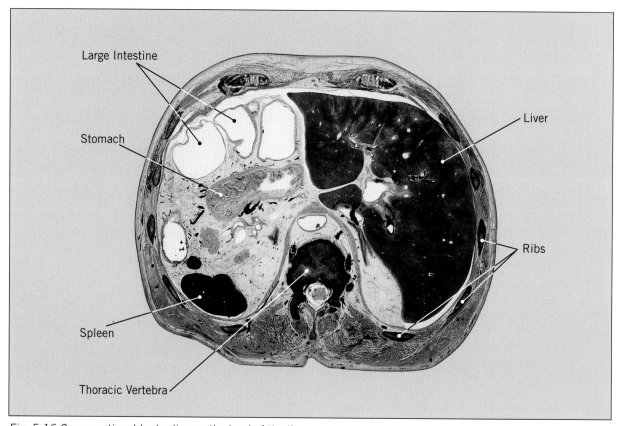

Large Intestine

Stomach

Liver

Spleen

Ribs

Thoracic Vertebra

Fig. 5.16 Cross-sectional body slice on the level of the liver

The liver gets its dark reddish-brown colour from its rich blood flow (Figs. 5.14 and 5.16). This rich blood flow is also a reason that metastases from malignant tumours frequently settle in the liver. When a tumour breaks into the vascular system, individual cells can separate from the organism and be carried away with the blood. They can then become stuck in the capillary network of other organs as in a filter; there they can grow into new tumours. They stick out on the surface of the liver or of a slice as light-coloured lumps (Figs. 5.19 and 5.20).

Melanomas, called "black cancer," are an especially malignant skin cancer. They develop from the cells that form melanin, a dark brown pigment of the skin, and thus look black. Melanoma cancer cells have a tendency to infiltrate blood and lymph vessels very quickly so that often after only a short time numerous small metastases turn up in other parts of the skin. The most frequent and most severe complication is the proliferation of tumours in the vital organs through metastases. In the body slices shown in Figs. 5.21 a and b, numerous me-

tastases can be seen in the abdominal and chest cavities as well as in the brain.

The abdominal organs are surrounded by the abdominal wall, which consists mainly of muscles. These are necessary for the movements of the torso. When they contract, they exert substantial pressure on the abdominal cavity (abdominal press). If the abdominal wall gives way to this pressure at a weak point, for example, where there is only connective tissue but not muscle, abdominal organs (usually loops of the small intestine) may protrude through a resulting rupture of the abdominal wall, which is known as a hernia. The organs then push the thin, transparent membrane that lines the walls of the abdominal cavity and folds inward to enclose the abdominal organs (peritoneum) outward like a sac (hernial sac). One weak point that is frequently affected is the groin (Fig. 5.23). Men are more likely than women to develop these so-called inguinal hernias, as with men the spermatic cord passes through the inner layers of the abdominal wall at this point, thereby creating a natural opening in the outer wall.

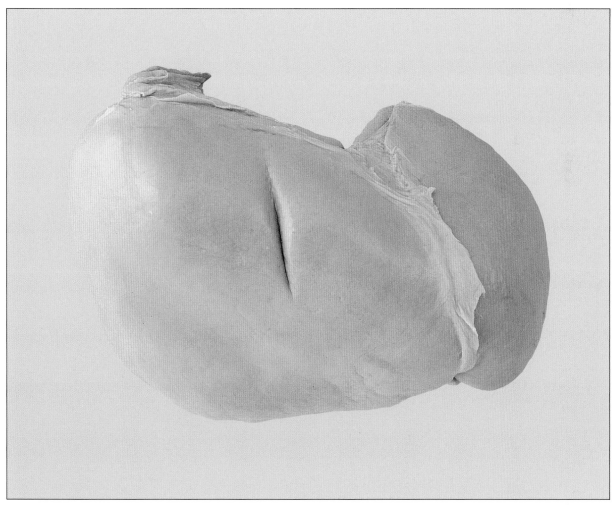

Fig. 5.17 Fatty liver

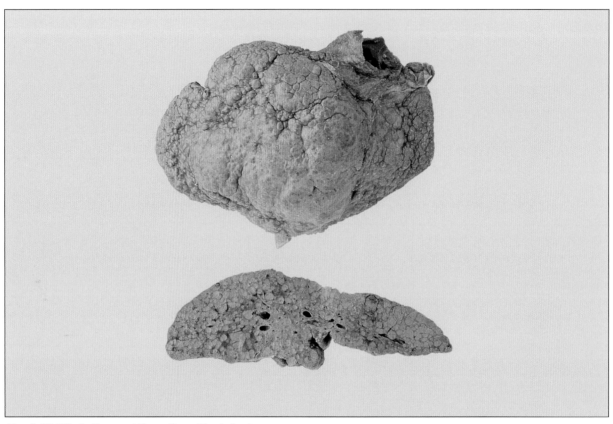

Fig. 5.18 Whole liver and liver slice with cirrhosis

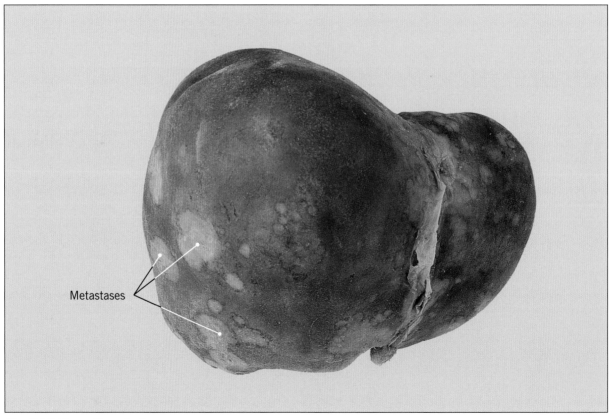

Metastases

Fig. 5.19 Liver with metastases

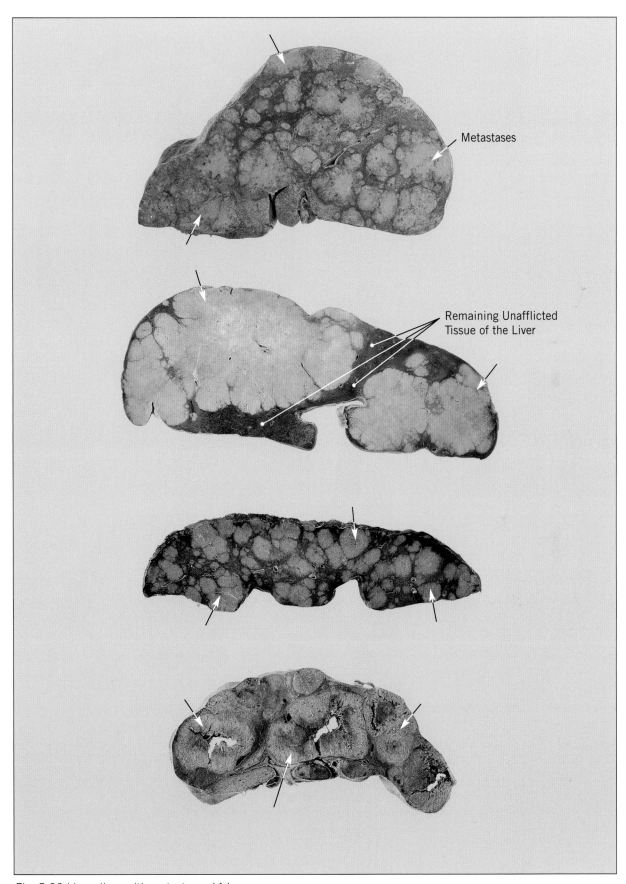

Metastases

Remaining Unafflicted
Tissue of the Liver

Fig. 5.20 Liver slices with metastases (←)

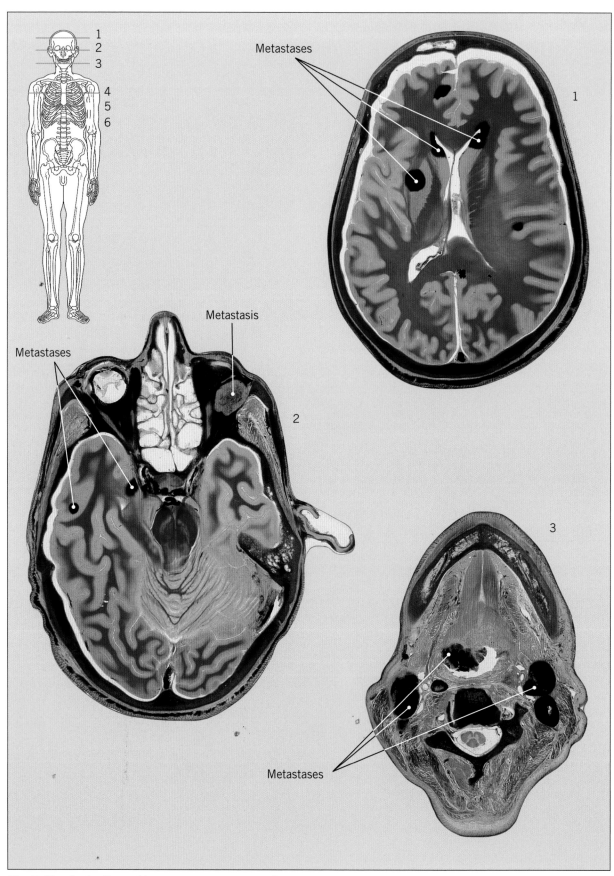

Metastases

Metastasis

Metastases

Metastases

Metastases

1

2

3

1
2
3
4
5
6

Fig. 5.21 a Body slices with numerous metastases of melanomas

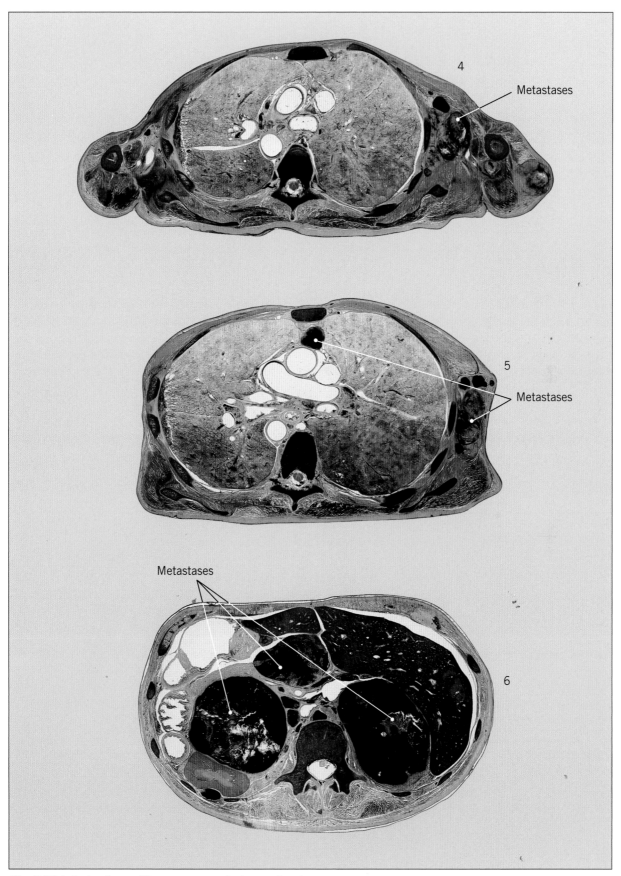

4

Metastases

5

Metastases

Metastases

6

Fig. 5.21 b Body slices with numerous metastases of melanomas

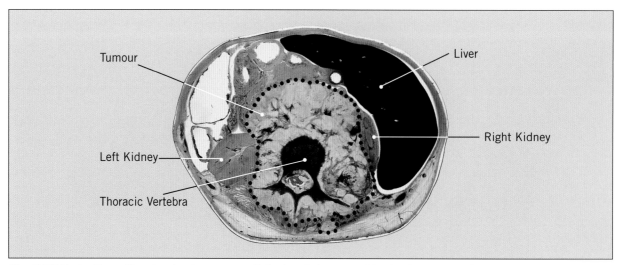

Fig. 5.22 Body slice with extensive tumour growth in the abdomen and in the dorsal wall of the torso

The spleen (Fig. 5.24) is not a part of the digestive tract but is directly adjacent to the stomach and pancreas on the left side of the upper abdomen.

It is a lymphatic organ. Breaking down old blood cells is, inter alia, one of its functions. Moreover, it plays a key role in the body's immune system. The spleen is normally about 12 cm long and weighs between 80 and 120 grams. With certain liver and blood diseases, it can enlarge substantially and in extreme cases can weigh up to 10 kilograms.

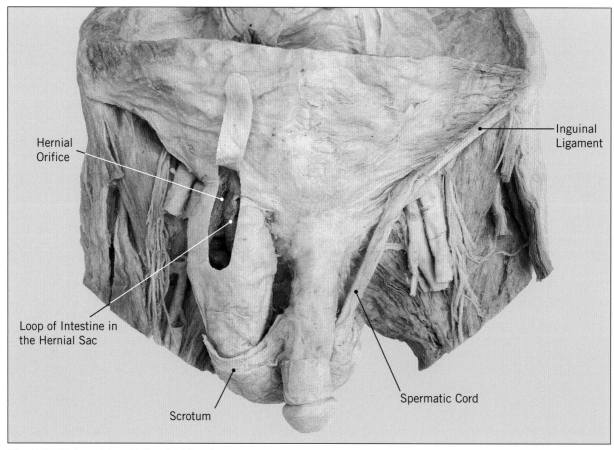

Fig. 5.23 Male pelvis with inguinal hernia

Fig. 5.24 Spleens, normal (above) and enlarged

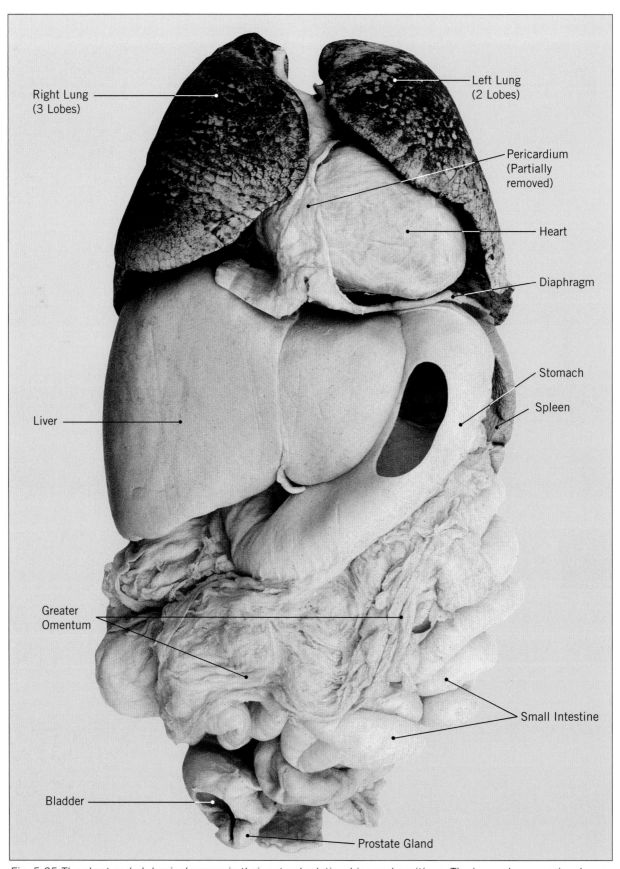

Right Lung
(3 Lobes)

Left Lung
(2 Lobes)

Pericardium
(Partially
removed)

Heart

Diaphragm

Stomach

Spleen

Liver

Greater
Omentum

Small Intestine

Bladder

Prostate Gland

Fig. 5.25 The chest and abdominal organs in their natural relationships and positions. The lungs show massive deposits of tars.

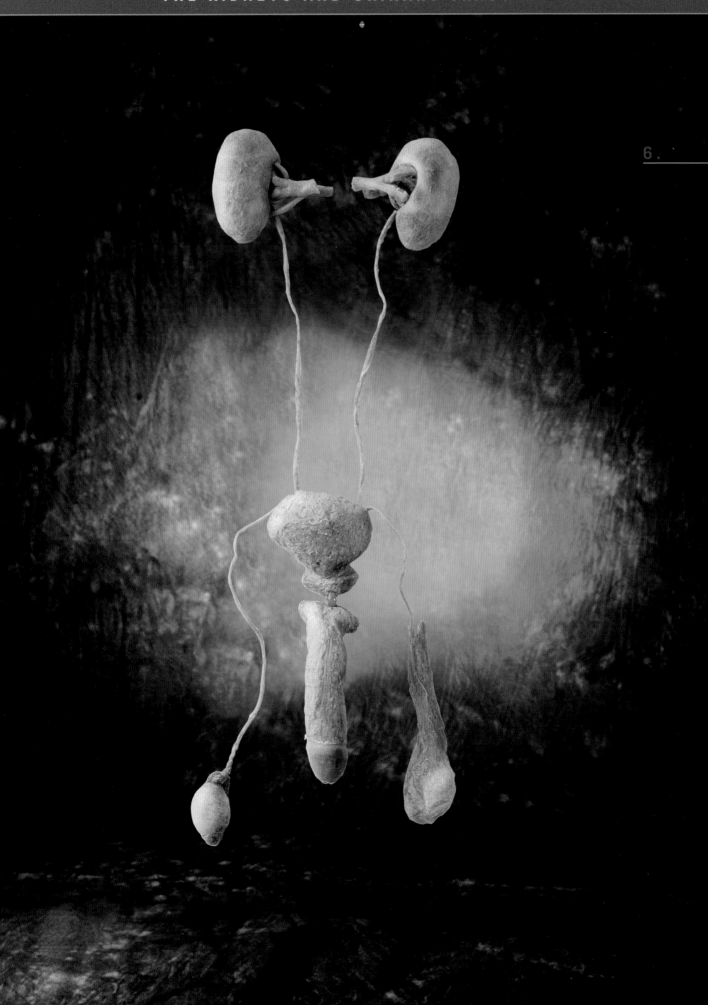

6. The Kidneys and Urinary Tract

Like any complex machinery, the human body also produces waste. Part of these waste products is discharged through the urine. In addition, the kidneys constantly filter dissolved waste products and water out of the blood. The total volume of blood in a body flows through the kidneys approx. 15 times per hour; that means 1800 litres of blood per day. At the same time, the kidneys maintain the balance between fluids, minerals and trace elements in the body.

(Fig. 6.1). They are situated on either side of the spinal column at the back wall of the upper abdomen. They are protected by the ribs in a renal bed (Fig. 6.4). In the kidney that has been cut open, a distinction can be made between the cortex, in which the blood is filtered, and the inner medulla that consists of white cone–shaped blocks of tissue called pyramids, in which the urine is concentrated (Fig. 6.2). The fine collection structures in the medulla open into cuplike calyces, from which urine empties into the renal pelvis. From there, the urine flows downward through long tube-like ducts (ureters) into the bladder where it is stored.

Finally, it is discharged from the body via the urethra, which in men is surrounded by a chestnut-sized prostate gland at its upper end, directly under the bladder (Fig. 6.3).

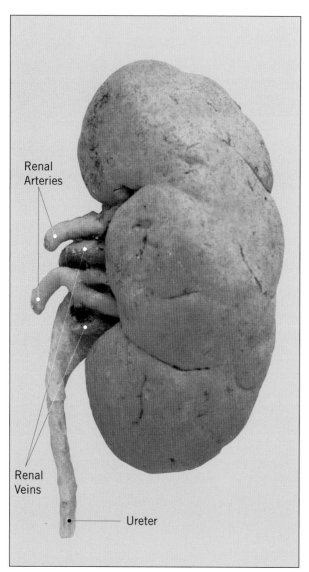

Renal Arteries

Renal Veins

Ureter

Fig. 6.1 Human kidney

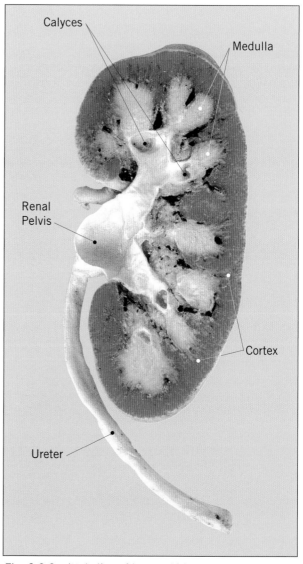

Calyces

Medulla

Renal Pelvis

Cortex

Ureter

Fig. 6.2 Sagittal slice of human kidney

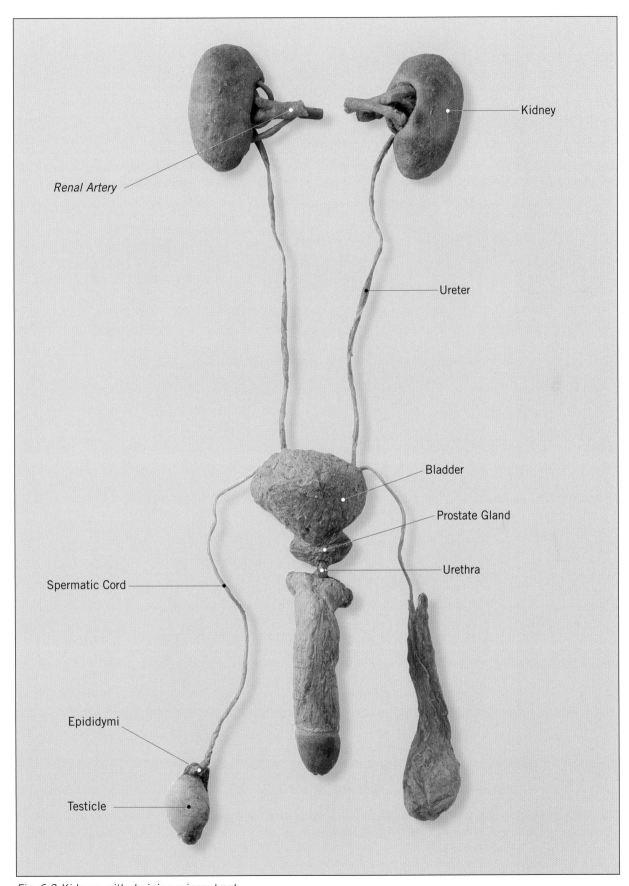

Renal Artery

Kidney

Ureter

Bladder

Prostate Gland

Urethra

Spermatic Cord

Epididymi

Testicle

Fig. 6.3 Kidneys with draining urinary tract

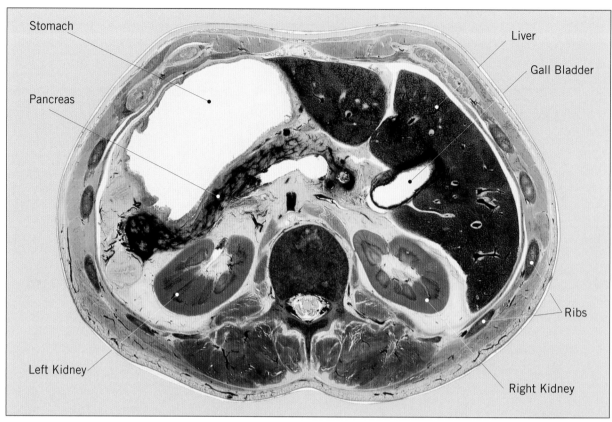

Stomach

Liver

Gall Bladder

Pancreas

Ribs

Left Kidney

Right Kidney

Fig. 6.4 Cross-section through the upper abdomen

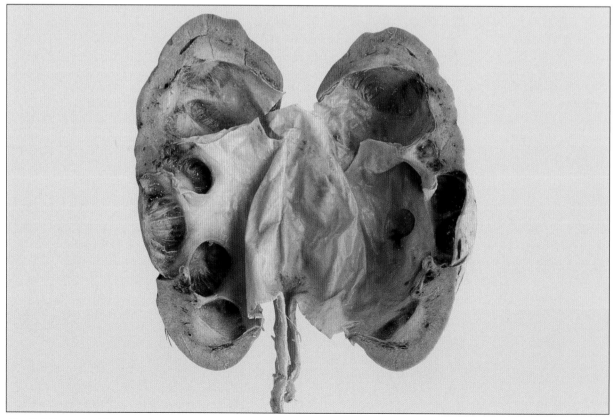

Fig. 6.5 Saccular kidney, cut open

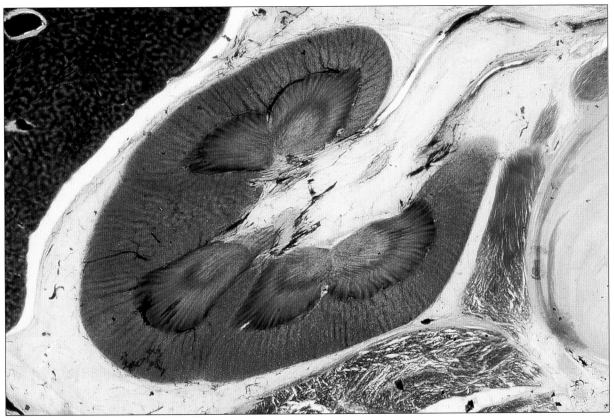

Fig. 6.6 Cross-section of kidney, detail

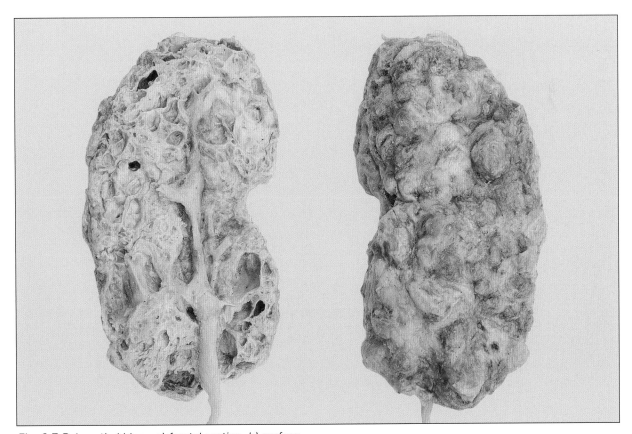

Fig. 6.7 Polycystic kidney, a) frontal section, b) surface

The internal diameter of ureters is less than 3 mm. For this reason, they can easily be blocked, e.g., by a kidney stone or by external compression. As urine is constantly being produced, such blockage causes it to back up in the renal pelvis, which in turn makes it distend and stretch the kidney tissue, which will become thinner if the pressure continues. This syndrome is called sacciform kidneys (hydronephrosis; Fig. 6.5).

Fig. 6.7 shows a polycystic kidney, a congenital deformation of the kidneys, in which the entire organ is infiltrated with small, fluid-filled cavities (cysts), which cause severe dilation of the organ. This disorder also causes severe kidney dysfunction and can only be treated by haemodialysis or a kidney transplant. Conversely, individual kidney cysts (Fig. 6.9) alone generally do not cause any problems. They are usually detected by coincidence, e.g., during an ultrasound examination of the abdomen and are encountered in approx. 10 % of the populace.

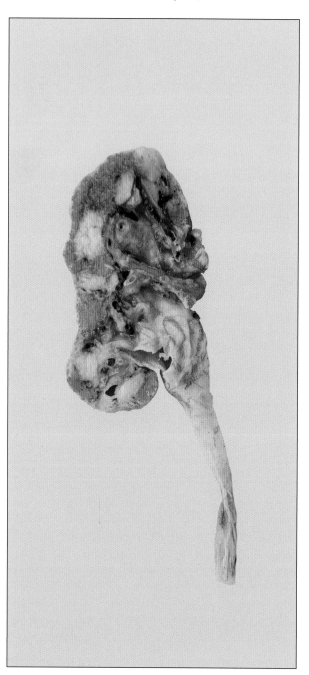

Fig. 6.8 Shrunken kidney caused by chronic infectious processes

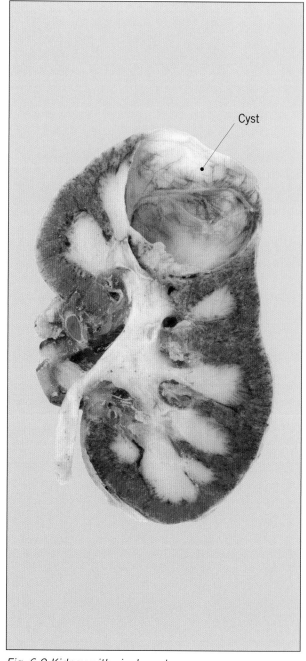

Cyst

Fig. 6.9 Kidney with single cyst

7. The Reproductive Organs

Reproduction is an essential aspect of life. New life is created when a male sperm fertilizes a female egg. These eggs and sperm are produced in the sexual organs.

Part of the male sexual organs are visible outside the body, and part is concealed within the body. The visible parts include the penis and the scrotum, which contains the two, egg-shaped testes and the epididymides. Inside the body, there is the prostate gland, the seminal vesicles and a number of tubes, such as the sperm duct, which connect the entire system (Fig. 7.1).

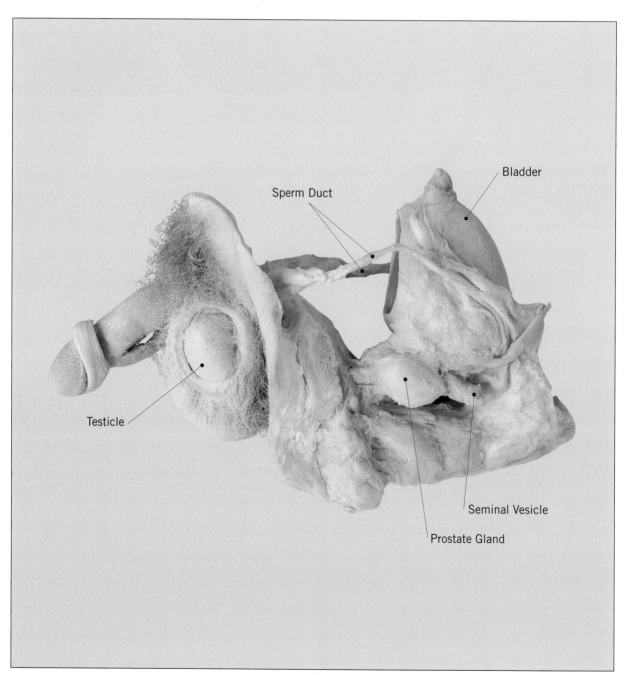

Fig. 7.1 Male sexual organs

The two testes are approximately the size of walnuts and consist of thousands of seminiferous tubules, in which about 500 million sperm mature every day. As they are in the scrotum outside the body, their temperature is always slightly below normal body temperature, which is necessary in forming sperm cells. Sperm are stored in the epididymides, which envelop the testes like a hood (Fig. 7.2). During sexual arousal, sperm is pumped toward the urethra by rhythmic contractions at the moment of ejaculation. There fluids from the prostate gland and the seminal vesicles are mixed with the sperm before it is ejaculated by means of rhythmic contractions of the urethral muscles.

The prostate gland is directly below the bladder and surrounds the urethra (Fig. 7.3). Its secretions, which are mixed with semen at ejaculation, facilitate movement of the sperm. With advancing age, the prostate gland tends to distend (Fig. 7.4). Its immediate proximity to the urethra then leads to problems with urination in aging men.

Female sexual organs are largely contained within the body. They not only produce the eggs necessary for fertilization,

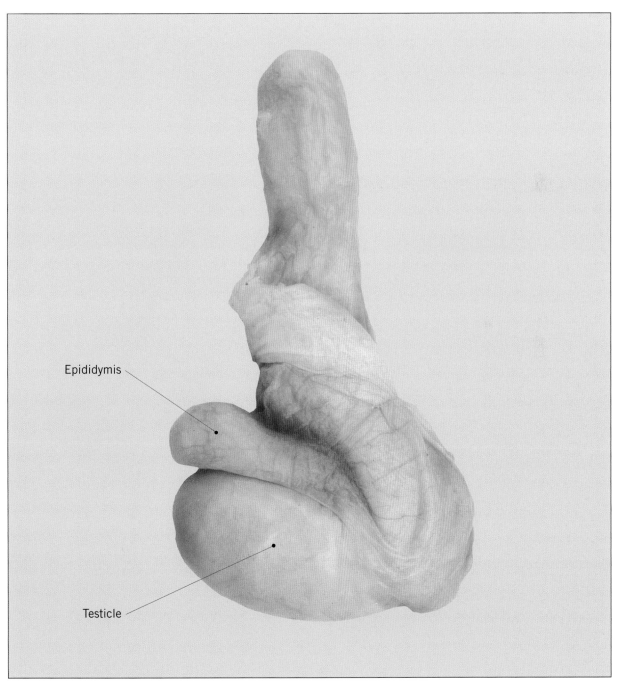

Epididymis

Testicle

Fig. 7.2 Testicle with epididymis

but are also involved in the development and birth of the foetus. Female reproductive organs include the two ovaries, the two Fallopian tubes, the uterus, the vagina and the external genitalia (Fig. 7.5).

Unlike male sperm, which constantly has to be reproduced, female egg cells are already implanted in the ovaries at birth, as so-called gametocytes. The ovaries, which are about the size of a peach stone, are situated at the side walls of the pelvis and are attached to the uterus by ligaments of connective tissue.

In sexually mature women, eggs ripen in the ovaries in a regular cycle of about four weeks; as a rule, each ovary alternates releasing a ripe egg for each cycle. When the egg is ripe, it is released into the abdomen (ovulation) where it is captured by the funnel-like end of the Fallopian tubes.

The function of the approx. 7–10-cm long Fallopian tubes is to convey the egg into the uterus. Fertilization generally occurs on the way to the uterus. The sperm swim at a speed of three to five millimetres per minute through the uterus and the Fallopian tubes. If there was ovulation with-

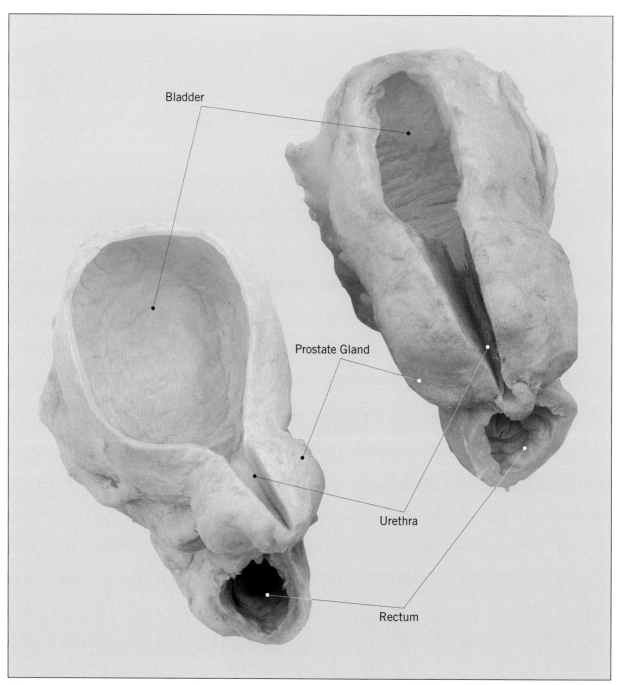

Bladder

Prostate Gland

Urethra

Rectum

Fig. 7.3 Bladder with prostate gland

Fig. 7.4 Bladder with severely distended prostate gland

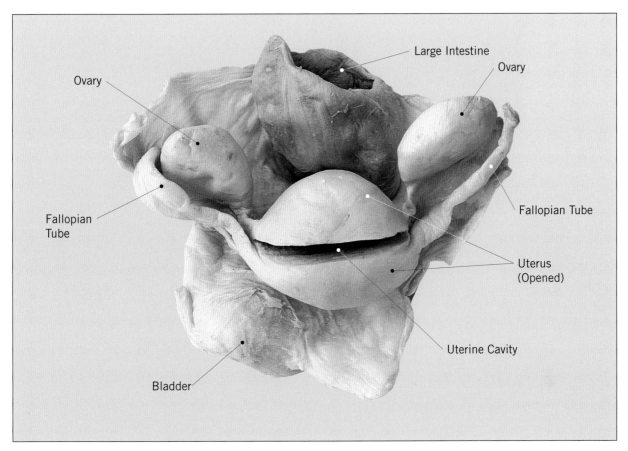

Fig. 7.5 Female internal sexual organs

in the last 48 hours, the sperm will encounter the egg. Should an egg deviate from its course to the Fallopian tube after ovulation, it can be fertilized in the abdomen (extrauterine pregnancy). On the other hand, if the egg is impeded on its way through the Fallopian tube, e.g., due to adhesions, pregnancy can develop there in the Fallopian tube.

The uterus measures approx. 6–8 cm and weighs around 50 grams; it is located in the middle of the pelvis, slightly above and behind the bladder. It is a pear-shaped, hollow organ with thick walls of muscle fibres. The upper part, the uterine body, accepts the fertilized egg and nourishes both the embryo and later the foetus as they develop during pregnancy by means of the blood vessels in its lining. In the course of pregnancy, the uterus gradually enlarges to a considerable extent, occupying most of the abdominal cavity (Fig. 8.8, p. 128). In non-pregnant women, the uterus is only about 2–3-cm^3 large; shortly before birth, the volume is 5–7 litres (or 300 to over 425 cubic inches). In the lower section of the uterus, there is the cylinder-shaped cervix, which opens into the vagina.

Fig. 7.6 shows a uterus, whose walls are covered with several small, benign tumours (myomas). Generally speaking, such tumours do not cause any problems; however, they could lead to menstrual disorders or complications during pregnancy.

Female breasts are actually appendages of the skin. As they, nevertheless, play a major part in human reproduction, they are also included with the external sexual organs. The mammary glands basically consist of fatty tissue that is permeated by milk glands and a network of glandular ducts that is so fine as to be scarcely visible to the naked eye (Figs. 7.8, 7.10–7.11). Small milk ducts empty into ever-larger collection ducts, which finally find an outlet at the nipples.

During pregnancy, the effects of hormones cause the number of milk glands and glandular ducts to increase significantly. Fig. 7.9 shows a sagittal slice of a female breast that has been almost completely infiltrated by the hard tissue of breast cancer. By comparison, the slice of healthy mammary glands in Fig. 7.8 shows pliable tissue interspersed with fatty cells. Breast cancer is a relatively common disease; it is the most frequent form of organic cancer in women.

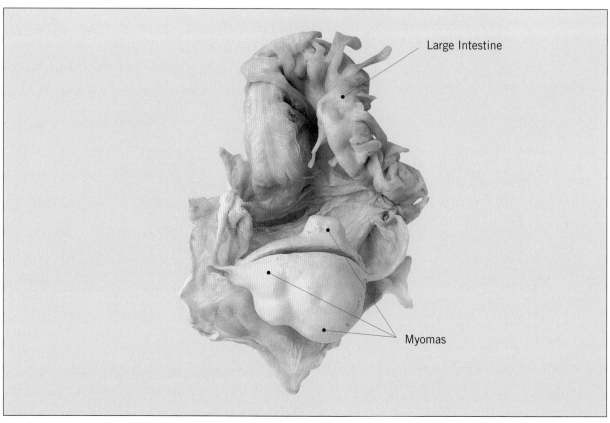

Fig. 7.6 Myomas (Benign tumours made of muscle fibres) on the uterus

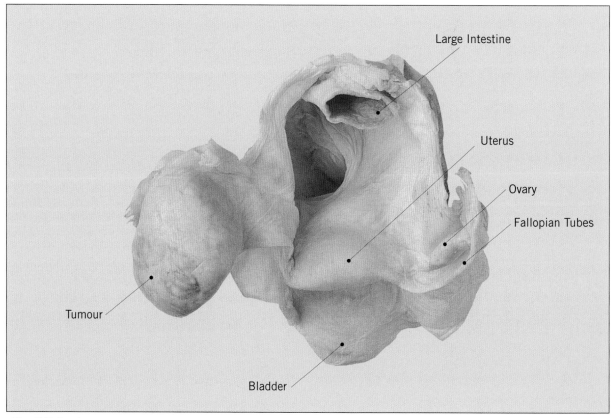

Fig. 7.7 Ovarian tumour

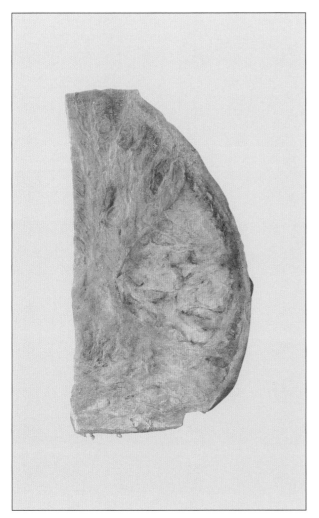

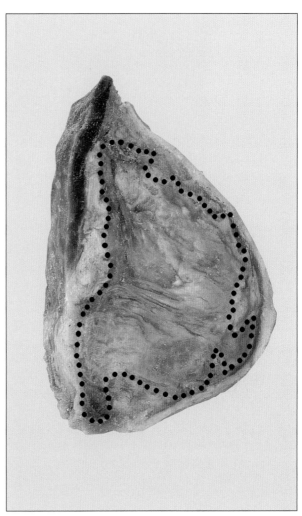

Fig. 7.8 Sagittal slice through a female breast

Fig. 7.9 Sagittal slice through a female breast with breast cancer (marked area)

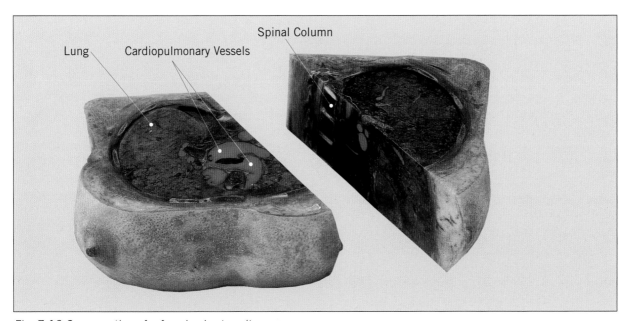

Fig. 7.10 Cross-section of a female chest cavity

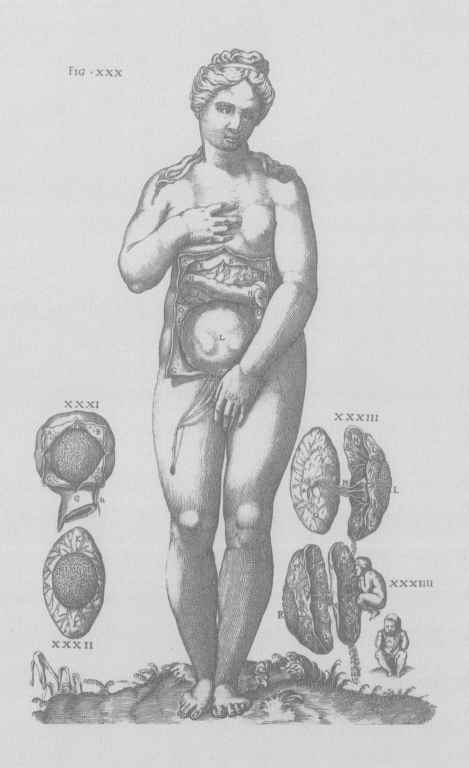

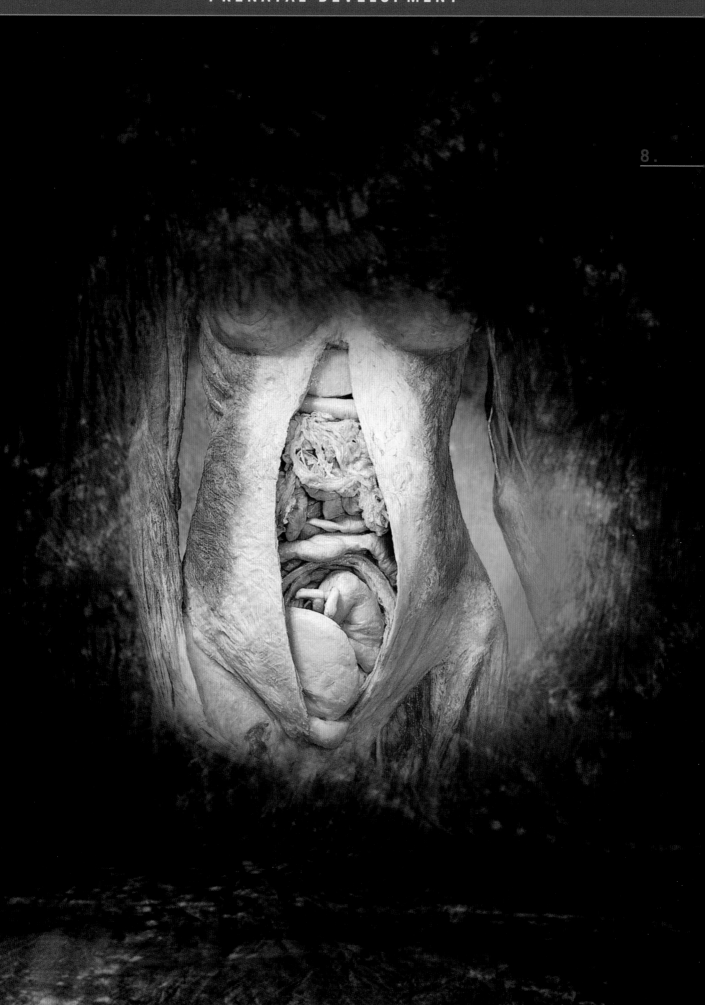

8. Prenatal Development

The first period of human life takes place invisibly in the mother's body. It begins when an egg is fertilized by sperm and ends with birth. With humans, pregnancy lasts an average of 266 days (by comparison: elephants deliver their young after 660- and mice after 20-day pregnancies). Eggs fertilized in the Fallopian tubes travel to the uterine cavity; the cells divide several times before embedding themselves in the lining of the uterus. The cells continue to di-

vide and begin to specialize in order to form all of the tissue and organs. After only four weeks, the baby already has a heart, eyes and four buds, from which the extremities will develop. After eight weeks, the period of organ differentiation is largely completed, and the baby now already begins to resemble a tiny child. During the first eight weeks, it is called an embryo. It is called a foetus during the next phase, which is primarily characterized by growth and organ ma-

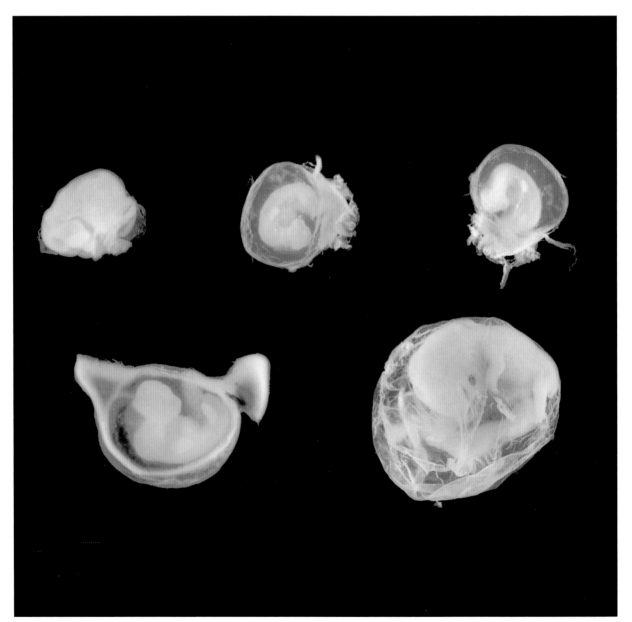

Fig. 8.1 Developmental stages from the fourth to the eighth week of pregnancy. During the first eight weeks of pregnancy, the developing organism is called an embryo. During this time, all organs are present.

turation. By the fourth month, the liver, pancreas, the intestines and the kidneys have been developed; hair and nails begin to grow. In the fifth month, maturing of the nervous system begins and the mother can feel the foetus move. After the seventh month, the foetus is developed to such an extent that it would be capable of surviving in case of premature birth. During the last two months, the foetus mainly gains in size and weight.

Nourishment for the developing foetus is provided by the pancake-shaped placenta (Figs. 8.4 and 8.5). The placenta exists only during pregnancy, measures approx. 18 cm in diameter and weighs about 500 grams. It develops during the first 10 weeks of pregnancy at the point where the fertilized egg embedded itself in the lining of the uterus. It is connected to the foetus via the umbilical cord. The heart of developing foetuses pumps blood through the artery of the umbilical cord to the vascular bed of the placenta, which is bathed in the mother's blood from the lining of the uterus. Here the exchange of substances such as oxygen and nutrients as well as waste and CO_2 can occur without mixing the blood of mother and child. Afterwards, blood that has been enriched with nutrients and oxygen flows back to the foetal organism via the umbilical cord.

Twins are individuals developed jointly in the same pregnancy. They are conceived when either the fertilized egg divides into two blastoderms (=identical or monozygotic twins)

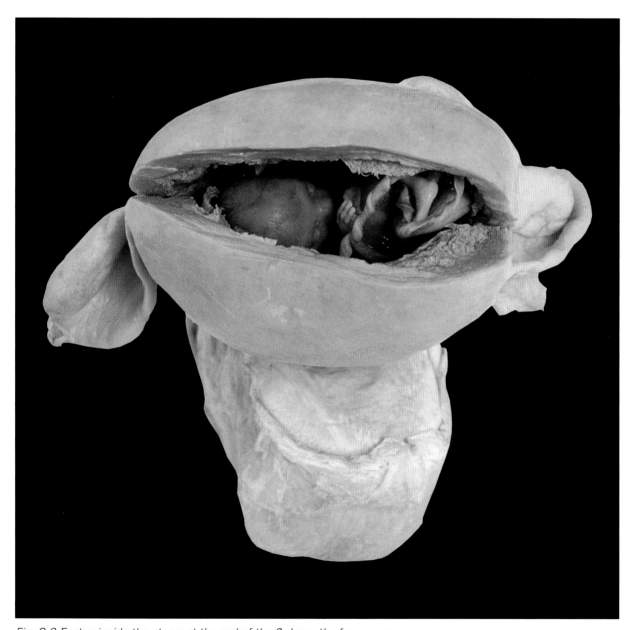

Fig. 8.2 Foetus inside the uterus at the end of the 3rd month of pregnancy

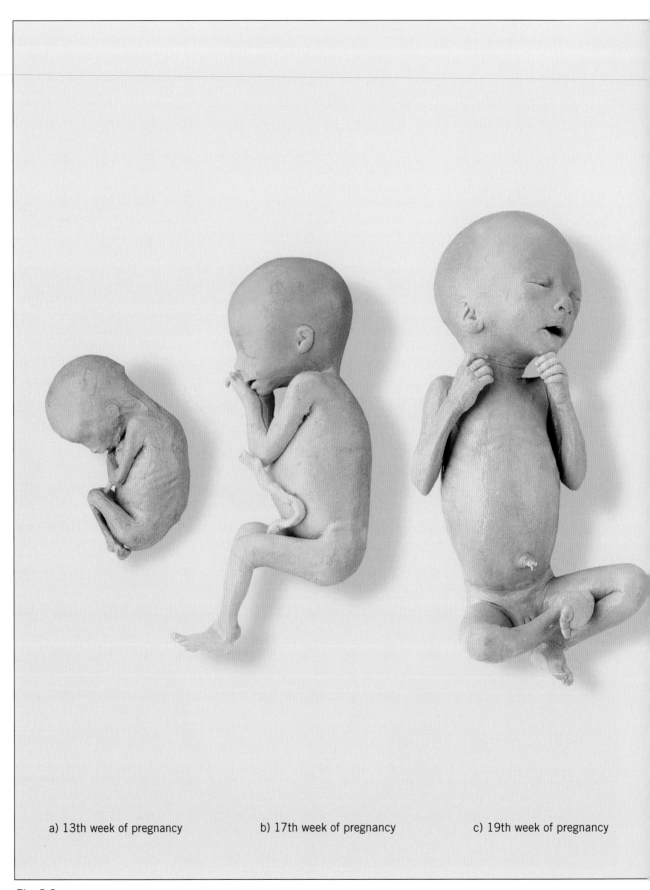

a) 13th week of pregnancy   b) 17th week of pregnancy   c) 19th week of pregnancy

Fig. 8.3

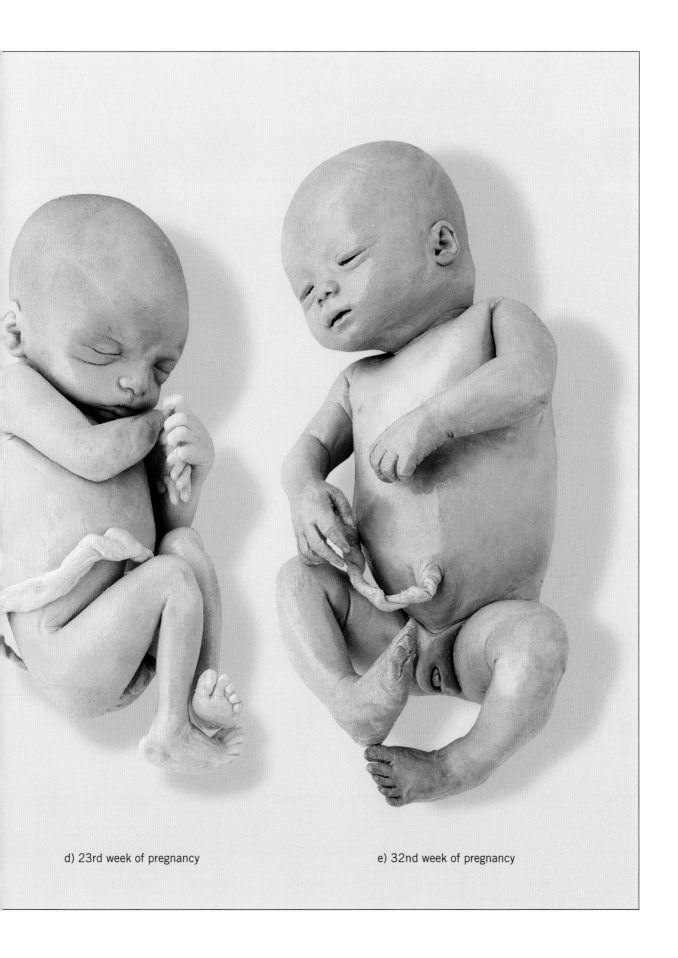

d) 23rd week of pregnancy   e) 32nd week of pregnancy

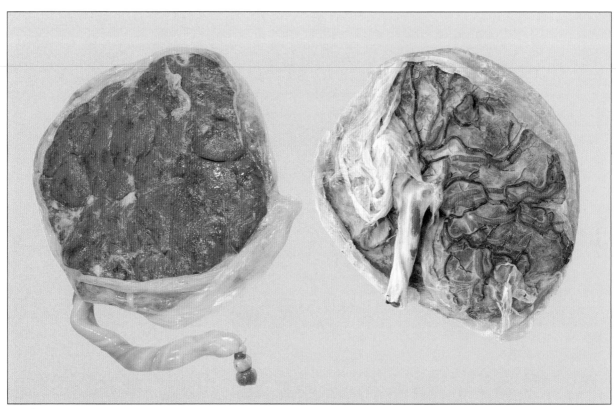

Fig. 8.4 Placenta. The uterine side shows the dense vascular bed, in which the exchange of nourishment and oxygen takes place

Fig. 8.5 Placenta. On the surface of the foetal side, the arteries and veins of the umbilical cord vessels branch out.

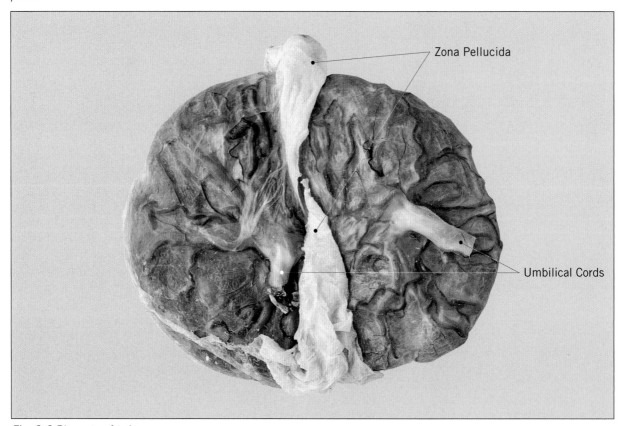

Zona Pellucida

Umbilical Cords

Fig. 8.6 Placenta of twins

or from two eggs (= fraternal or dizygotic twins) fertilized at the same time. In the first case, the children are syngeneic (sharing the same genetic code) and always of the same sex. In the second case, they are as genetically similar or different as any siblings. Identical twins can share a single placenta or each can have his or her own; conversely, with fraternal twins, there are always two separate placentas. Fig. 8.6 shows a large placenta of identical twins. On its surface, the stumps of two umbilical cords can be seen and remnants of the zona pellucida (oolemma) that encased the foetuses in the uterus.

Fig. 8.7 shows a foetus in the uterus at the end of the third month of pregnancy (embedded in a block). The bones appear through the soft tissue due to a special colouration.

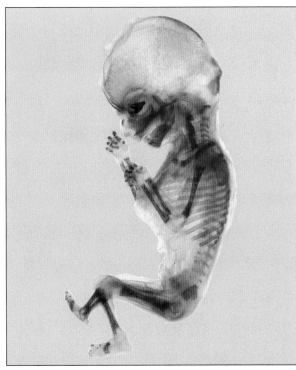

Fig. 8.7 Foetus at the end of the third month of pregnancy. Special dyes have been used to colour the bones

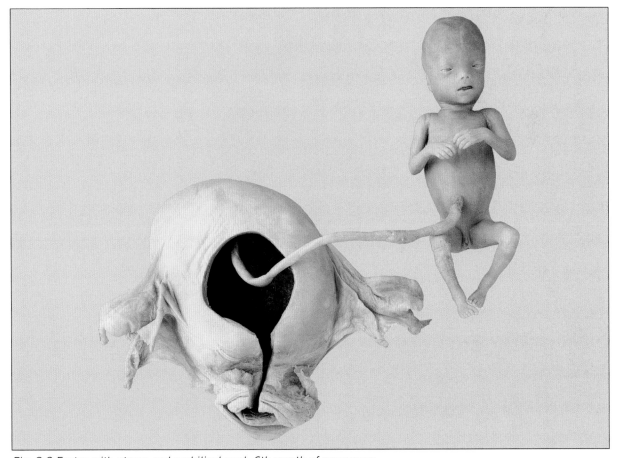

Fig. 8.8 Foetus with uterus and umbilical cord; 6th month of pregnancy

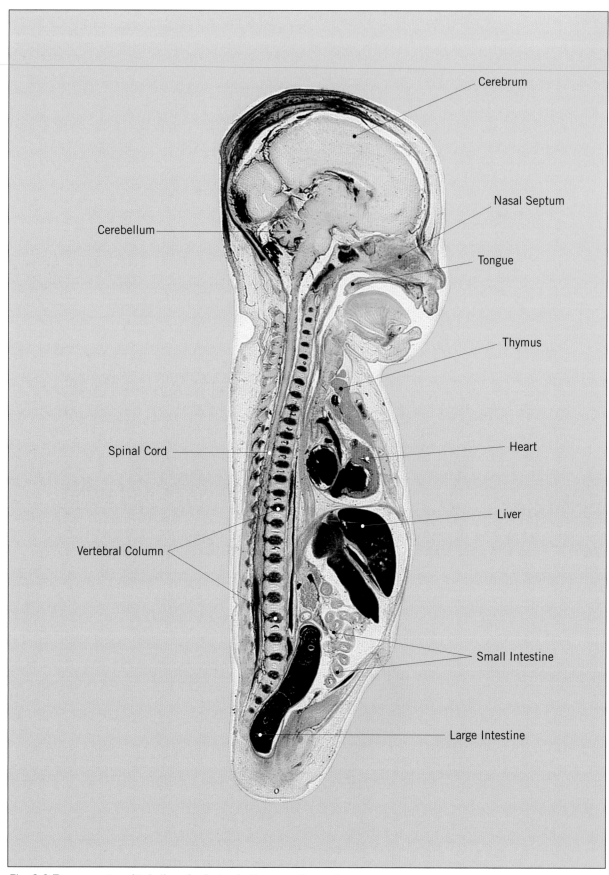

Cerebrum

Nasal Septum

Cerebellum

Tongue

Thymus

Spinal Cord

Heart

Liver

Vertebral Column

Small Intestine

Large Intestine

Fig. 8.9 Transparent sagittal slice of a foetus in the seventh month

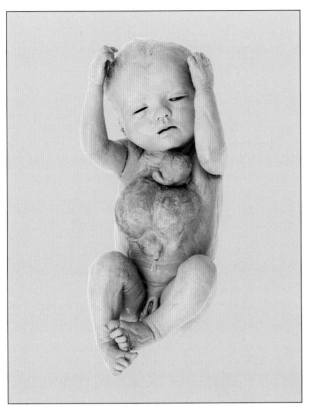

Fig. 8.10 Foetus with chest and abdominal defects: the heart and parts of the abdominal organs protrude outwardly.

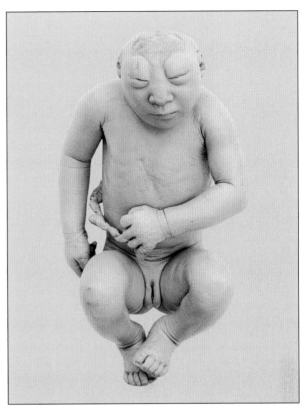

Fig. 8.12 Foetus with a most severe deformation of the brain, in which the cranium and extensive parts of the brain are missing.

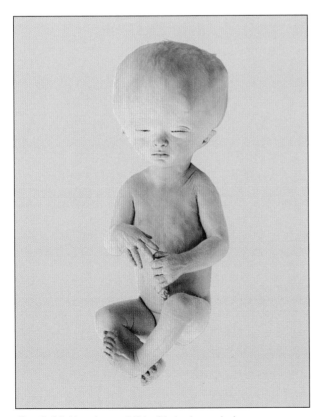

Fig. 8.11 New-born child with hydrocephalus

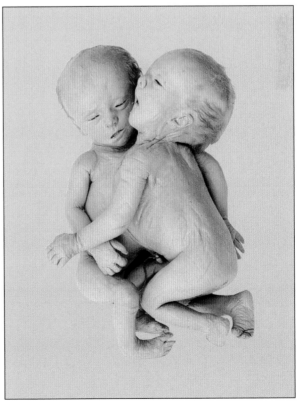

Fig. 8.13 Siamese twins

Congenital Deformities

Congenital deformities can either be the result of pathological genetic factors or abnormal development of the foetus caused by damage from external sources (e.g., from alcohol or drug abuse of the mother or from infectious diseases). During the period from the third to the eighth weeks of pregnancy, embryos are especially susceptible to such influences as at this time the rate of cell division is particularly high and organ differentiation is in progress. Here abnormal development of individual cells can lead to malformation of the entire organism.

Fig. 8.11 shows a newborn child with hydrocephalus. This syndrome is caused by abnormal accumulation of fluid in the brain due to blockage, which leads to a backup of the cerebrospinal fluid in the cerebral ventricles. With foetuses and small children, this increase in pressure not only makes the ventricles dilate, but also causes the entire skull to enlarge. The reason for this is that the cranial sutures have not yet become ossified because of anticipated cranial growth; they thus give way to the increased internal pressure. Normally, the circumference of the head corresponds to that of the chest.

Siamese twins (Fig. 8.13) are identical twins who are joined or to one another at some point. They result when individual cells or clusters of cells divide incompletely during early embryonic development.
The chances for survival for Siamese twins depend on the severity of this adhesion to one another. In simple cases, the twins are only joined by a flap of skin and can be easily separated through surgery. In severe cases, both individuals share vital organs, such as the heart and/or the liver.

Fig. 8.12 shows a foetus afflicted with anencephaly. This is the most severe deformation of the brain, in which the cranium and extensive parts of the brain are missing. Such foetuses have no chance of surviving.

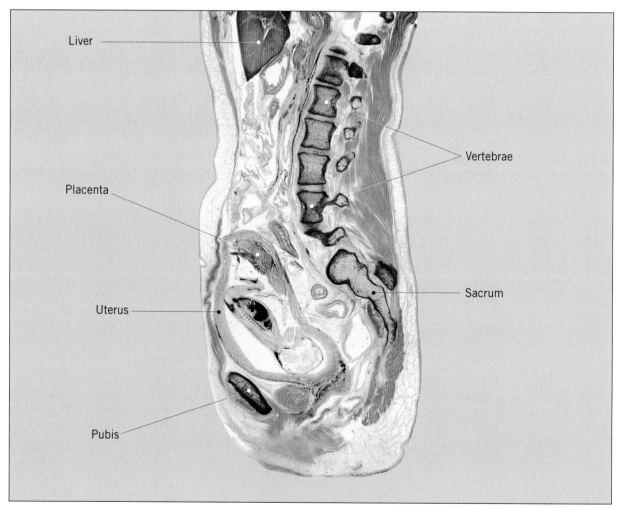

Fig. 8.14 Sagittal slice through a woman in the fifth month of pregnancy

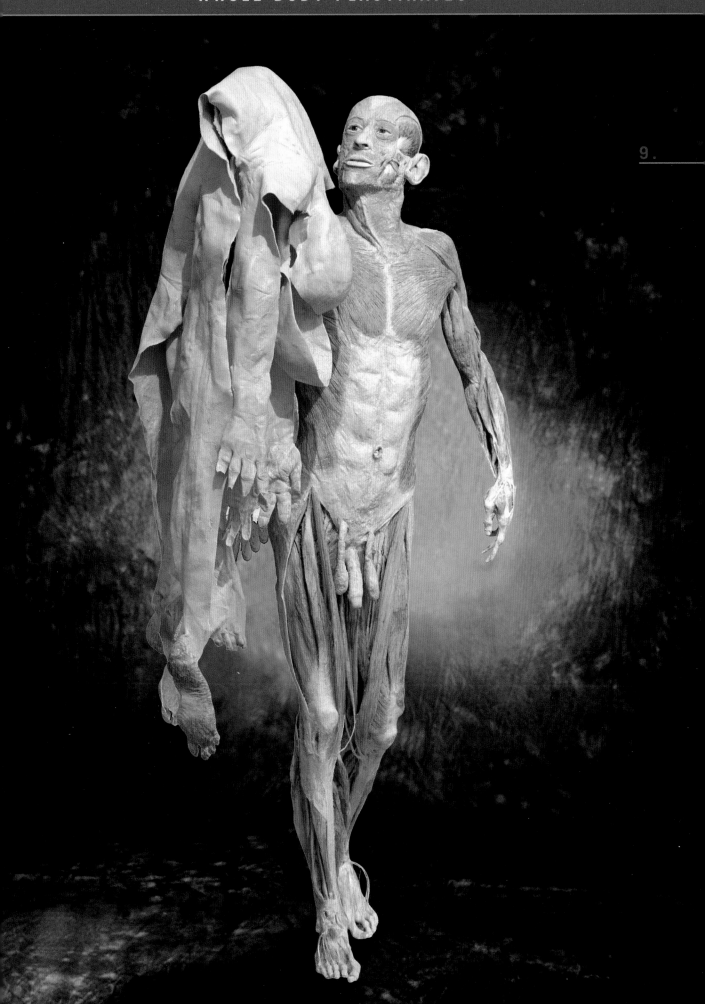

9. Whole Body Plastinates

Fig. 9.1 bis 9.3

Whole body plastinate of a woman in the 5th month of pregnancy. At this stage of the pregnancy, the foetus is 17 centimetres (ca. 6.5 inches) long from crown-to-rump and causes the abdomen to bulge.

The superficial muscles have been exposed on the front side of this body, while the back shows the deeper muscles. On the left side of the back, the thoracic cavity has been opened, revealing a smoker's lung, as can be clearly seen by the black pigmentation. On the right side, the torso has been opened to show the right kidney.

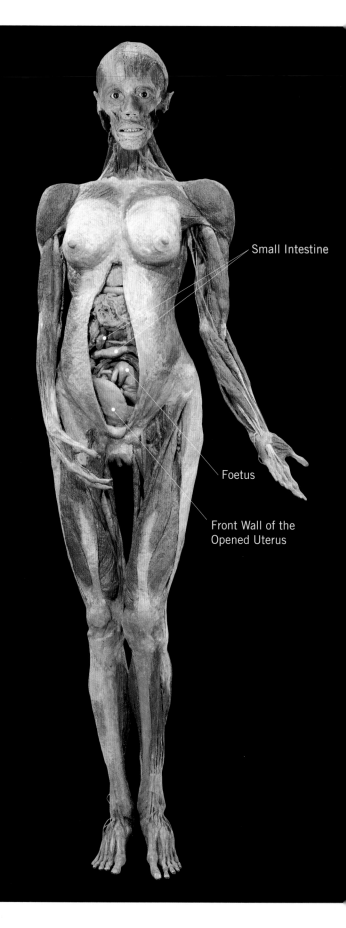

Small Intestine

Foetus

Front Wall of the Opened Uterus

Fig. 9.1

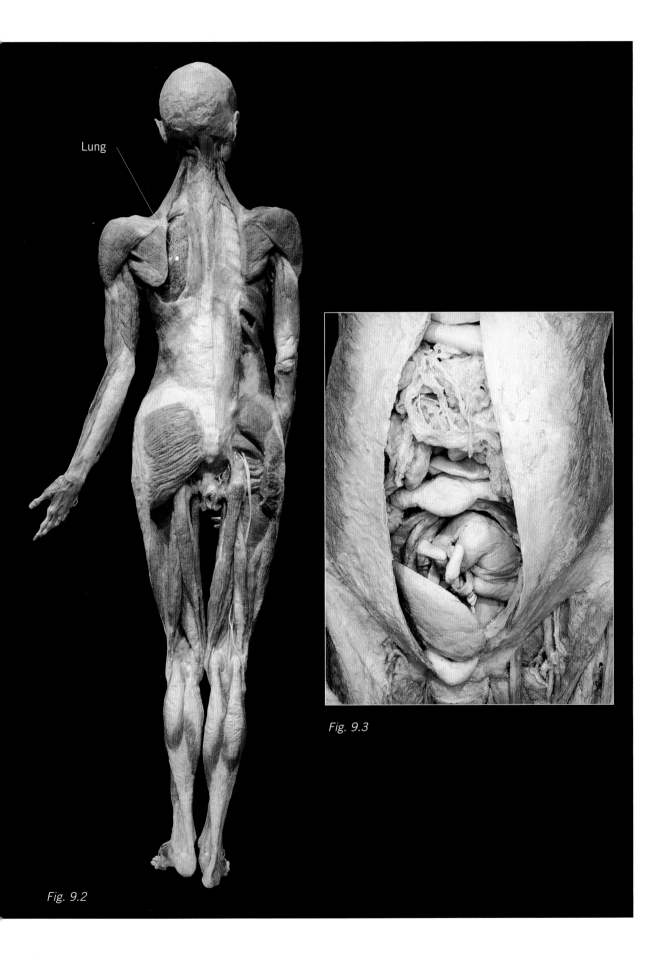

Lung

Fig. 9.2

Fig. 9.3

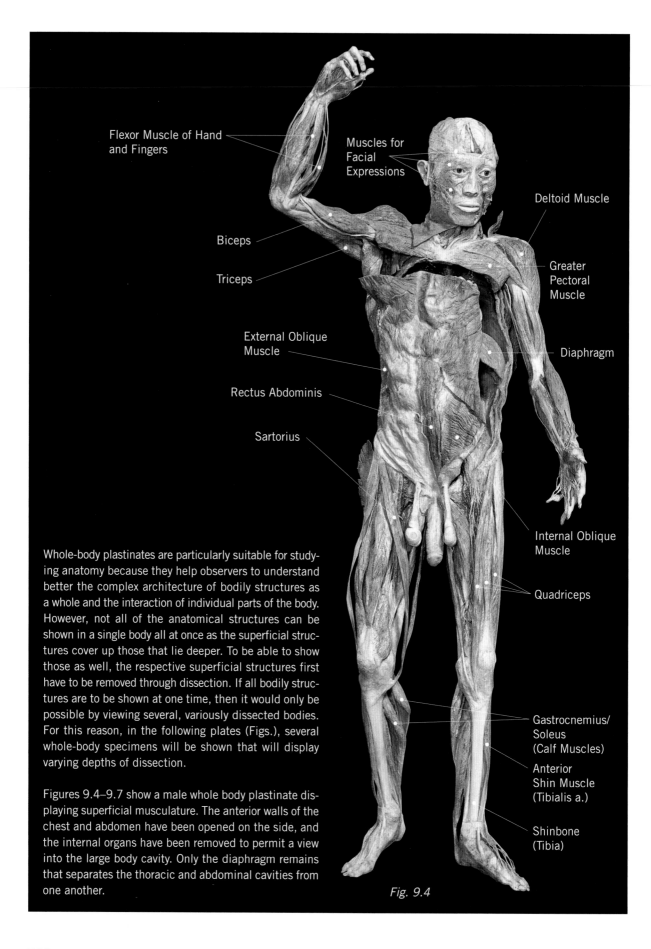

Flexor Muscle of Hand
and Fingers

Muscles for
Facial
Expressions

Deltoid Muscle

Biceps

Greater
Pectoral
Muscle

Triceps

External Oblique
Muscle

Diaphragm

Rectus Abdominis

Sartorius

Internal Oblique
Muscle

Quadriceps

Whole-body plastinates are particularly suitable for study-ing anatomy because they help observers to understand better the complex architecture of bodily structures as a whole and the interaction of individual parts of the body. However, not all of the anatomical structures can be shown in a single body all at once as the superficial struc-tures cover up those that lie deeper. To be able to show those as well, the respective superficial structures first have to be removed through dissection. If all bodily struc-tures are to be shown at one time, then it would only be possible by viewing several, variously dissected bodies. For this reason, in the following plates (Figs.), several whole-body specimens will be shown that will display varying depths of dissection.

Figures 9.4–9.7 show a male whole body plastinate dis-playing superficial musculature. The anterior walls of the chest and abdomen have been opened on the side, and the internal organs have been removed to permit a view into the large body cavity. Only the diaphragm remains that separates the thoracic and abdominal cavities from one another.

Gastrocnemius/
Soleus
(Calf Muscles)

Anterior
Shin Muscle
(Tibialis a.)

Shinbone
(Tibia)

Fig. 9.4

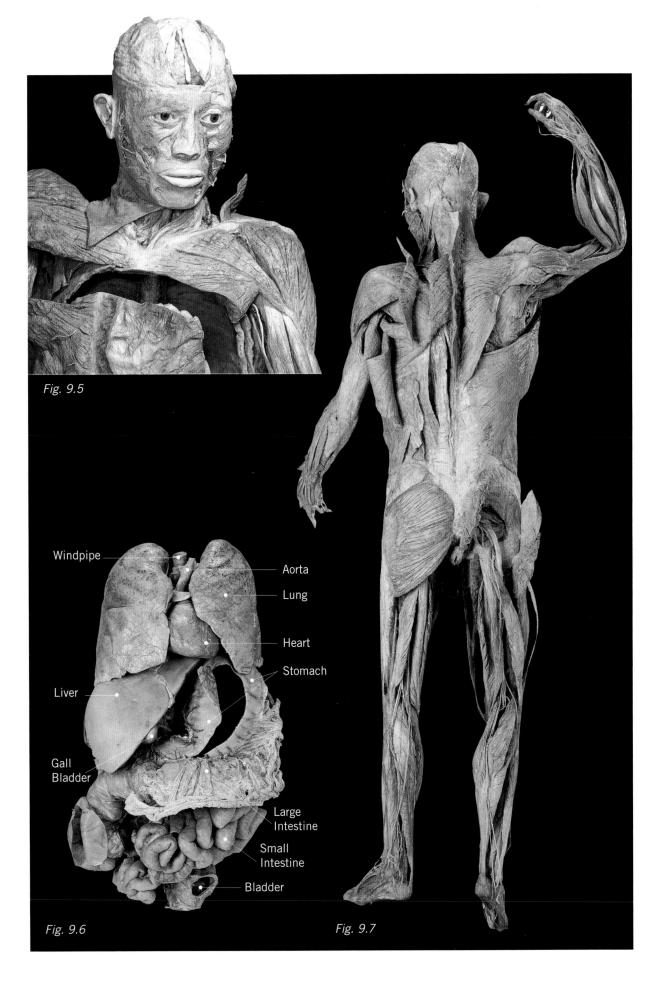

Fig. 9.5

Fig. 9.6

Windpipe
Aorta
Lung
Heart
Stomach
Liver
Gall
Bladder
Large
Intestine
Small
Intestine
Bladder

Fig. 9.7

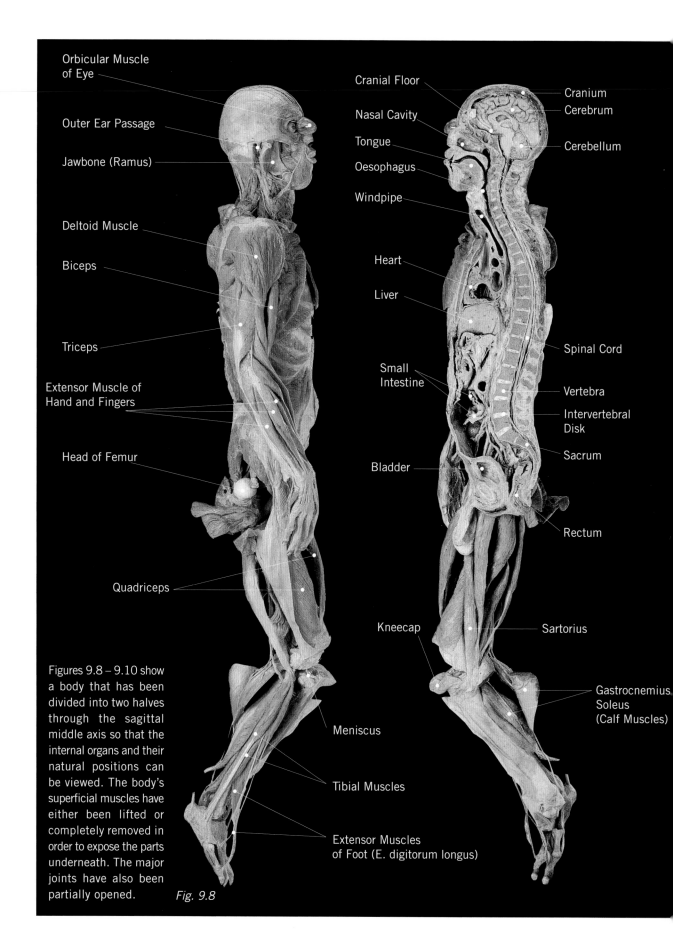

Orbicular Muscle of Eye

Outer Ear Passage

Jawbone (Ramus)

Deltoid Muscle

Biceps

Triceps

Extensor Muscle of Hand and Fingers

Head of Femur

Quadriceps

Cranial Floor

Nasal Cavity

Tongue

Oesophagus

Windpipe

Heart

Liver

Small Intestine

Bladder

Cranium

Cerebrum

Cerebellum

Spinal Cord

Vertebra

Intervertebral Disk

Sacrum

Rectum

Kneecap

Sartorius

Gastrocnemius, Soleus (Calf Muscles)

Meniscus

Tibial Muscles

Extensor Muscles of Foot (E. digitorum longus)

Figures 9.8 – 9.10 show a body that has been divided into two halves through the sagittal middle axis so that the internal organs and their natural positions can be viewed. The body's superficial muscles have either been lifted or completely removed in order to expose the parts underneath. The major joints have also been partially opened. *Fig. 9.8*

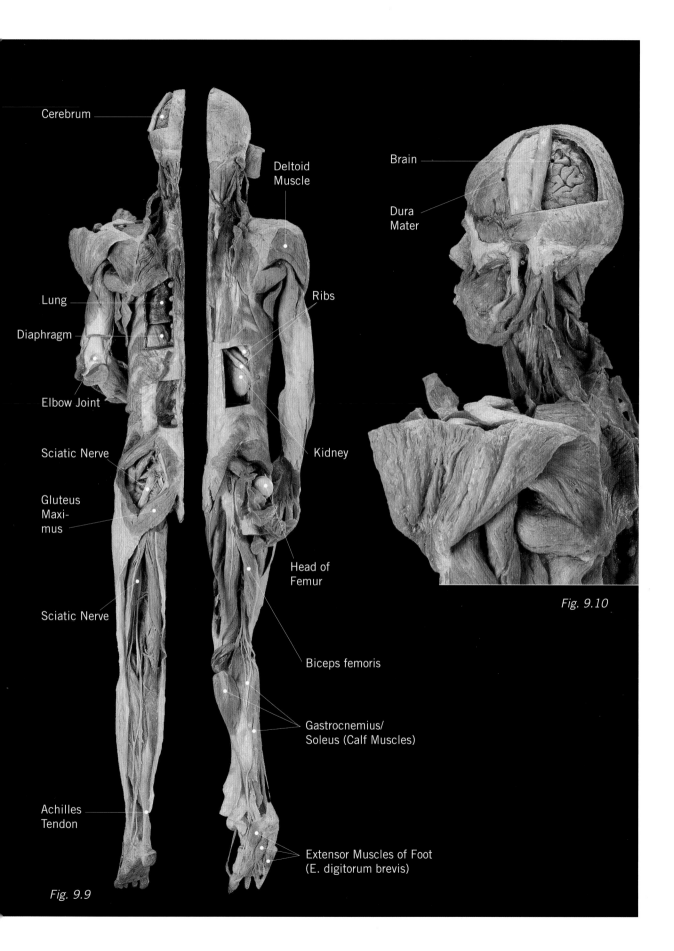

Cerebrum

Deltoid Muscle

Lung

Diaphragm

Elbow Joint

Sciatic Nerve

Gluteus Maximus

Sciatic Nerve

Achilles Tendon

Ribs

Kidney

Head of Femur

Biceps femoris

Gastrocnemius/ Soleus (Calf Muscles)

Extensor Muscles of Foot (E. digitorum brevis)

Fig. 9.9

Brain

Dura Mater

Fig. 9.10

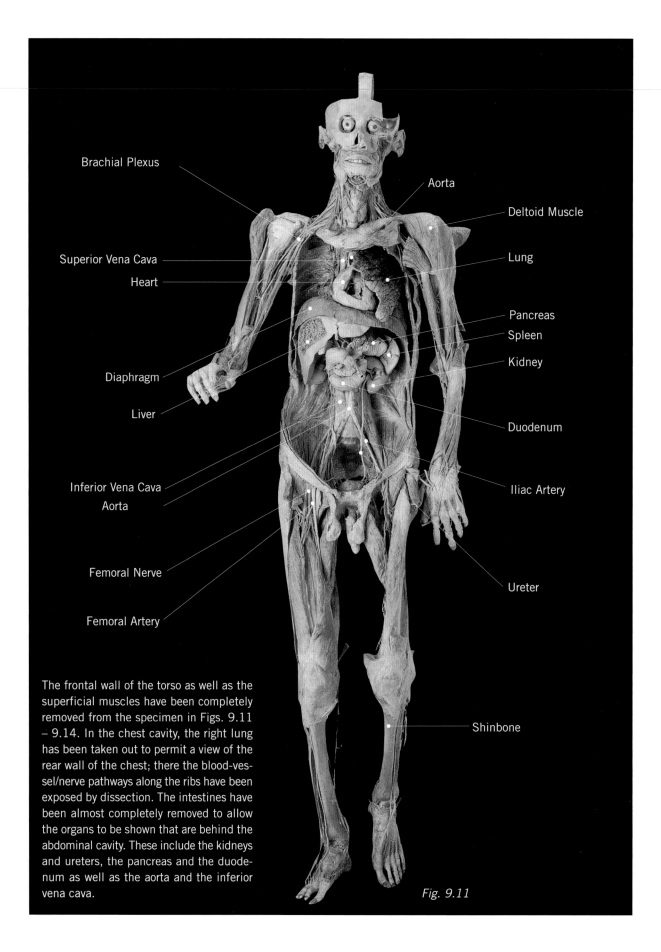

Brachial Plexus

Aorta

Deltoid Muscle

Superior Vena Cava

Lung

Heart

Pancreas

Spleen

Kidney

Diaphragm

Liver

Duodenum

Inferior Vena Cava

Aorta

Iliac Artery

Femoral Nerve

Ureter

Femoral Artery

Shinbone

The frontal wall of the torso as well as the superficial muscles have been completely removed from the specimen in Figs. 9.11 – 9.14. In the chest cavity, the right lung has been taken out to permit a view of the rear wall of the chest; there the blood-vessel/nerve pathways along the ribs have been exposed by dissection. The intestines have been almost completely removed to allow the organs to be shown that are behind the abdominal cavity. These include the kidneys and ureters, the pancreas and the duodenum as well as the aorta and the inferior vena cava.

Fig. 9.11

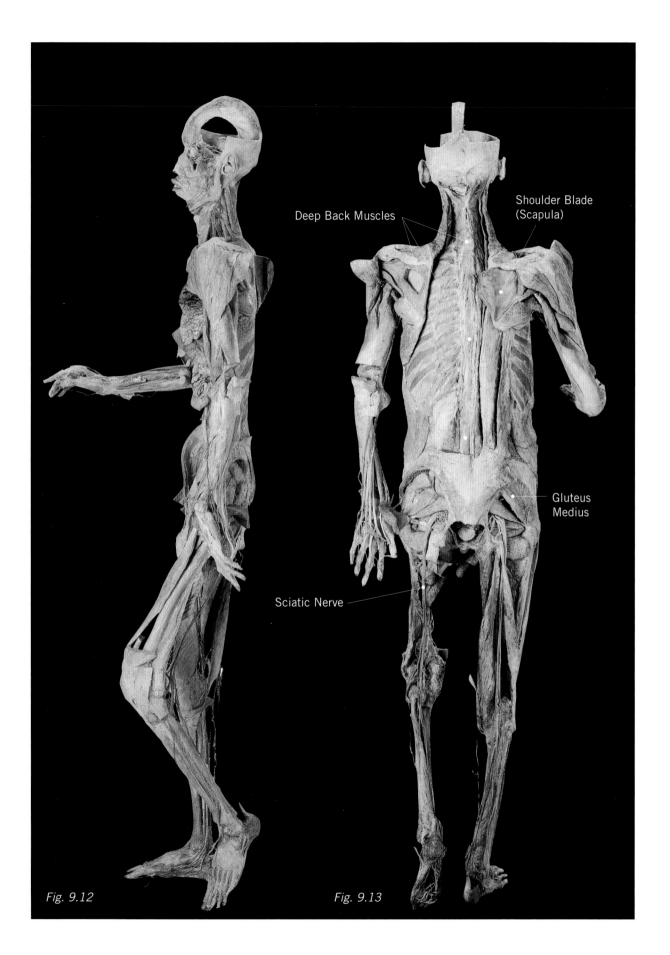

Deep Back Muscles

Shoulder Blade
(Scapula)

Gluteus
Medius

Sciatic Nerve

Fig. 9.12

Fig. 9.13

137

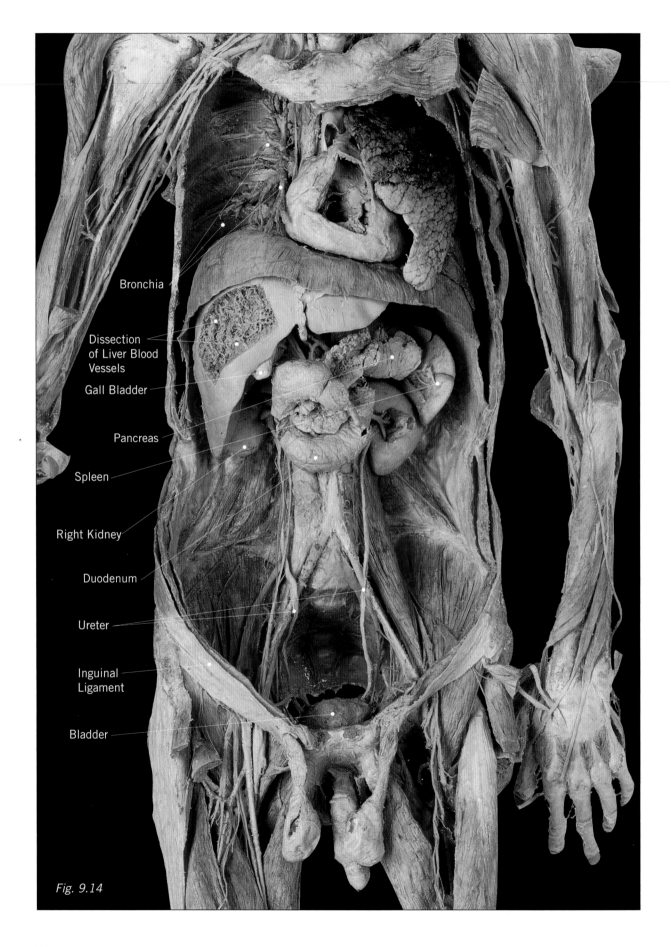

Bronchia

Dissection
of Liver Blood
Vessels

Gall Bladder

Pancreas

Spleen

Right Kidney

Duodenum

Ureter

Inguinal
Ligament

Bladder

Fig. 9.14

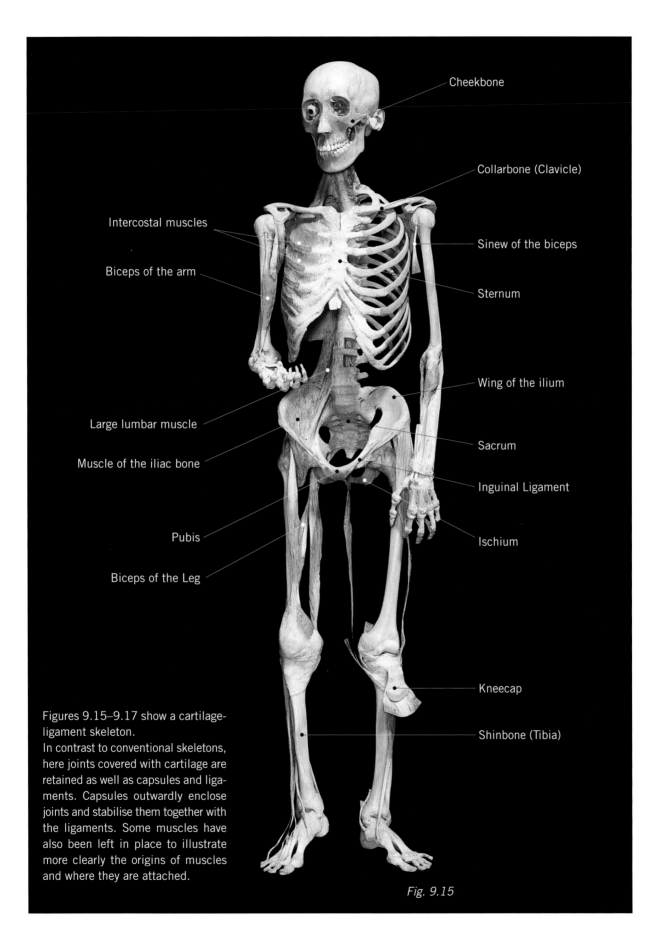

Cheekbone

Collarbone (Clavicle)

Intercostal muscles

Sinew of the biceps

Biceps of the arm

Sternum

Wing of the ilium

Large lumbar muscle

Sacrum

Muscle of the iliac bone

Inguinal Ligament

Pubis

Ischium

Biceps of the Leg

Kneecap

Figures 9.15–9.17 show a cartilage-ligament skeleton.
In contrast to conventional skeletons, here joints covered with cartilage are retained as well as capsules and ligaments. Capsules outwardly enclose joints and stabilise them together with the ligaments. Some muscles have also been left in place to illustrate more clearly the origins of muscles and where they are attached.

Shinbone (Tibia)

Fig. 9.15

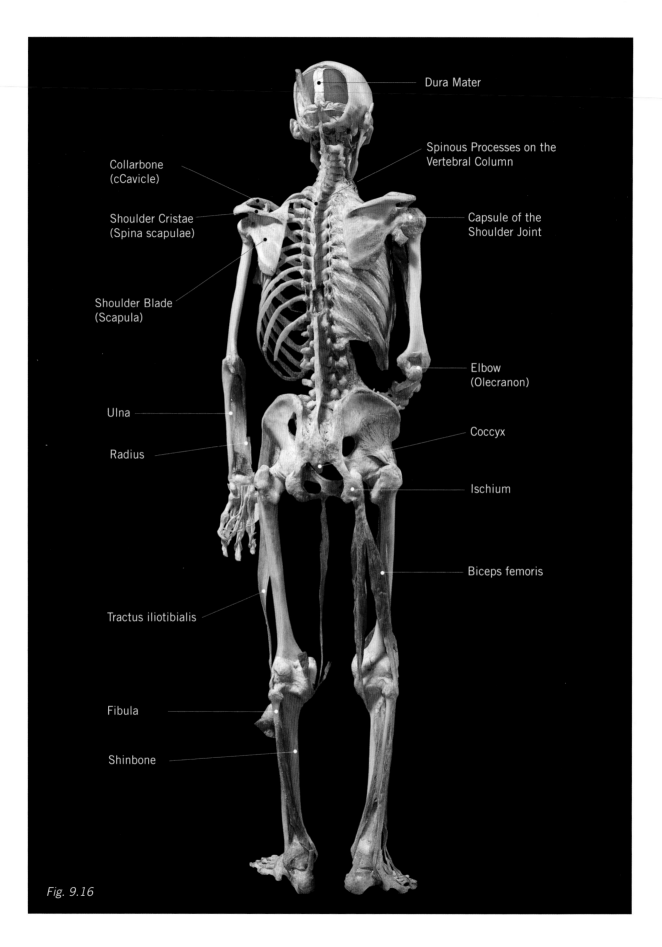

Dura Mater

Spinous Processes on the
Vertebral Column

Collarbone
(cCavicle)

Capsule of the
Shoulder Joint

Shoulder Cristae
(Spina scapulae)

Shoulder Blade
(Scapula)

Elbow
(Olecranon)

Ulna

Coccyx

Radius

Ischium

Biceps femoris

Tractus iliotibialis

Fibula

Shinbone

Fig. 9.16

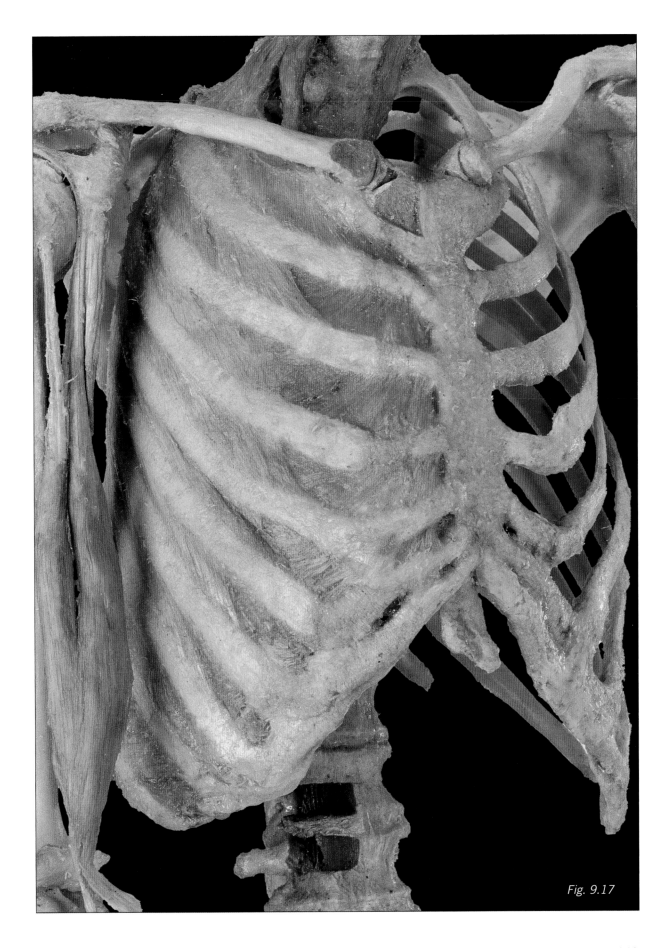

Fig. 9.17

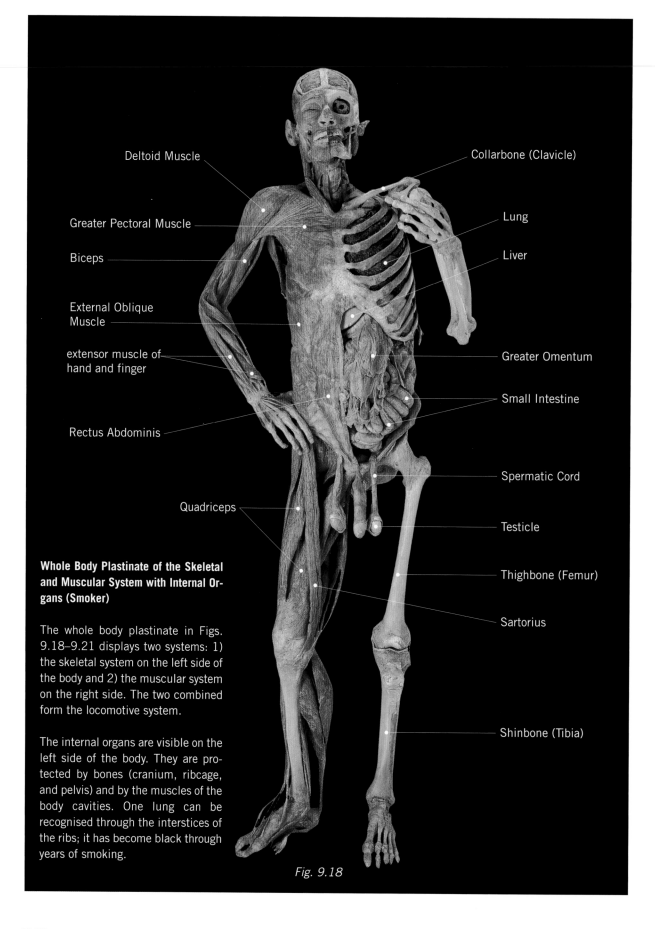

Deltoid Muscle

Greater Pectoral Muscle

Biceps

External Oblique
Muscle

extensor muscle of
hand and finger

Rectus Abdominis

Quadriceps

Collarbone (Clavicle)

Lung

Liver

Greater Omentum

Small Intestine

Spermatic Cord

Testicle

Thighbone (Femur)

Sartorius

Shinbone (Tibia)

**Whole Body Plastinate of the Skeletal
and Muscular System with Internal Organs (Smoker)**

The whole body plastinate in Figs.
9.18–9.21 displays two systems: 1)
the skeletal system on the left side of
the body and 2) the muscular system
on the right side. The two combined
form the locomotive system.

The internal organs are visible on the
left side of the body. They are protected by bones (cranium, ribcage,
and pelvis) and by the muscles of the
body cavities. One lung can be
recognised through the interstices of
the ribs; it has become black through
years of smoking.

Fig. 9.18

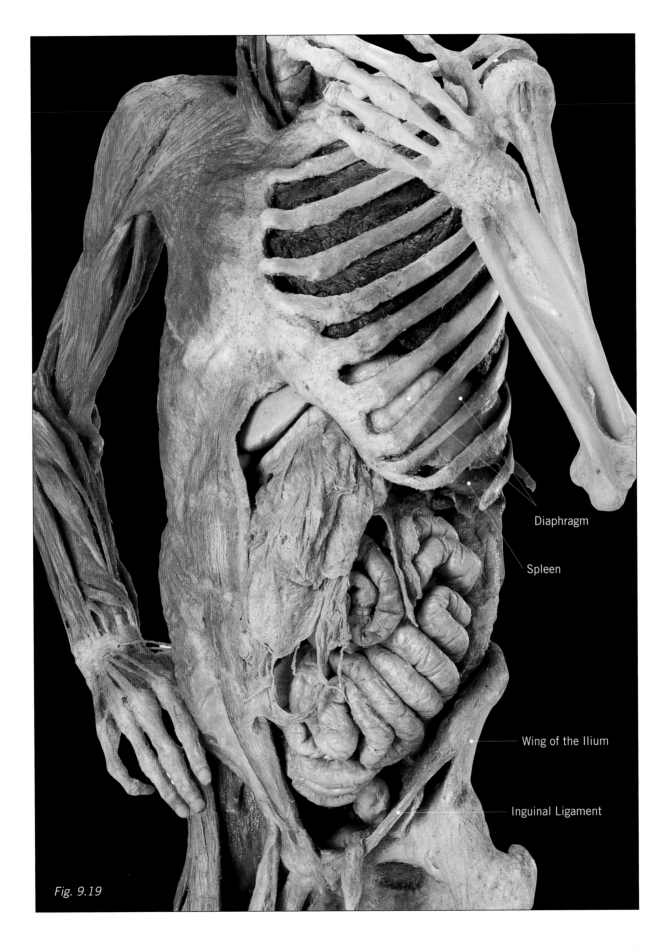

Diaphragm

Spleen

Wing of the Ilium

Inguinal Ligament

Fig. 9.19

143

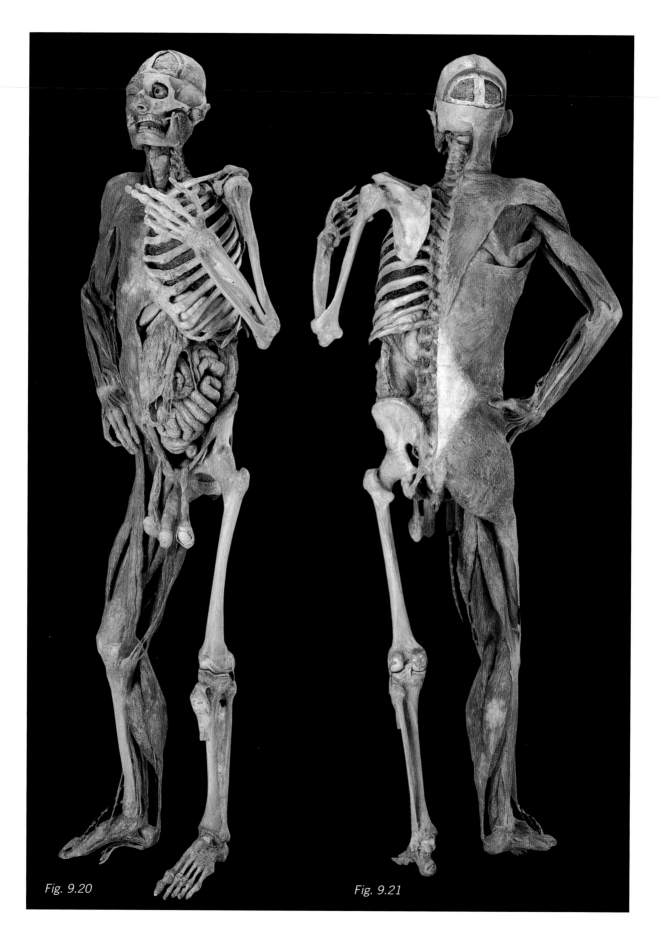

Fig. 9.20

Fig. 9.21

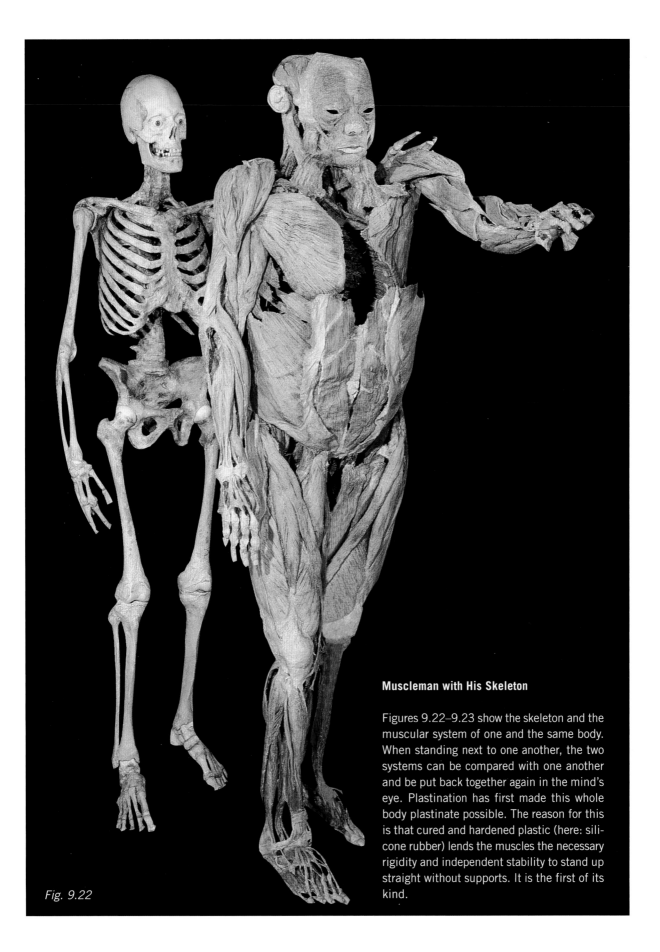

Musicleman with His Skeleton

Figures 9.22–9.23 show the skeleton and the muscular system of one and the same body. When standing next to one another, the two systems can be compared with one another and be put back together again in the mind's eye. Plastination has first made this whole body plastinate possible. The reason for this is that cured and hardened plastic (here: silicone rubber) lends the muscles the necessary rigidity and independent stability to stand up straight without supports. It is the first of its kind.

Fig. 9.22

Fig. 9.23

Whole Body Gestalt Plastinate with Skin

The whole body plastinate demonstrates on the one hand how vulnerable man looks without the skin to protect him, and on the other hand the nature of the skin as an independent organ when there is no longer a body inside. Only when the skin has been carefully removed through dissection does the anatomical nakedness become readily apparent, namely, the bones and muscles that in turn enclose the organs.

The skin is the organ that is noticed the least, and yet it is the largest and heaviest of our organs, without which we would not be able to exist. The skin lends individuality to our exteriors; it also imparts beauty and age. It is the buffer between the body and the environment. Its functions include transmitting pressure and tactile sensations as well as regulating our metabolism, e.g. our water metabolism.

Fig. 9.24

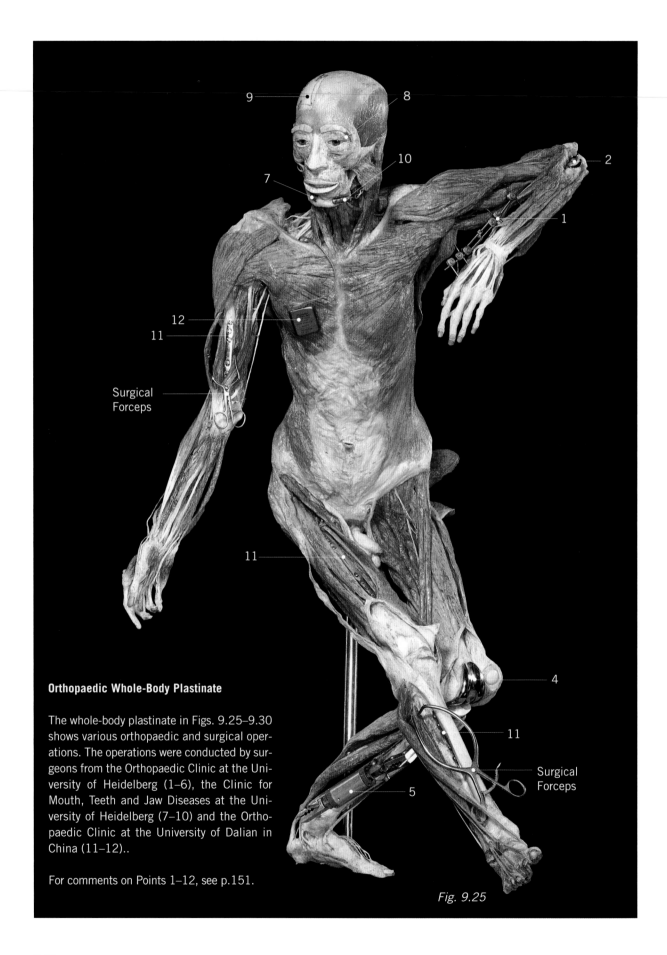

Surgical Forceps

Surgical Forceps

Orthopaedic Whole-Body Plastinate

The whole-body plastinate in Figs. 9.25–9.30 shows various orthopaedic and surgical operations. The operations were conducted by surgeons from the Orthopaedic Clinic at the University of Heidelberg (1–6), the Clinic for Mouth, Teeth and Jaw Diseases at the University of Heidelberg (7–10) and the Orthopaedic Clinic at the University of Dalian in China (11–12)..

For comments on Points 1–12, see p.151.

Fig. 9.25

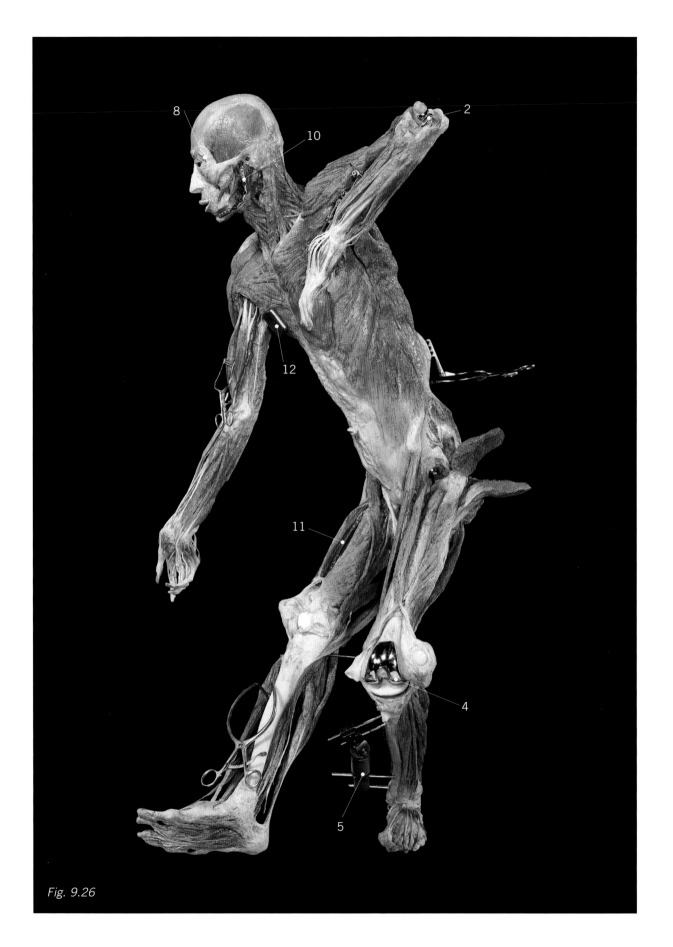

Fig. 9.26

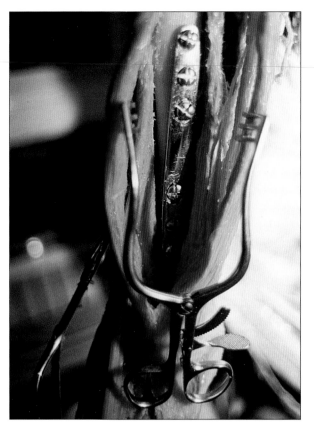

Fig. 9.27 Osteosynthesis with plate

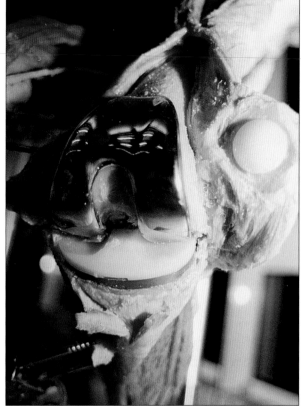

Fig. 9.28 Artificial knee joint

Fig. 9.29 External wrist fixation

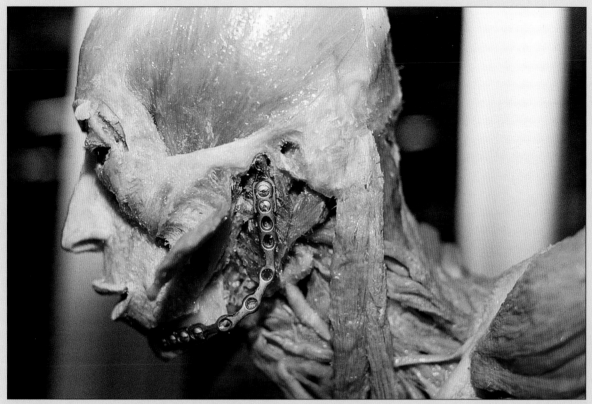

Fig. 9.30 Jawbone prosthesis after partial resection of the jawbone

Operations:

1   Left wrist: Fixation to immobilise wrist fracture.
2   Prosthesis in the left elbow joint.
3   Prosthesis in the left hip joint.
4   Prosthesis in the left knee joint.
5   Left shinbone: External fixation (to immobilise fractured tibia or to lengthen leg).
6   Spinal column: Stabilised with screws and connection pieces (for worn vertebrae).
7   Alignment of mandible fracture and osteosynthesis by means of mini plates.
8   Alignment of jaw bone fracture and osteosynthesis by means of mini plates.
9   Situation after cranial surgery; the removed skull piece has been put back in place and fixed by means of mini plates.
10   Partial resection of the jawbone and replacement with artificial joint.
11   Metal plates for osteosynthesis for internal stabilisation of fractures in long tubular bones (humerus, radius, femur and tibia).
12   Pacemaker (in front of right greater pectoral muscle).

Operations planned and performed by:

Joint transplants:
Dr. M. Schiltenwolf, Dr. M. Bucher, Dr. A. Reiter
Orthopaedic Clinic at the University of Heidelberg

Cranial surgery:
Dr. S. Haßfeld,
Clinic for Mouth, Teeth and Jaw Diseases at the University of Heidelberg

Osteosynthesis of large bones:
Prof. Chen, M.D.
Orthopaedic Clinic, Medical University in Dalian, China

Our thanks to our sponsors:
Aesculap AG, Tuttlingen
Zimmer AG, Tuttlingen
Johnson & Johnson

This specimen shows the variety and versatility of the individual muscles in the body. The skeleton is almost completely covered by musculature of some kind. To be able to show both systems simultaneously in one specimen, the muscles were detached from their original positions on the bones and then either folded back or laterally shifted. It thus becomes obvious how tenuously the sinewy muscles are attached to the bones. Lifelike positioning of this whole body plastinate in a running pose permits a detailed all-around view of each extremity.

Fig. 9.31 Whole body plastinate of the locomotive system (The Runner)

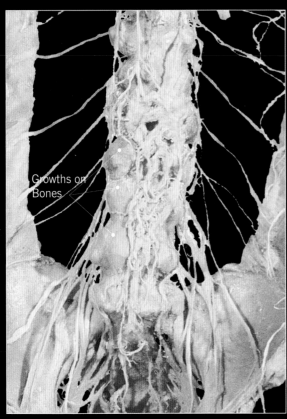

Growths on Bones

Fig. 9.32

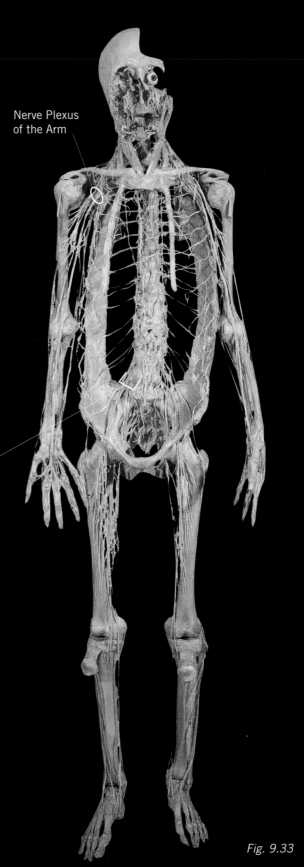

Nerve Plexus of the Arm

Nerve Plexus of the Leg

Posed Specimen of the Nervous System

This specimen shows the nervous system and the skeleton together with its cartilage and ligaments (Figs. 9.32–9.35).

All of the parts of the nervous system can be seen:
1. The central nervous system,
    consisting of the brain and spinal cord;
2. The peripheral nervous system,
    consisting of the cranial nerves and the spinal nerves emerging laterally from the spinal cord and extending to the tips of the fingers and toes;
3. The autonomic nervous system,
    which regulates the activities of the internal organs
Moreover, this specimen displays severe arthrosis of the spine; growths on the vertebrae can be clearly recognised.

Fig. 9.33

153

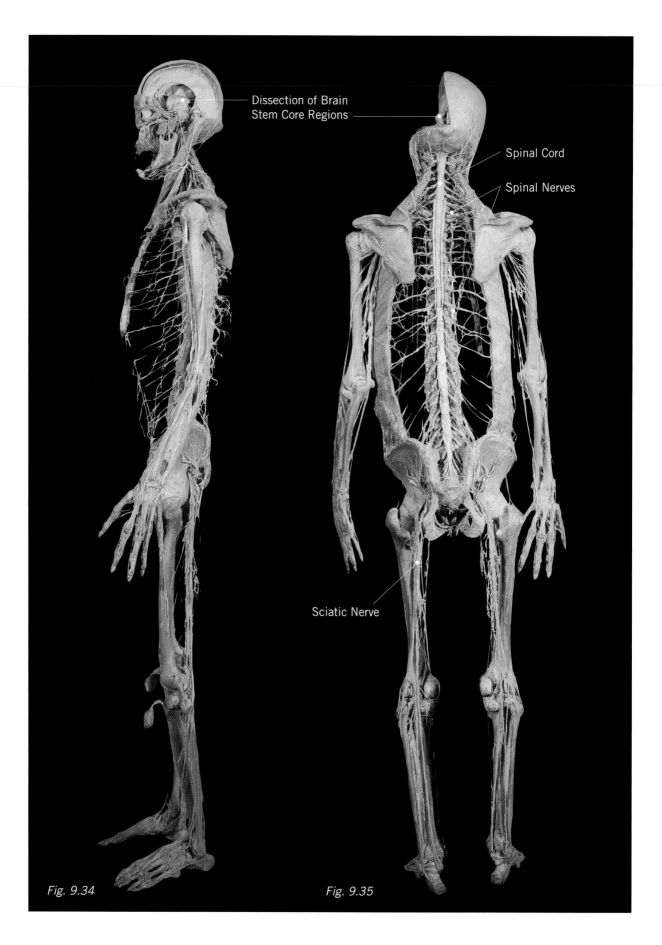

Dissection of Brain
Stem Core Regions

Spinal Cord

Spinal Nerves

Sciatic Nerve

Fig. 9.34

Fig. 9.35

Fig. 9.36 Whole body plastinate with dissection of the central and peripheral nervous systems (The Chess Player)

Fig. 9.37

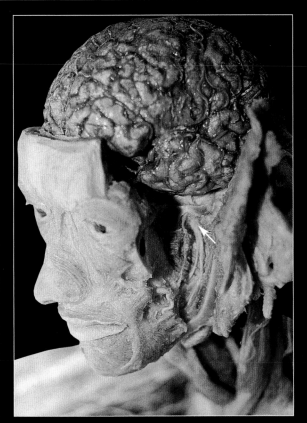

Fig. 9.38 Dissection of the facial nerves
(Trigeminal nerve; arrow)

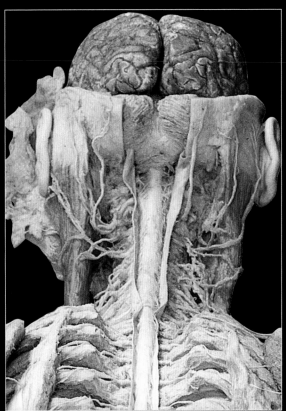

Fig. 9.39 Spinal cord in opened vertebral canal with
emerging peripheral nerves

Fig. 9.40

Exploded Body Specimen

Exploded views of whole-body specimens are a new form of anatomical dissections. Whereas in traditional specimens individual structures were successively removed in order to reveal deeper bodily regions, here they remain a part of the total specimen. Organs hidden in the depths of the body can now be seen by creating interspaces and by shifting the organs away from one another. Shifting and/or expansion can be in any direction, for example, sideways (Figs. 9.46–9.49), upwards (Figs. 9.41–9.45), forward or for that matter in every direction equally (Fig. 9.50).

Exploded body specimens were first made possible by Plastination because the plastics used in this process provide the individual body parts with the necessary stability to stand on their own.

(Figs. 9.41–9.45) In this specimen, the body shell has been cut through at the head, chest, and abdominal levels. The sections thus obtained were then shifted upwards. In this way, the skull reveals a view of the brain; the heart and lungs are visible in the deeper chest region and the abdominal organs below. The body has been given a sitting position to facilitate viewing.

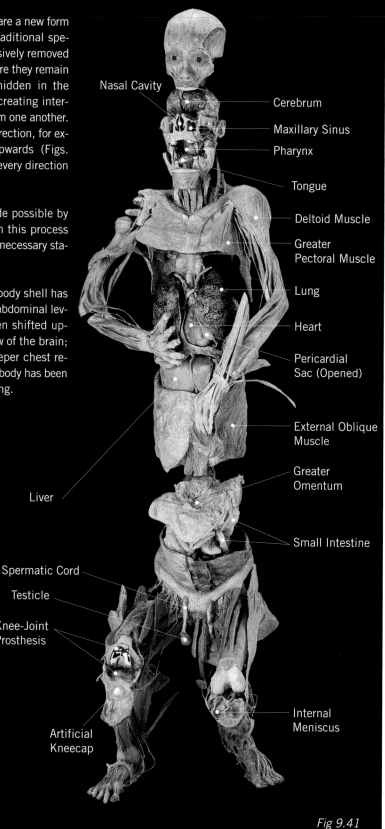

Nasal Cavity

Cerebrum

Maxillary Sinus

Pharynx

Tongue

Deltoid Muscle

Greater Pectoral Muscle

Lung

Heart

Pericardial Sac (Opened)

External Oblique Muscle

Greater Omentum

Small Intestine

Liver

Spermatic Cord

Testicle

Knee-Joint Prosthesis

Artificial Kneecap

Internal Meniscus

Fig 9.41

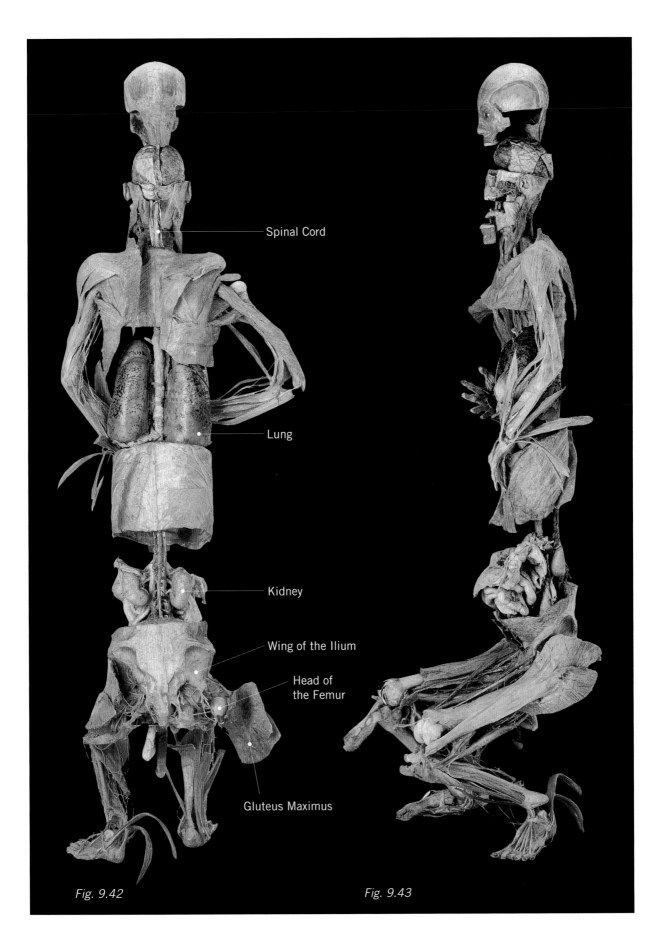

Spinal Cord

Lung

Kidney

Wing of the Ilium

Head of
the Femur

Gluteus Maximus

Fig. 9.42

Fig. 9.43

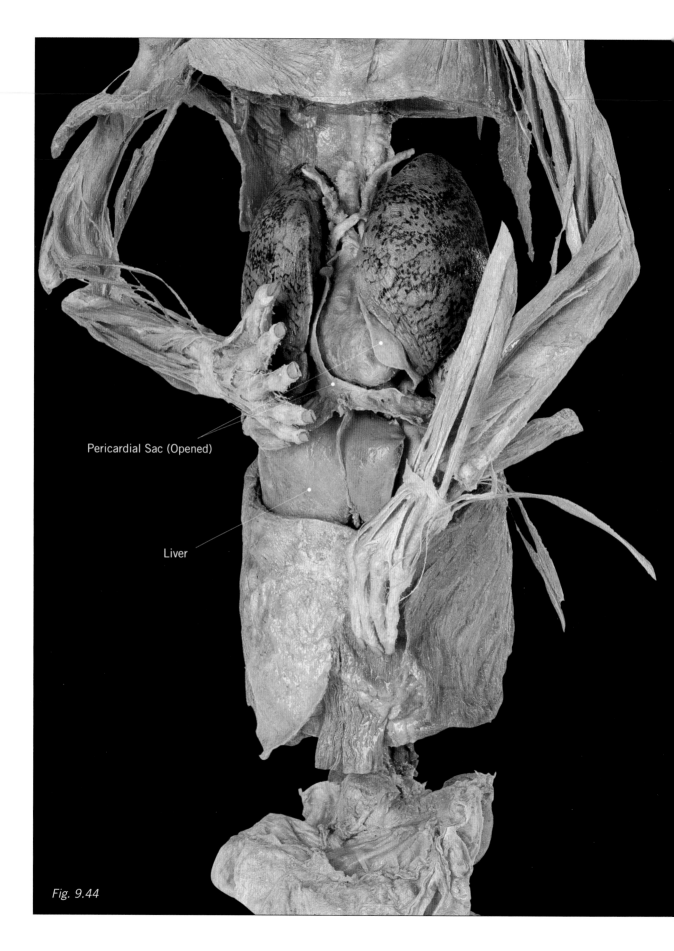

Pericardial Sac (Opened)

Liver

Fig. 9.44

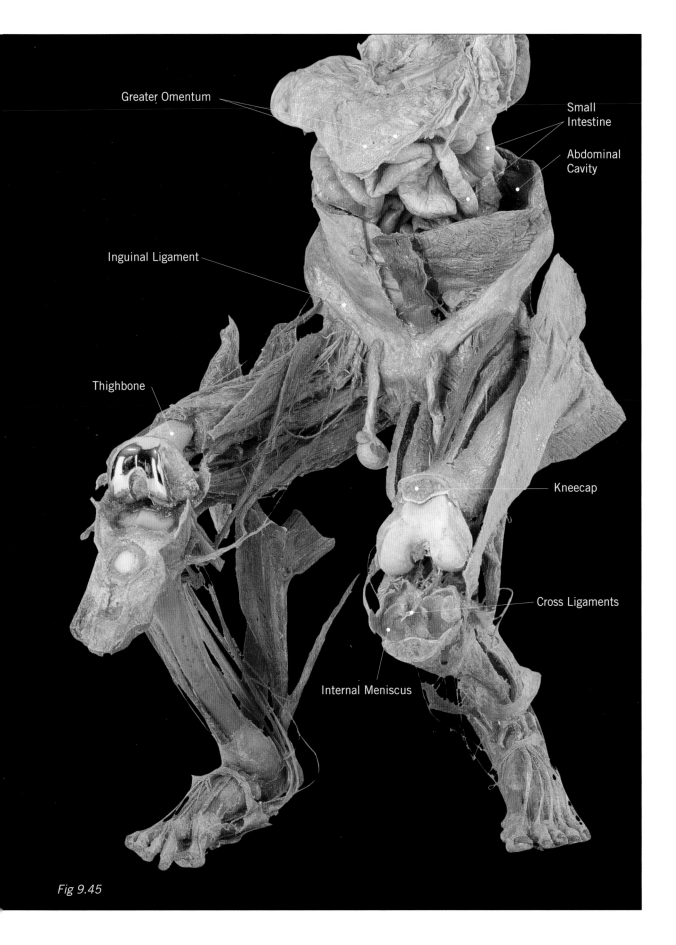

Greater Omentum

Small Intestine

Abdominal Cavity

Inguinal Ligament

Thighbone

Kneecap

Cross Ligaments

Internal Meniscus

Fig 9.45

161

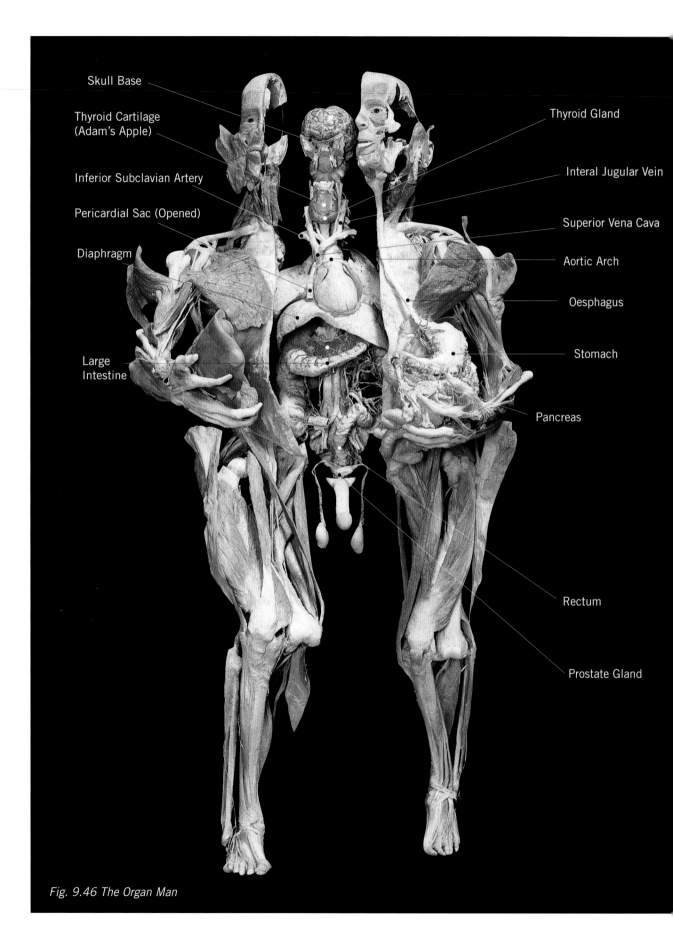

Skull Base

Thyroid Cartilage
(Adam's Apple)

Inferior Subclavian Artery

Pericardial Sac (Opened)

Diaphragm

Large
Intestine

Thyroid Gland

Interal Jugular Vein

Superior Vena Cava

Aortic Arch

Oesphagus

Stomach

Pancreas

Rectum

Prostate Gland

Fig. 9.46 The Organ Man

Figures 9.467–9.49 show a laterally exploded male body. The body shell was divided sagitally through the middle axis, and the two halves together with the extremities were then shifted outwardly to the respective sides. In this way, the eyes fall on the internal organs. To achieve a better view of the organs located near the rear wall of the abdomen, the specimen holds the gastrointestinal tract in the left hand and the liver in the right hand. At the back, the spinal column with the spinal cord and the brain remain along the middle axis.

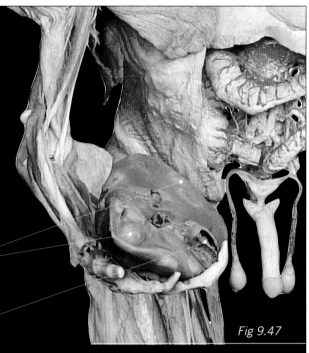

Tumour Metastases

Gallbladder with Gallstones

Fig 9.47

Fig. 9.48

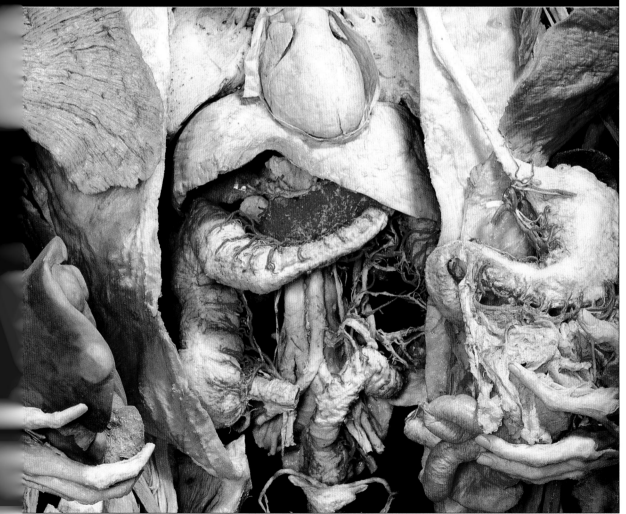

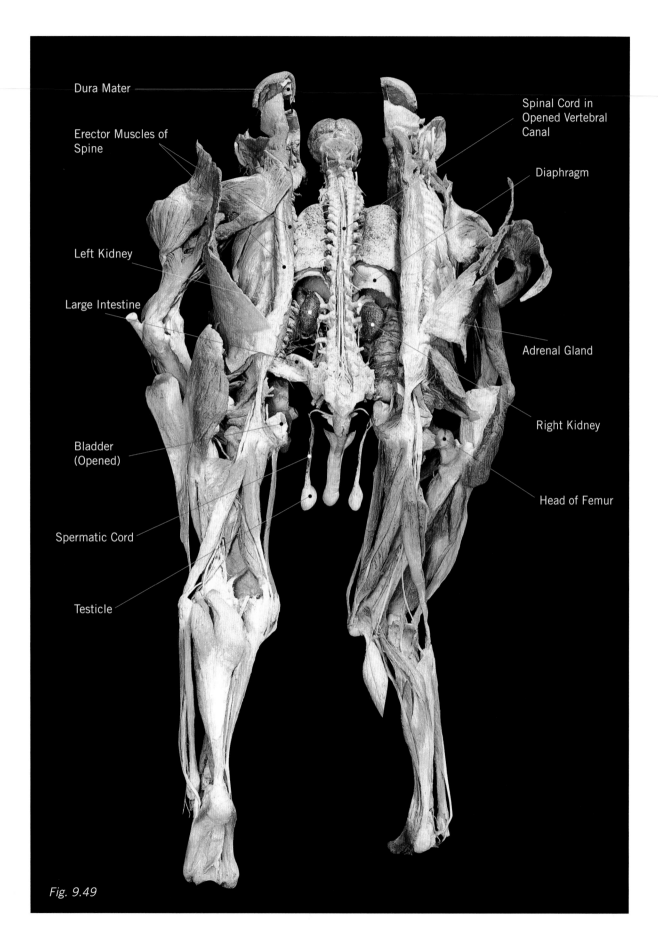

Dura Mater

Spinal Cord in
Opened Vertebral
Canal

Erector Muscles of
Spine

Diaphragm

Left Kidney

Large Intestine

Adrenal Gland

Right Kidney

Bladder
(Opened)

Head of Femur

Spermatic Cord

Testicle

Fig. 9.49

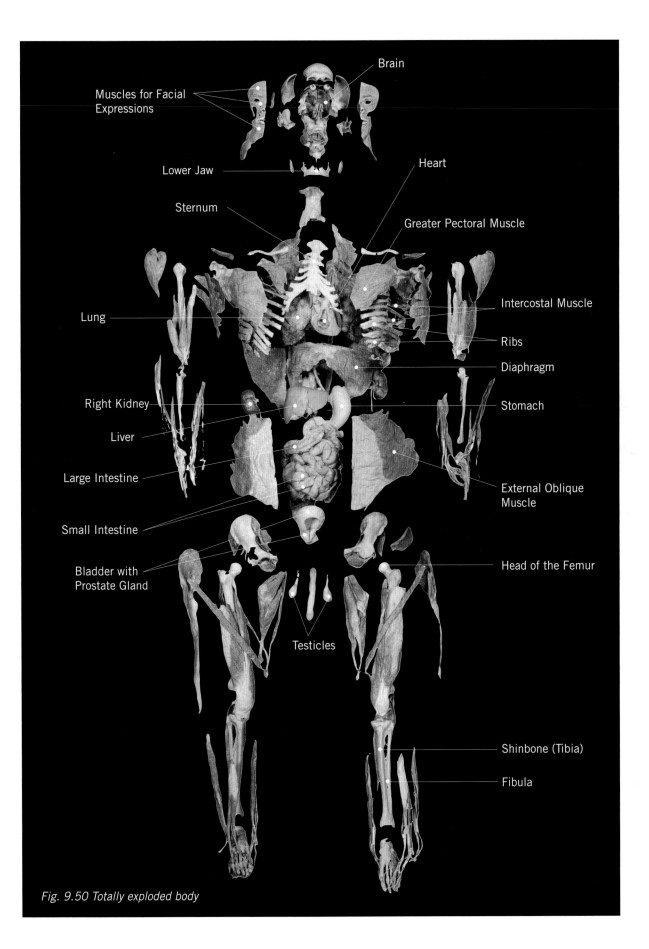

Brain

Muscles for Facial
Expressions

Lower Jaw

Heart

Sternum

Greater Pectoral Muscle

Intercostal Muscle

Lung

Ribs

Diaphragm

Right Kidney

Stomach

Liver

Large Intestine

External Oblique
Muscle

Small Intestine

Bladder with
Prostate Gland

Head of the Femur

Testicles

Shinbone (Tibia)

Fibula

Fig. 9.50 Totally exploded body

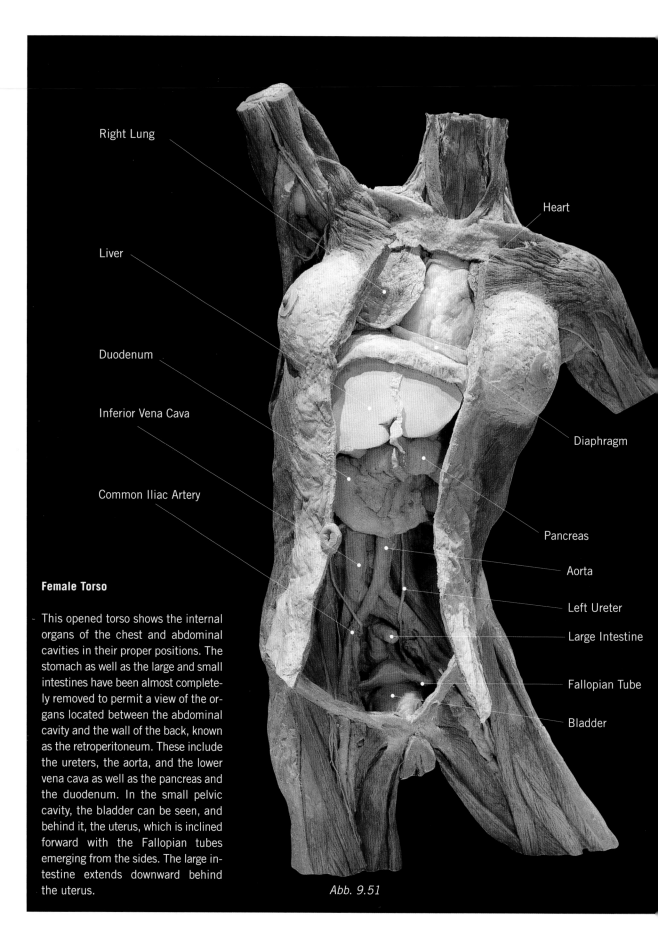

Right Lung

Heart

Liver

Duodenum

Inferior Vena Cava

Diaphragm

Common Iliac Artery

Pancreas

Aorta

Female Torso

This opened torso shows the internal organs of the chest and abdominal cavities in their proper positions. The stomach as well as the large and small intestines have been almost completely removed to permit a view of the organs located between the abdominal cavity and the wall of the back, known as the retroperitoneum. These include the ureters, the aorta, and the lower vena cava as well as the pancreas and the duodenum. In the small pelvic cavity, the bladder can be seen, and behind it, the uterus, which is inclined forward with the Fallopian tubes emerging from the sides. The large intestine extends downward behind the uterus.

Left Ureter

Large Intestine

Fallopian Tube

Bladder

Abb. 9.51

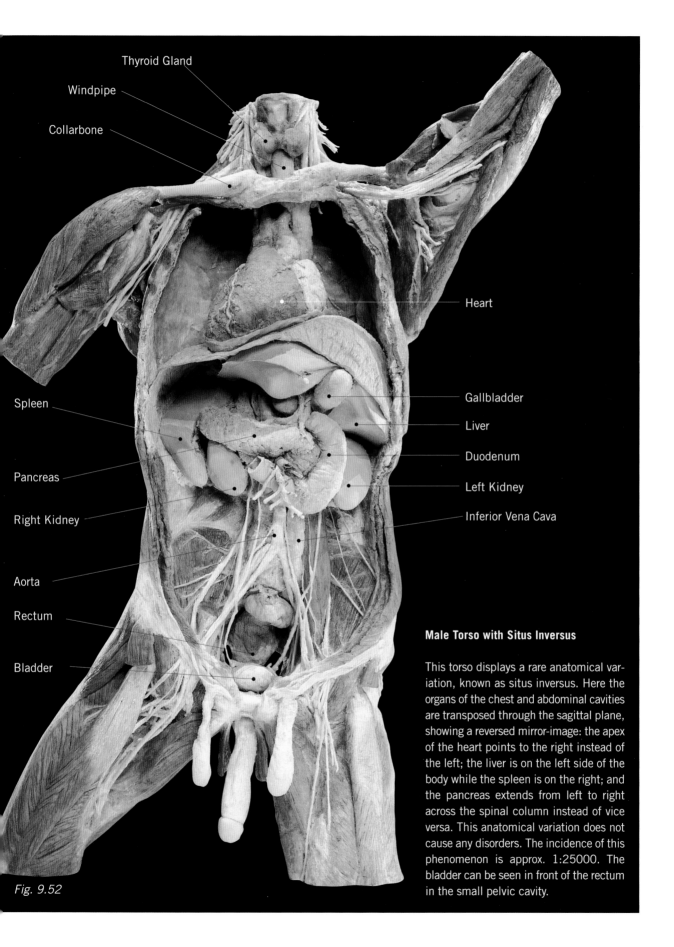

Thyroid Gland

Windpipe

Collarbone

Heart

Spleen

Gallbladder

Liver

Duodenum

Pancreas

Left Kidney

Right Kidney

Inferior Vena Cava

Aorta

Rectum

Bladder

Male Torso with Situs Inversus

This torso displays a rare anatomical variation, known as situs inversus. Here the organs of the chest and abdominal cavities are transposed through the sagittal plane, showing a reversed mirror-image: the apex of the heart points to the right instead of the left; the liver is on the left side of the body while the spleen is on the right; and the pancreas extends from left to right across the spinal column instead of vice versa. This anatomical variation does not cause any disorders. The incidence of this phenomenon is approx. 1:25000. The bladder can be seen in front of the rectum in the small pelvic cavity.

Fig. 9.52

167

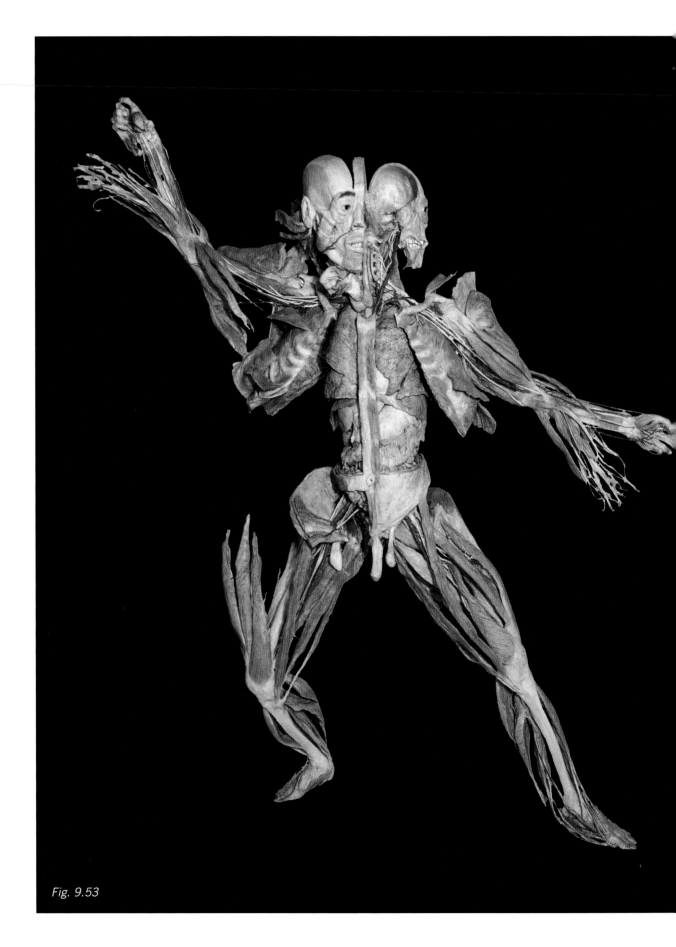

Fig. 9.53

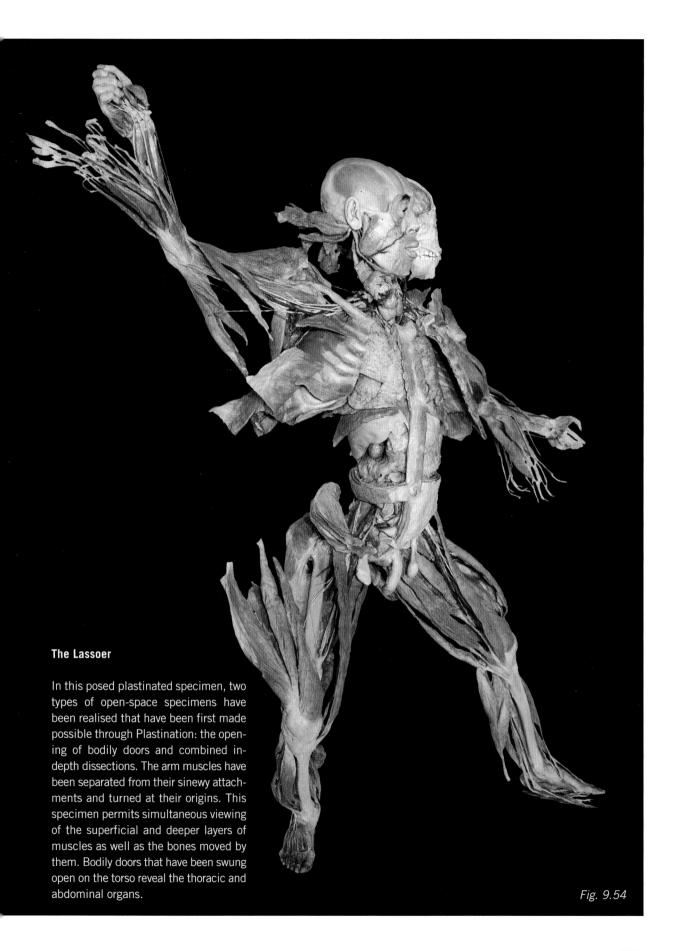

The Lassoer

In this posed plastinated specimen, two types of open-space specimens have been realised that have been first made possible through Plastination: the opening of bodily doors and combined in-depth dissections. The arm muscles have been separated from their sinewy attachments and turned at their origins. This specimen permits simultaneous viewing of the superficial and deeper layers of muscles as well as the bones moved by them. Bodily doors that have been swung open on the torso reveal the thoracic and abdominal organs.

Fig. 9.54

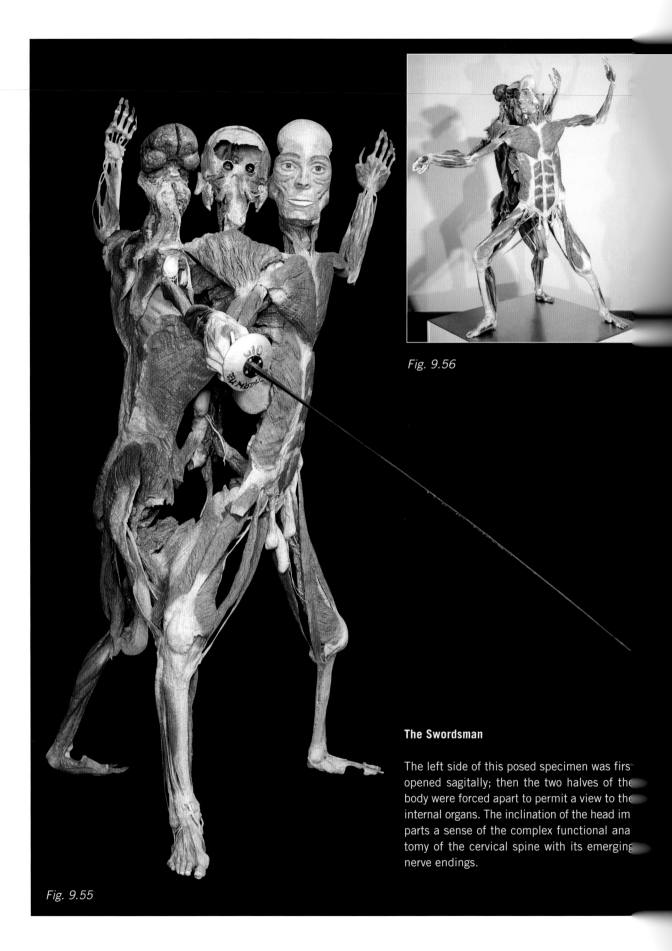

Fig. 9.56

The Swordsman

The left side of this posed specimen was firs
opened sagitally; then the two halves of the
body were forced apart to permit a view to the
internal organs. The inclination of the head im
parts a sense of the complex functional ana
tomy of the cervical spine with its emerging
nerve endings.

Fig. 9.55

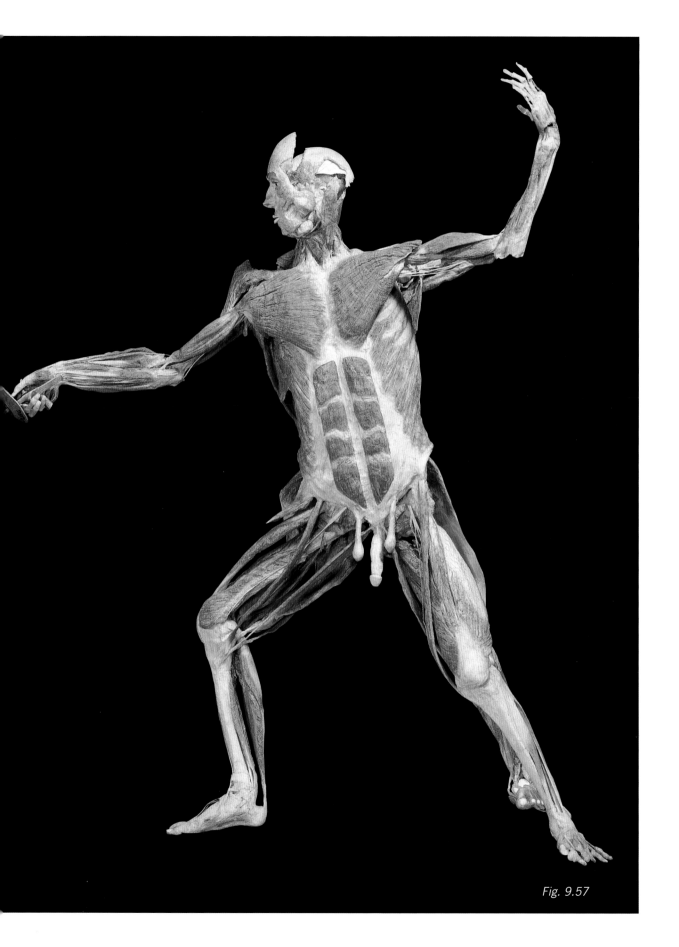

Fig. 9.57

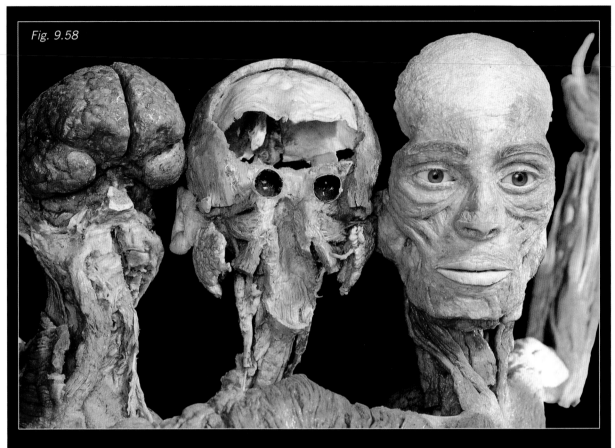

Fig. 9.58

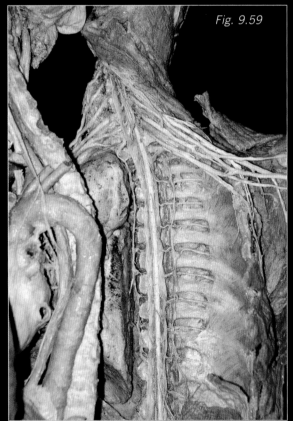

Fig. 9.59

Fig. 9.60

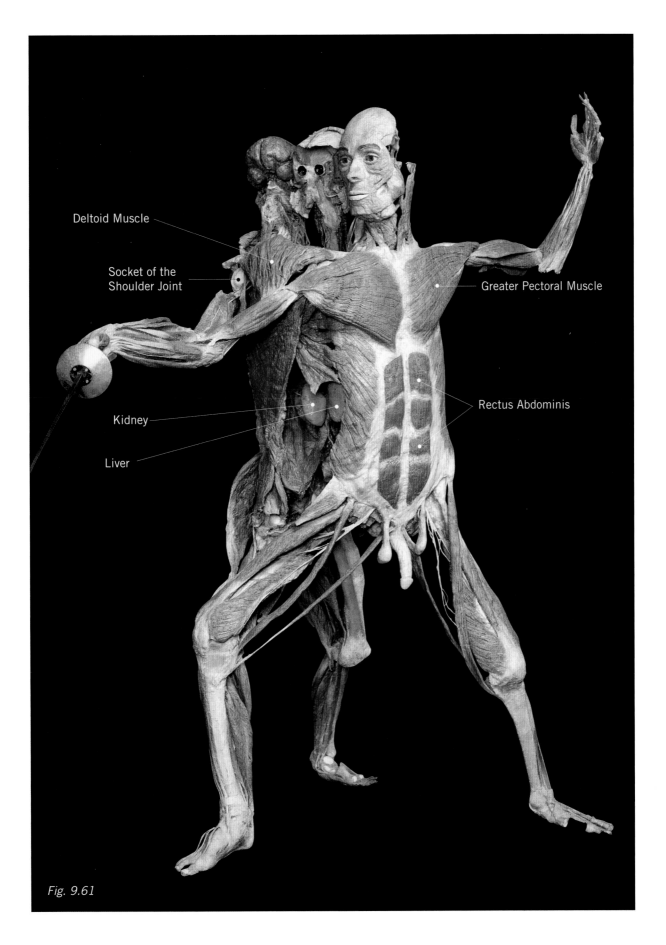

Deltoid Muscle

Socket of the
Shoulder Joint

Kidney

Liver

Greater Pectoral Muscle

Rectus Abdominis

Fig. 9.61

173

Fig. 9.63

The Thrower

With this gestalt plastinate, the muscles have been separated from their origins at the bones, combined into functional groups and turned in such a way that the musculature and skeleton system are simultaneously visible. Moreover, this plastinate permits us to look into all of the bodily joints. The lower jaw has been cut into two halves and shifted upwards.

Fig. 9.62

Fig. 9.64

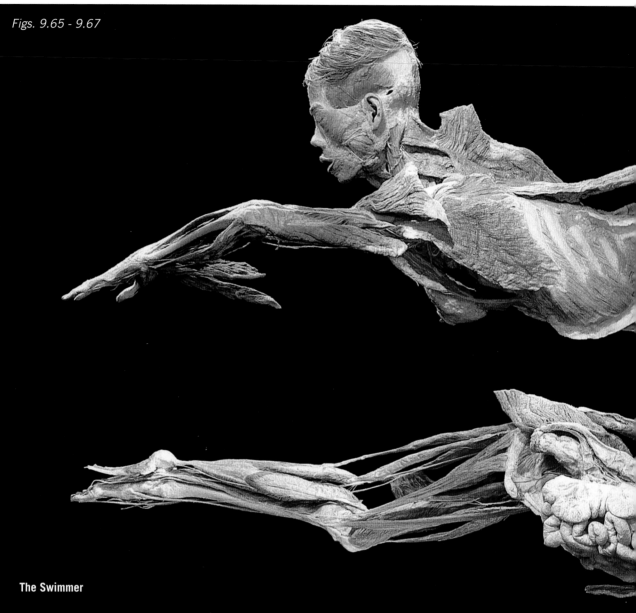

The Swimmer

The body shell has been laterally separated into two halves. Conversely, the inner organs have been left as they were in the left or right body half, respectively. On the respective sides opposite each organ, cavities indicate the position, form and size of the organs that have been removed. The vertebrae can thus be seen in the left half, with the oesophagus in front and the liver as well as the intestines in the abdominal cavity. The intervertebral disks are to be seen in the right half as well as the uterus with the ovaries and Fallopian tubes in the pelvic cavity.

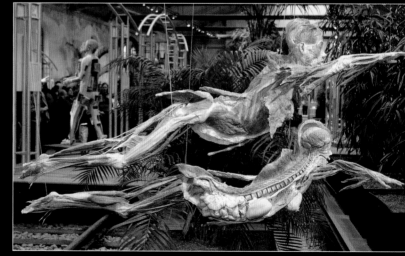

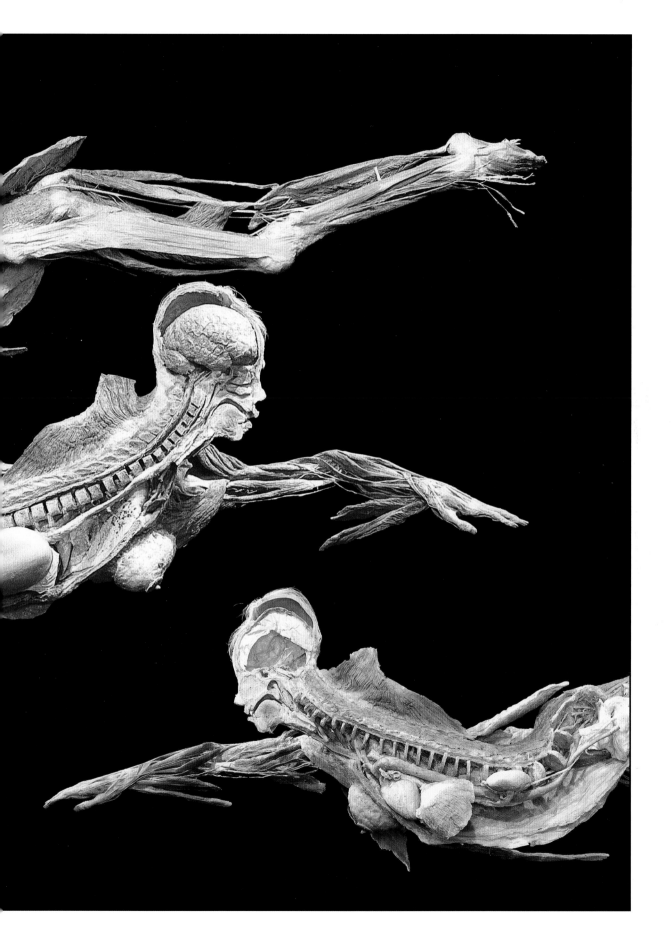

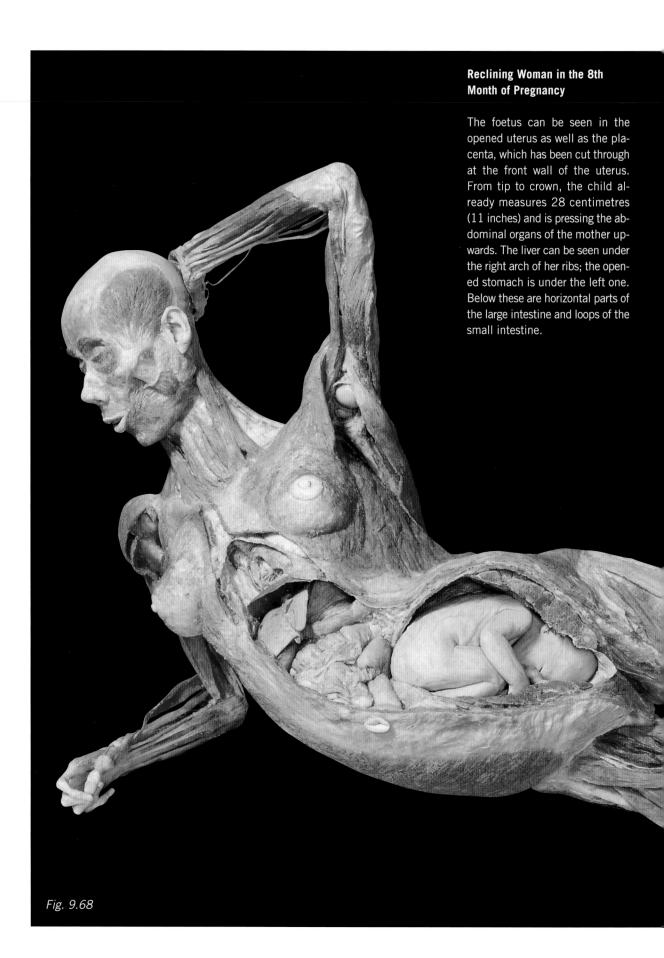

Reclining Woman in the 8th Month of Pregnancy

The foetus can be seen in the opened uterus as well as the placenta, which has been cut through at the front wall of the uterus. From tip to crown, the child already measures 28 centimetres (11 inches) and is pressing the abdominal organs of the mother upwards. The liver can be seen under the right arch of her ribs; the opened stomach is under the left one. Below these are horizontal parts of the large intestine and loops of the small intestine.

Fig. 9.68

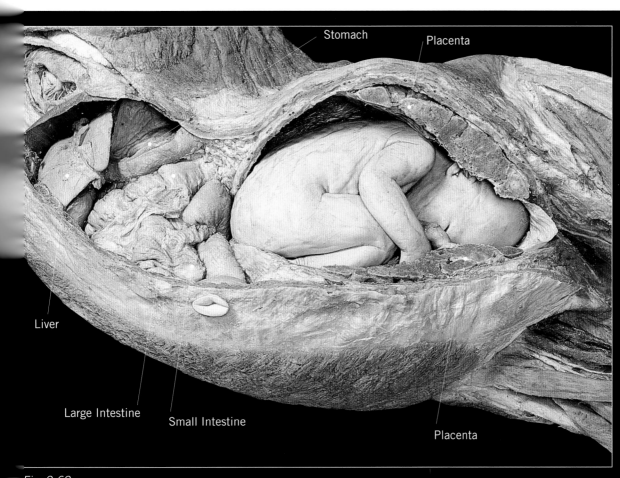

Fig. 9.69

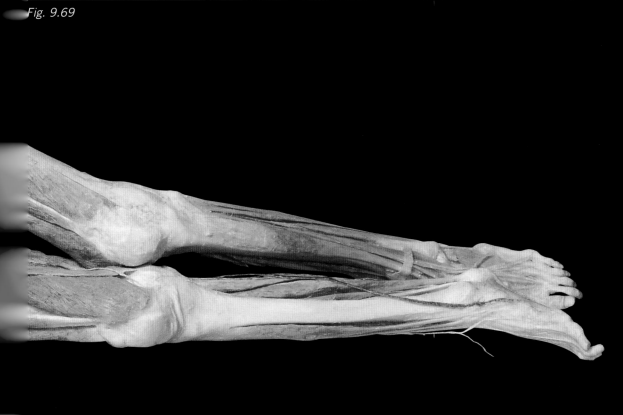

Fig. 9.70

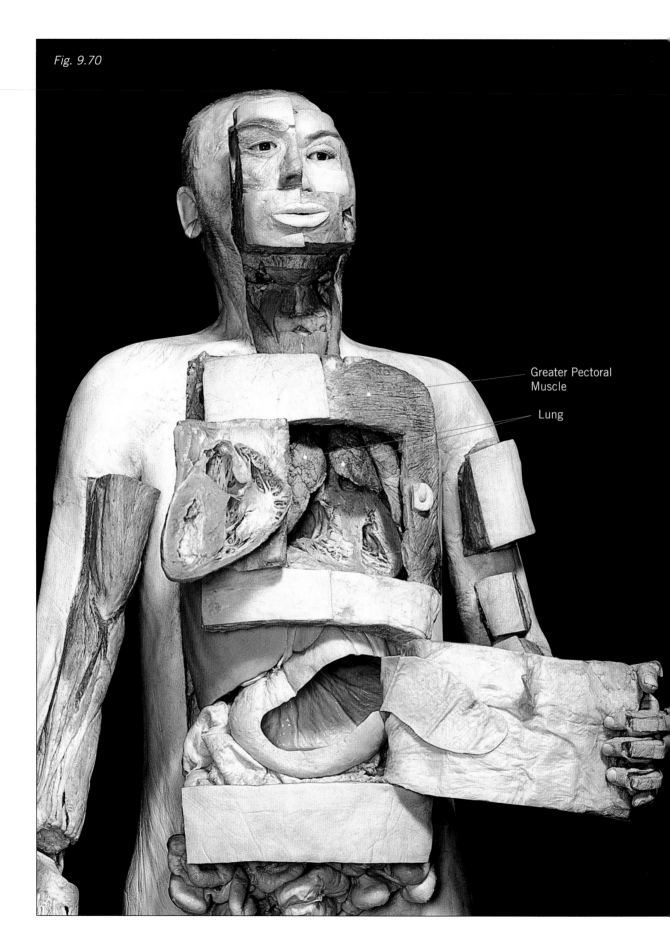

Greater Pectoral
Muscle

Lung

Fragmented Plastinate

Inside the body all of our organ systems are packed tightly together without much space in betweenr. Toillustrate this compactness of bodily interiors, fragments have been drawn out of this body's insides or have been swung open like doors.

The observer can also close the body again by returning the fragments to their original position in the mind's eye.

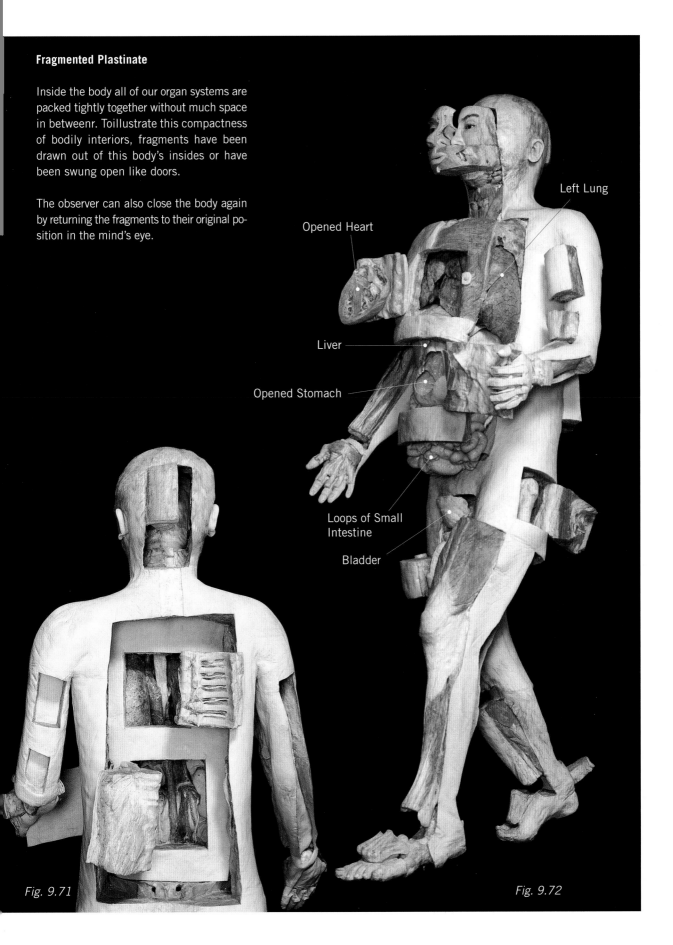

Opened Heart

Left Lung

Liver

Opened Stomach

Loops of Small Intestine

Bladder

Fig. 9.71

Fig. 9.72

Rearing Horse with Rider

Both the human and the horse have a very similar anatomical arrangement in form, position and microscopic structures of their organs and muscles. Conversely, there are major differences in the proportions. Compared to the horse, human musculature is rather puny, while, on the other hand, the larger human brain permits significantly higher intelligence. In humans, the humeri (long bones of the arm) and thighbones are relatively long, while the hands and feet are relatively short. With horses, the bones of the forelimbs and hind limbs by contrast are relatively short and closer to the trunk; conversely, the cannon bones, fetlocks, pasterns and hoofs are relatively long, and the number of phalanges of the toes is reduced so that the joints of the limbs have different positions.

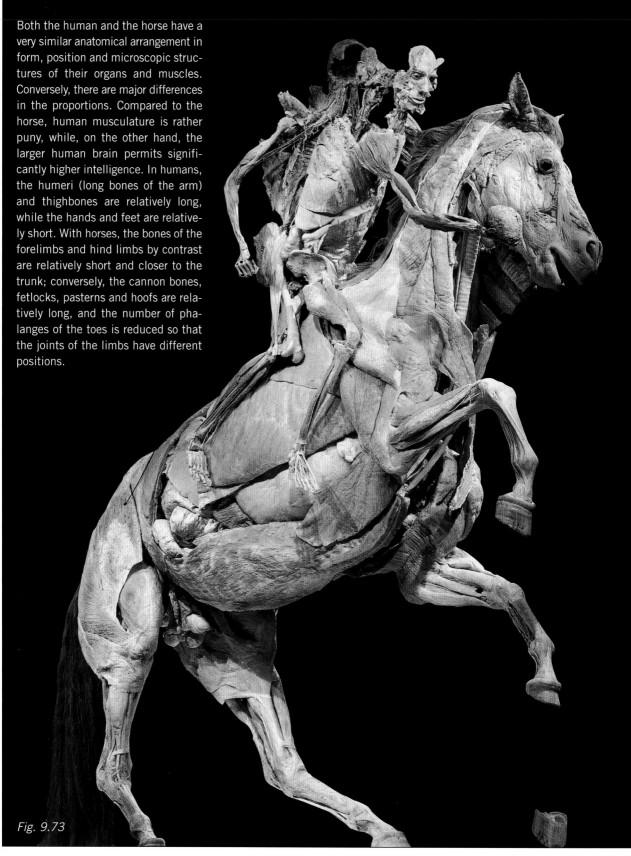

Fig. 9.73

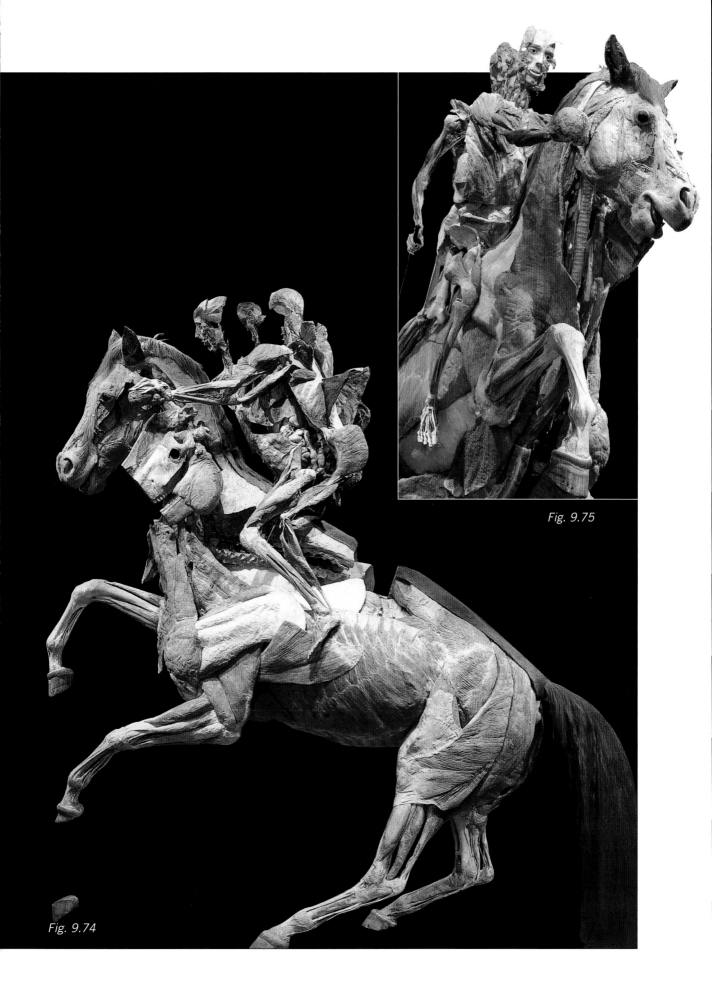

Fig. 9.74

Fig. 9.75

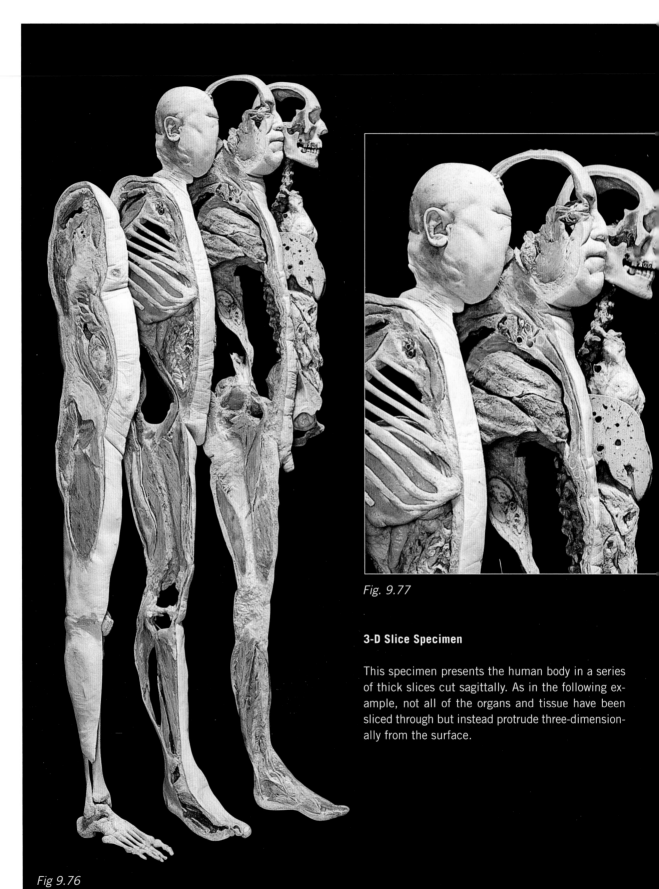

Fig. 9.77

3-D Slice Specimen

This specimen presents the human body in a series of thick slices cut sagittally. As in the following example, not all of the organs and tissue have been sliced through but instead protrude three-dimensionally from the surface.

Fig 9.76

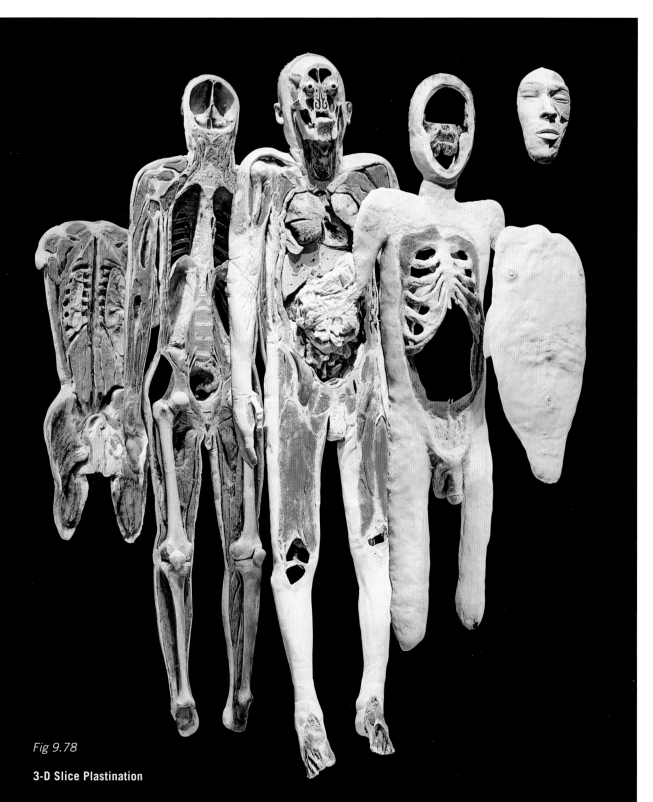

Fig 9.78

3-D Slice Plastination

This specimen shows a human body in thick, frontal slices. Nevertheless, not all of the organs and tissue have been sliced through but instead protrude three-dimensionally from the surface. These body parts are missing in the neighbouring slices and leave only gaps in those places that reflect the shape and size of the organs that have been removed or that correspond to the organ removed by dissection. The resulting negative and positive forms provide an instructional pattern of complementary protrusions and indentations.

Fig. 9.79

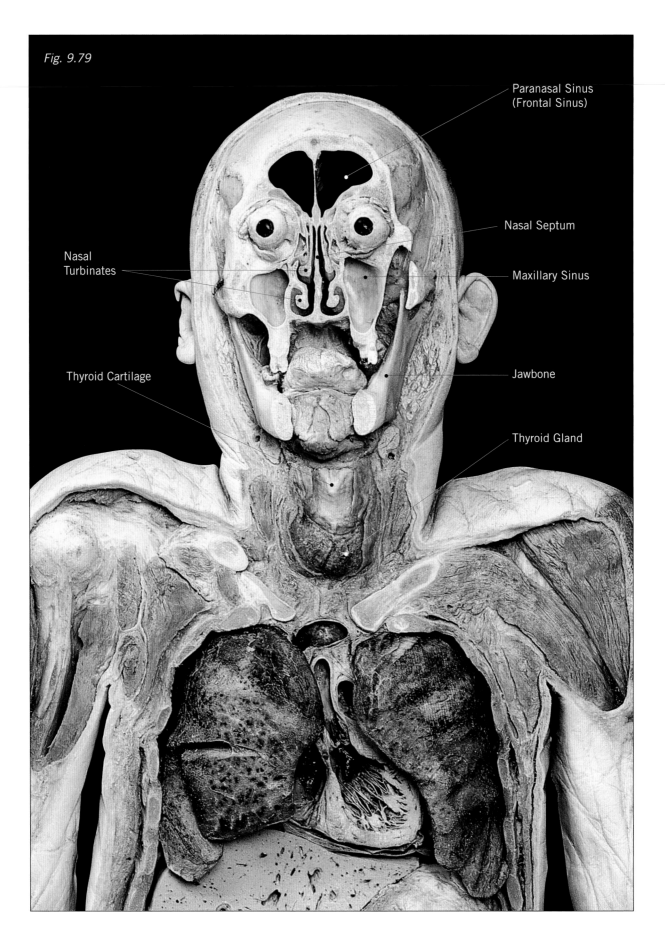

Paranasal Sinus
(Frontal Sinus)

Nasal Septum

Maxillary Sinus

Nasal
Turbinates

Jawbone

Thyroid Cartilage

Thyroid Gland

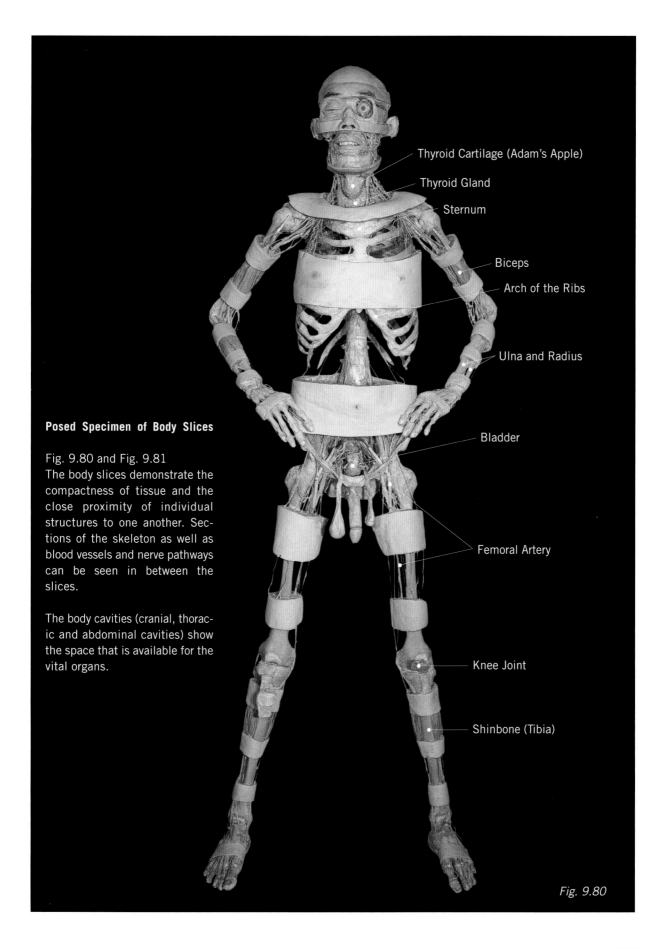

Thyroid Cartilage (Adam's Apple)

Thyroid Gland

Sternum

Biceps

Arch of the Ribs

Ulna and Radius

Bladder

Femoral Artery

Knee Joint

Shinbone (Tibia)

Posed Specimen of Body Slices

Fig. 9.80 and Fig. 9.81
The body slices demonstrate the compactness of tissue and the close proximity of individual structures to one another. Sections of the skeleton as well as blood vessels and nerve pathways can be seen in between the slices.

The body cavities (cranial, thoracic and abdominal cavities) show the space that is available for the vital organs.

Fig. 9.80

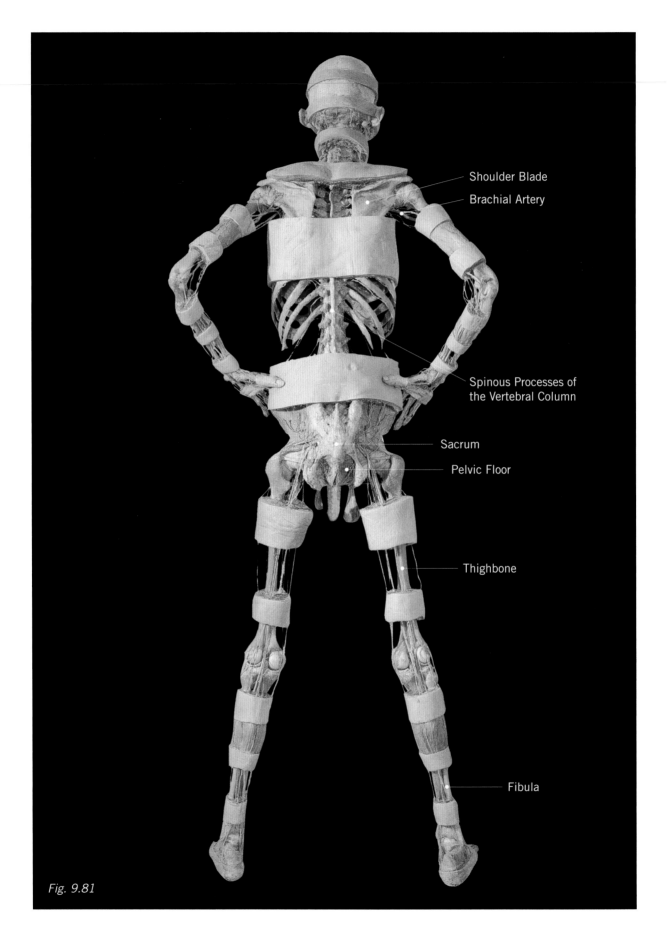

Shoulder Blade

Brachial Artery

Spinous Processes of
the Vertebral Column

Sacrum

Pelvic Floor

Thighbone

Fibula

Fig. 9.81

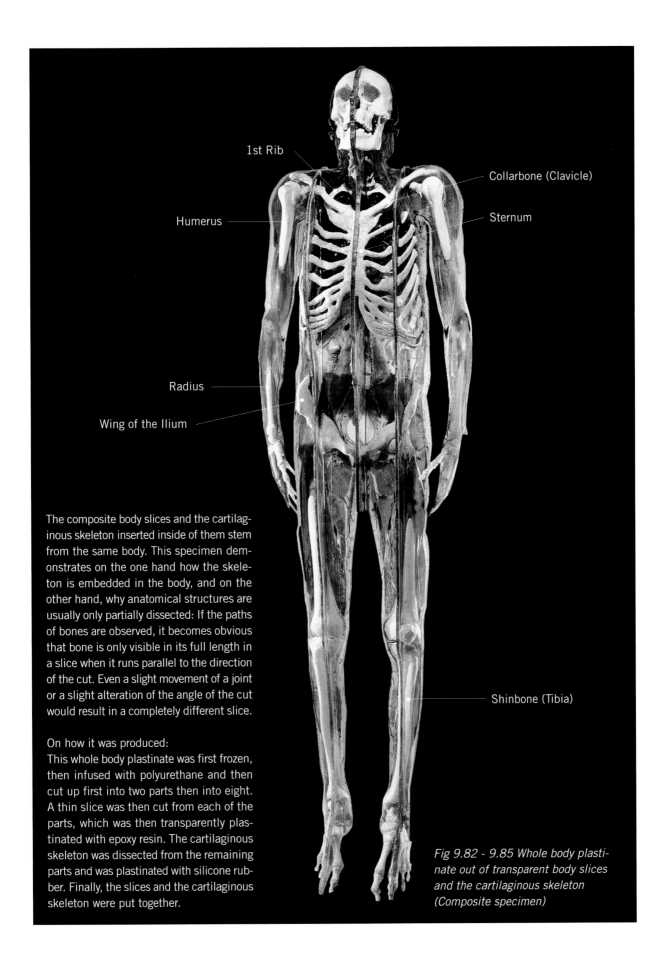

1st Rib

Collarbone (Clavicle)

Humerus

Sternum

Radius

Wing of the Ilium

Shinbone (Tibia)

The composite body slices and the cartilaginous skeleton inserted inside of them stem from the same body. This specimen demonstrates on the one hand how the skeleton is embedded in the body, and on the other hand, why anatomical structures are usually only partially dissected: If the paths of bones are observed, it becomes obvious that bone is only visible in its full length in a slice when it runs parallel to the direction of the cut. Even a slight movement of a joint or a slight alteration of the angle of the cut would result in a completely different slice.

On how it was produced:
This whole body plastinate was first frozen, then infused with polyurethane and then cut up first into two parts then into eight. A thin slice was then cut from each of the parts, which was then transparently plastinated with epoxy resin. The cartilaginous skeleton was dissected from the remaining parts and was plastinated with silicone rubber. Finally, the slices and the cartilaginous skeleton were put together.

Fig 9.82 - 9.85 Whole body plastinate out of transparent body slices and the cartilaginous skeleton (Composite specimen)

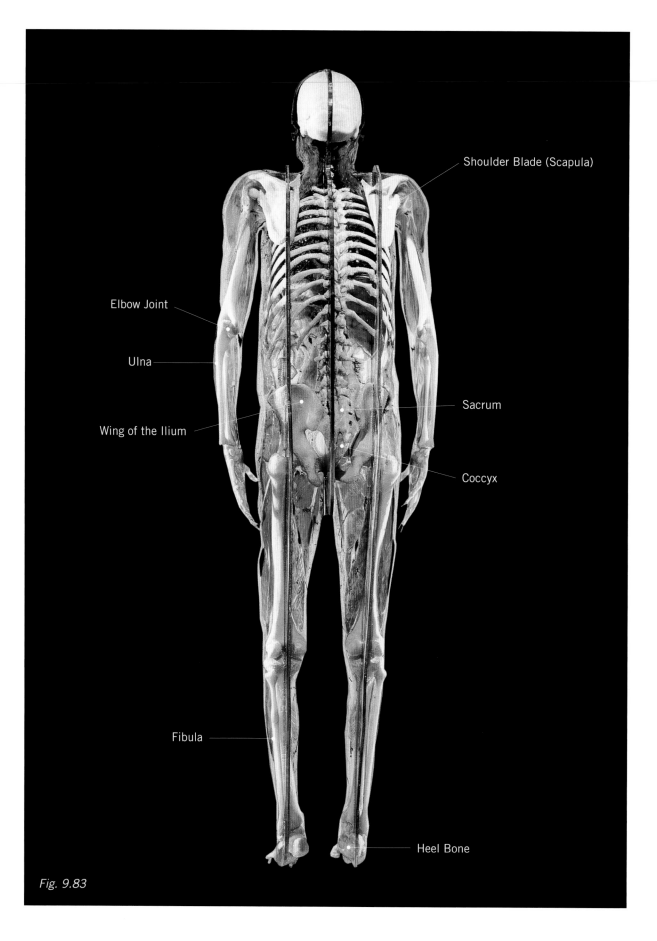

Shoulder Blade (Scapula)

Elbow Joint

Ulna

Wing of the Ilium

Sacrum

Coccyx

Fibula

Heel Bone

Fig. 9.83

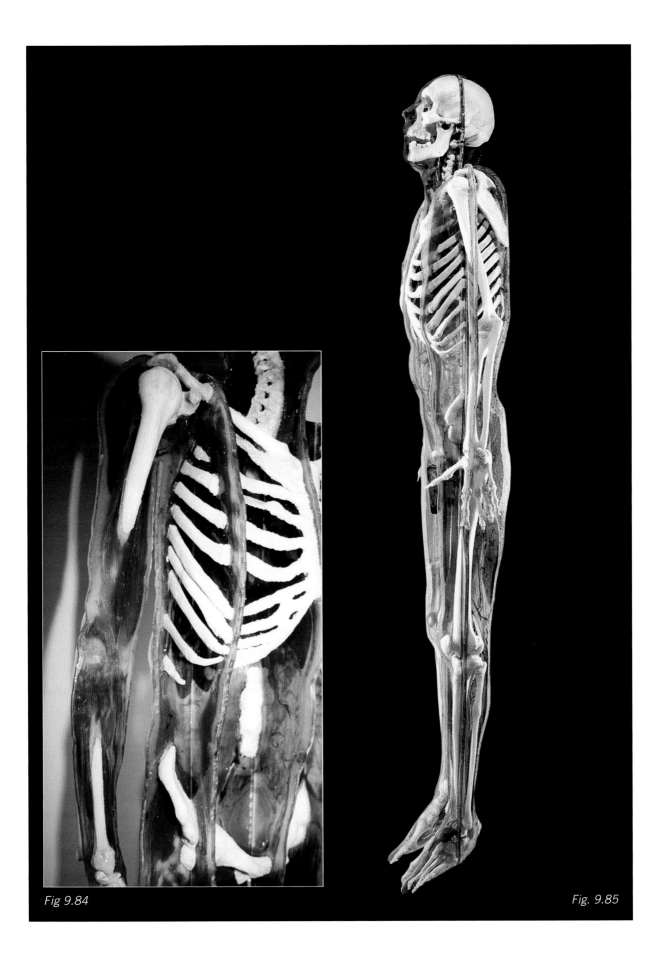

Fig 9.84

Fig. 9.85

Figure 9.86 shows a transparent body, comprising 83 slices representing all of the body's regions. The torso and the extremities have largely been cut horizontally; conversely, the head, elbows, hands, knees and feet have been cut sagittally to afford a better view. Placement of the slices at intervals of 12 cm permits viewers to look more deeply into the body.

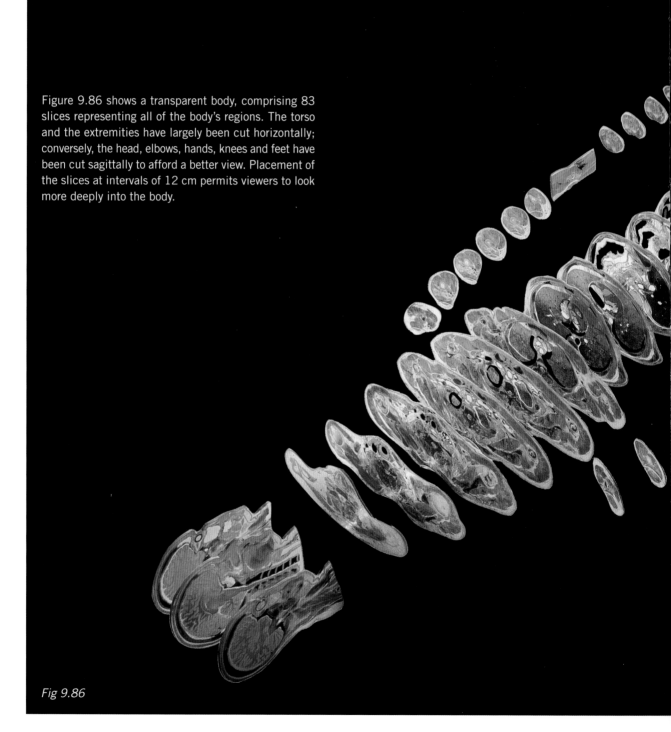

Fig 9.86

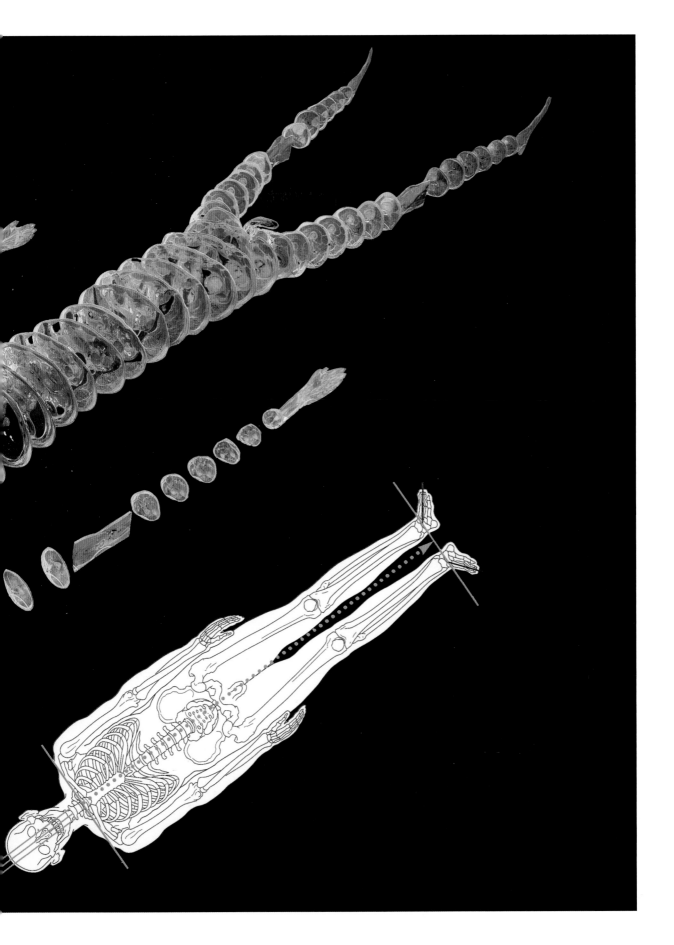

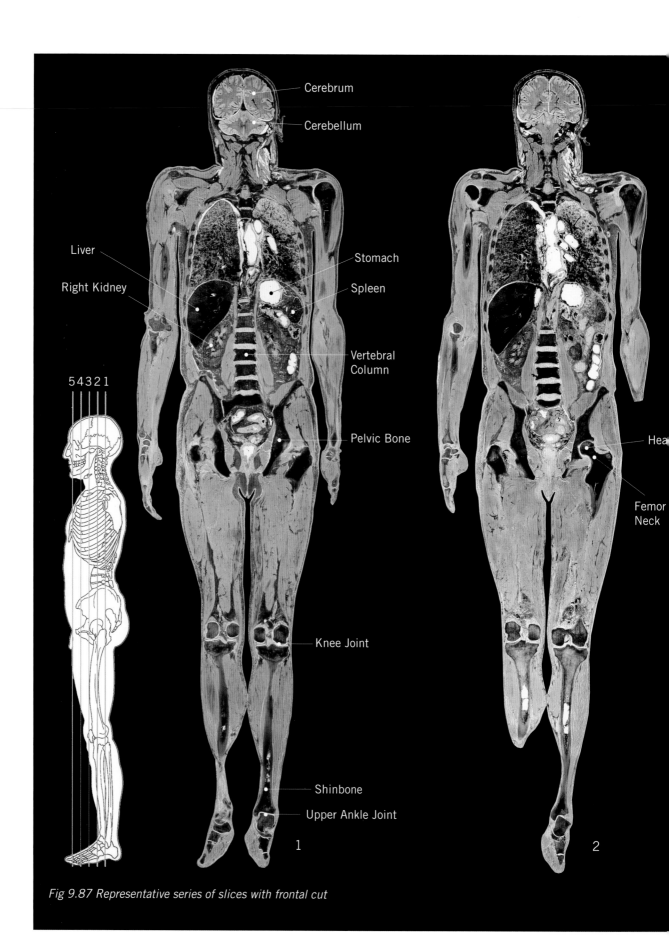

Cerebrum

Cerebellum

Liver

Right Kidney

Stomach

Spleen

Vertebral
Column

5 4 3 2 1

Pelvic Bone

Hea

Femor
Neck

Knee Joint

Shinbone

Upper Ankle Joint

1

2

Fig 9.87 Representative series of slices with frontal cut

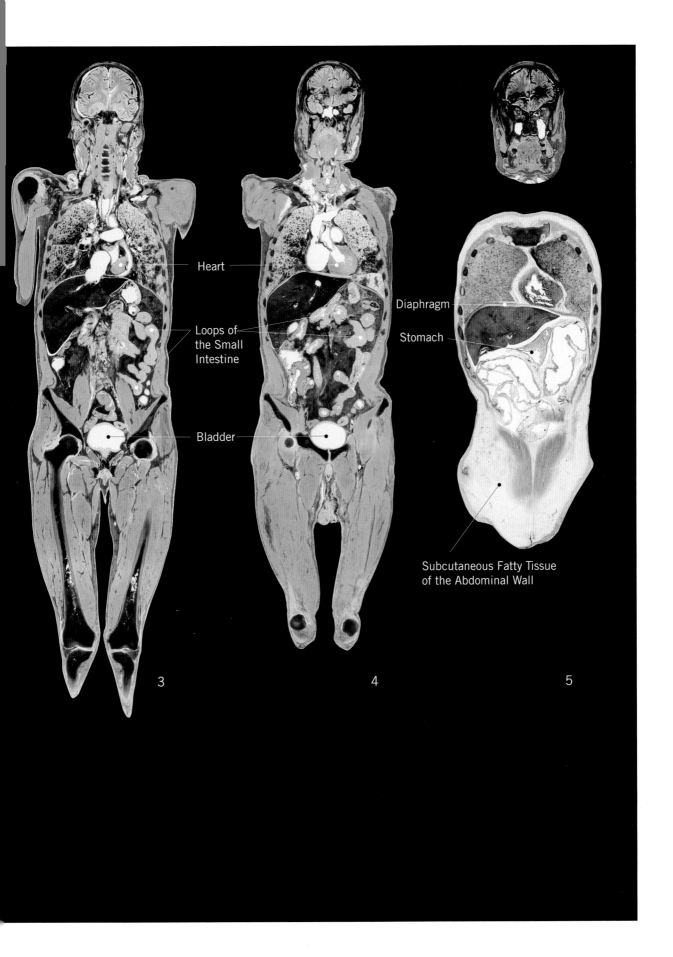

Heart

Loops of
the Small
Intestine

Bladder

Diaphragm

Stomach

Subcutaneous Fatty Tissue
of the Abdominal Wall

3

4

5

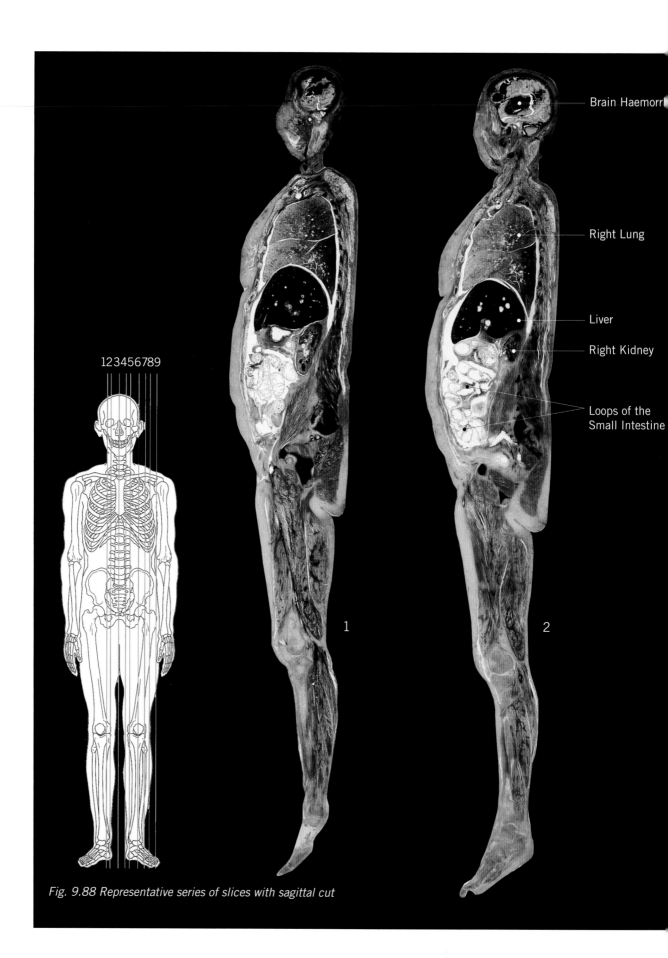

Brain Haemorr[...]

Right Lung

Liver

Right Kidney

Loops of the
Small Intestine

123456789

1

2

Fig. 9.88 Representative series of slices with sagittal cut

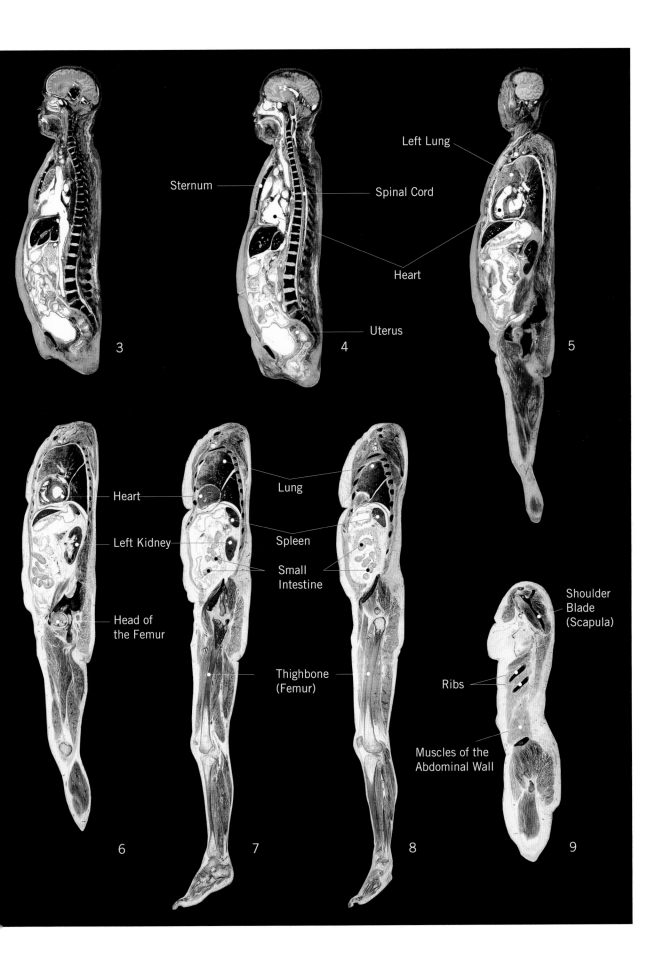

Left Lung

Sternum

Spinal Cord

Heart

Uterus

3

4

5

Heart

Lung

Left Kidney

Spleen

Small
Intestine

Head of
the Femur

Thighbone
(Femur)

Shoulder
Blade
(Scapula)

Ribs

Muscles of the
Abdominal Wall

6

7

8

9

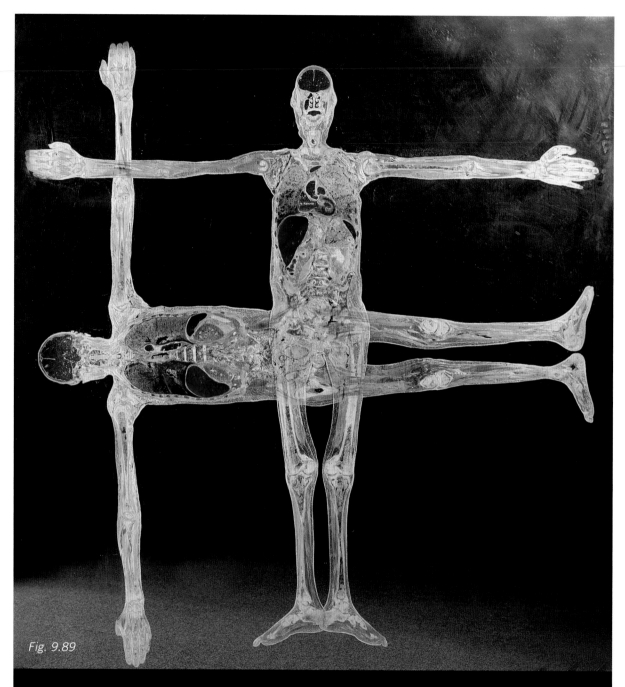

Fig. 9.89

Series of Slices

Transparent slices of a male body. This exhibit clearly shows that the span from fingertips to fingertips corresponds approximately to the height of the body.

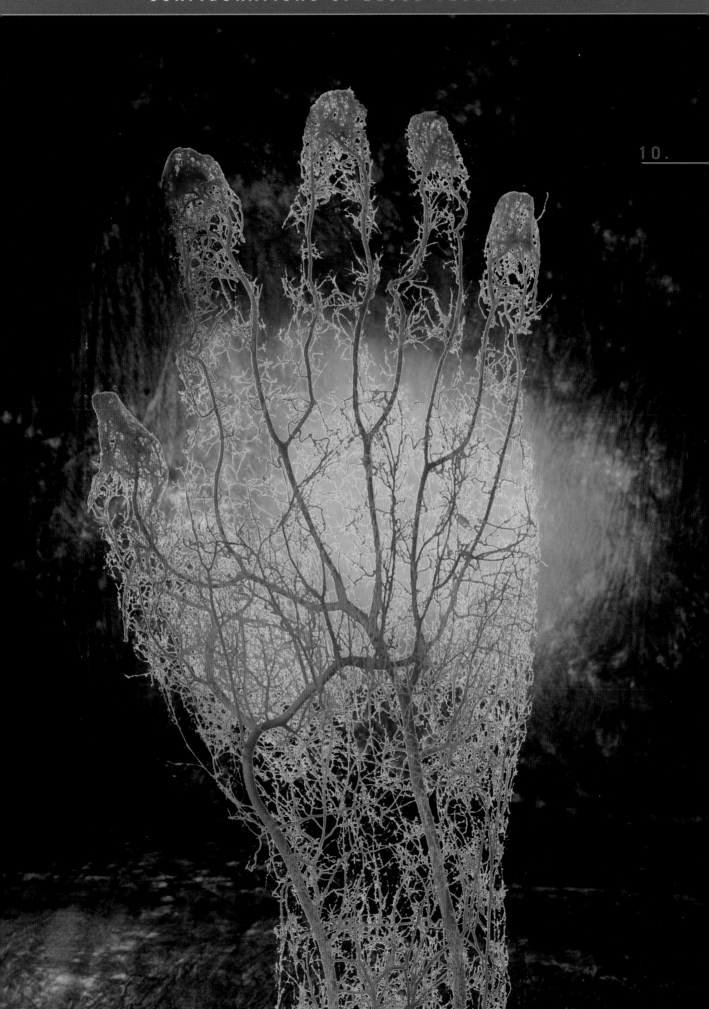

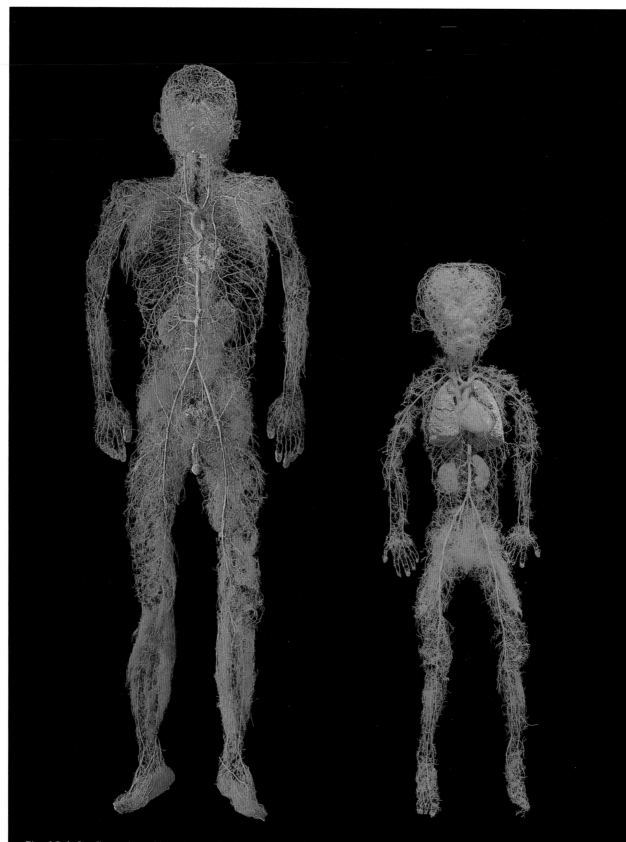

Fig. 10.1 Configuration of blood vessels of an adult male   Fig. 10.2 Configuration of blood vessels of a child

Fig. 10.3

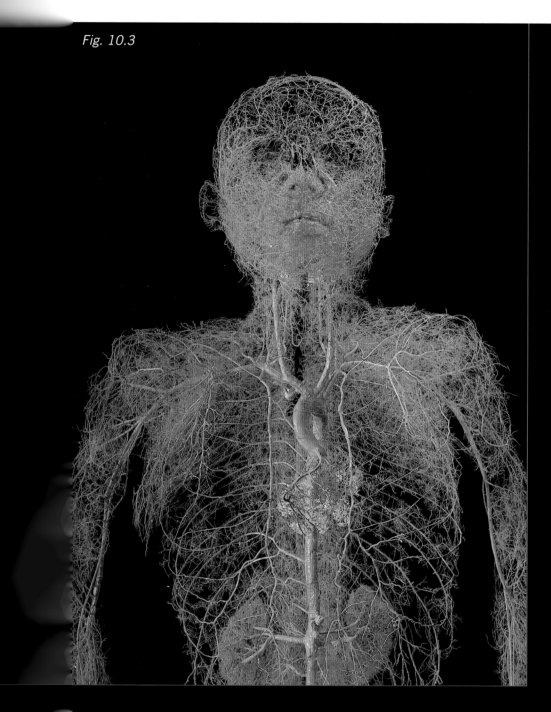

Configurations of Blood Vessels

These specimens are perfect embodiments of the inner profiles of blood vessels; the surround-ing tissue has been removed to facilitate visibility. These vessels are first injected with dyed plastic. Once the plastic has hardened, it has already taken on the shape formed by the ves-sels; the surrounding soft tissue can then be mechanically and chemically removed (corrod-ed) with the aid of ferments (collagenases, proteases). Sloughing and removal of remaining tissue is accomplished with ultrasound, a great deal of water, much patience and great care. In this way, arteries and their most minute clusters of blood vessels can be made visible.

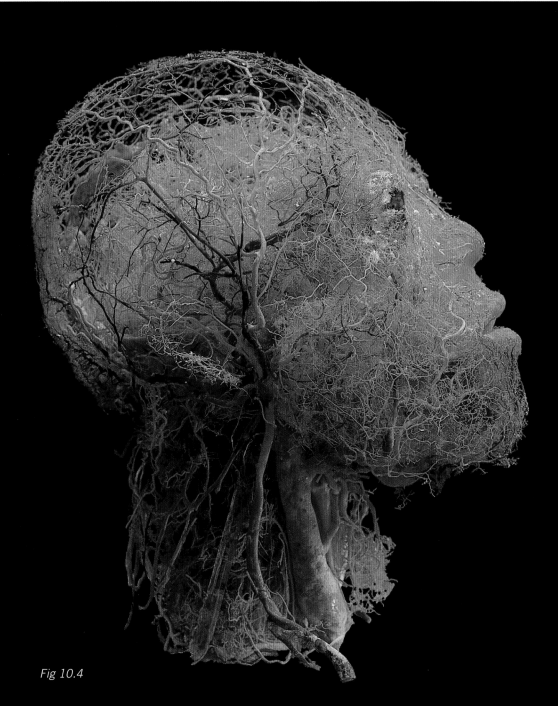

Fig 10.4

Configuration of the Arteries of the Head and Brain

The brain can only function properly when it receives a constant supply of oxygen-rich blood. For this purpose, the brain alone demands 15–20% of cardiac output although it only accounts for 2% of total body weight. The brain receives its blood supply via two sets of arteries, the internal carotid arteries left and right (A. carotis internae) and the vertebral arteries (A. vertebrales). All four arteries are connected with one another via a closed arterial circle (Circulus arteriosus cerebri) at the underside of the brain so that when blockage (occlusion) occurs in an artery, the flow of blood can be diverted via the circle and the endangered area of the brain can continue to be supplied with blood.

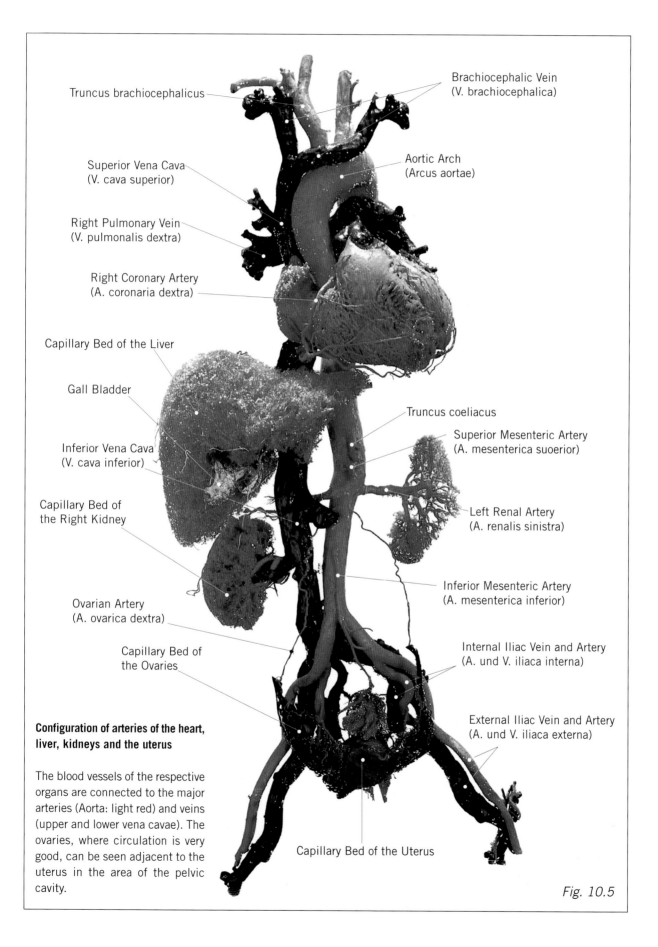

Truncus brachiocephalicus

Brachiocephalic Vein
(V. brachiocephalica)

Superior Vena Cava
(V. cava superior)

Aortic Arch
(Arcus aortae)

Right Pulmonary Vein
(V. pulmonalis dextra)

Right Coronary Artery
(A. coronaria dextra)

Capillary Bed of the Liver

Gall Bladder

Truncus coeliacus

Superior Mesenteric Artery
(A. mesenterica suoerior)

Inferior Vena Cava
(V. cava inferior)

Capillary Bed of
the Right Kidney

Left Renal Artery
(A. renalis sinistra)

Inferior Mesenteric Artery
(A. mesenterica inferior)

Ovarian Artery
(A. ovarica dextra)

Capillary Bed of
the Ovaries

Internal Iliac Vein and Artery
(A. und V. iliaca interna)

External Iliac Vein and Artery
(A. und V. iliaca externa)

**Configuration of arteries of the heart,
liver, kidneys and the uterus**

The blood vessels of the respective
organs are connected to the major
arteries (Aorta: light red) and veins
(upper and lower vena cavae). The
ovaries, where circulation is very
good, can be seen adjacent to the
uterus in the area of the pelvic
cavity.

Capillary Bed of the Uterus

Fig. 10.5

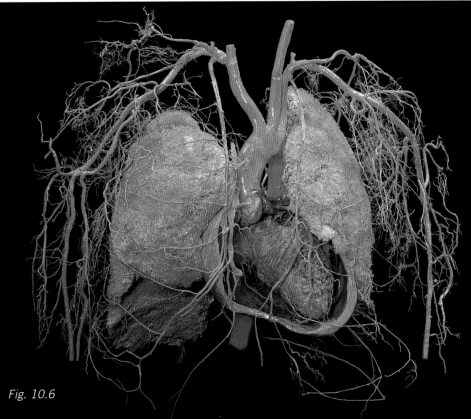

Fig. 10.6

Configuration of Arteries of the Thoracic Organs

In the area of the aortic arch, the arteries diverge to supply blood to the head, the upper extremeties and the upper half of the torso.

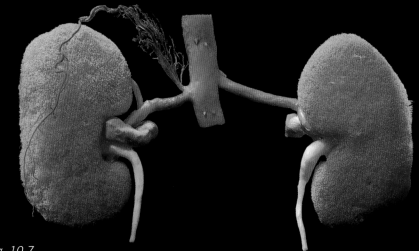

Fig. 10.7

Configuration of the Renal Arteries

(View from the rear) and the ureters that drain urine from the kidneys (yellow). The renal arteries flow into extremely fine capillary tufts or glomeruli (Malpighian or renal corpuscles) in the kidney tissue, which then filter the incoming blood.

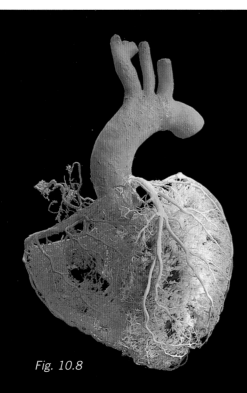

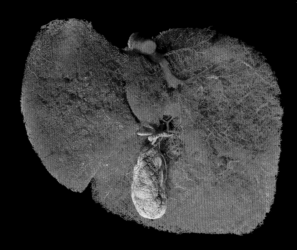

Fig. 10.9

Configuration of the Hepatic Arteries

(View from the rear) with the gallbladder (green). As the liver represents the central organ for processing nutrients and cleansing the blood, circulation through the liver is unusually strong. Approx. 1.5 litres (ca. 2.6 pints) flow through it every minute.

Fig. 10.8

Configuration of the Coronary Arteries

The vascular bed of the left coronary artery is highlighted with yellow plastic; it supplies the walls of the left ventricle and part of the right chamber, while the right coronary artery (red) primarily nourishes the right chamber.

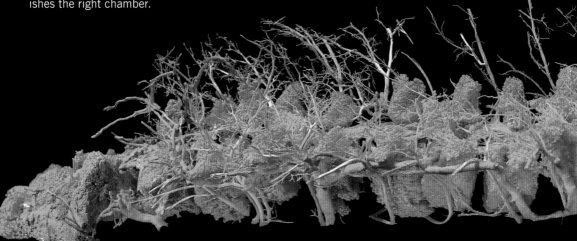

Fig. 10.10

Configuration of the Blood Vessels in the Spinal Column

The vertebrae contain a great deal of blood-forming (haematopoietic) bone marrow, in which blood cells are developed.

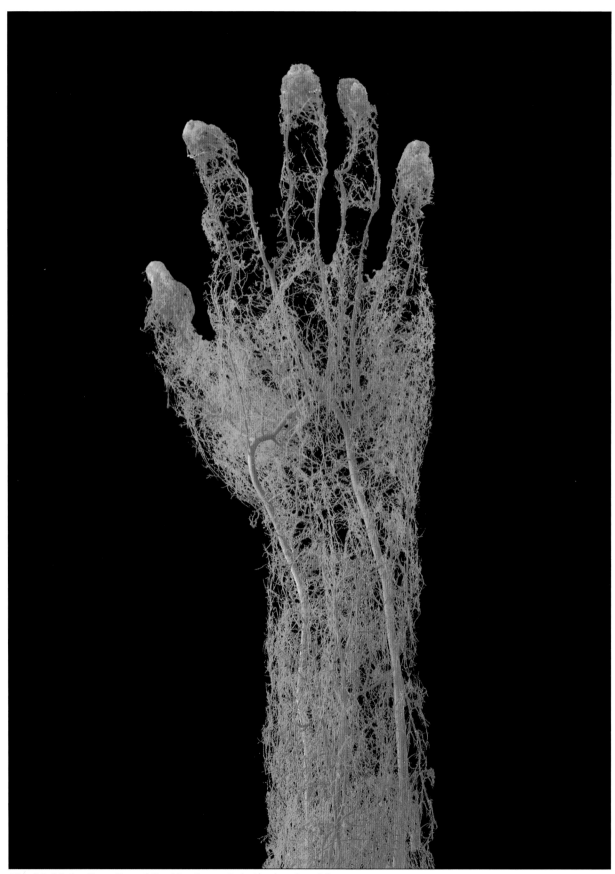

Fig. 10.11 Configuration of the blood vessels in the hand and forearm

Fig. 10.11 Configuration of the blood vessels of a rabbit

Ernst-D. Lantermann

KÖRPERWELTEN as Seen by Visitors

In recent years, probably no other exhibition in Germany has provoked such vigorous and controversial discussion among the public as KÖRPERWELTEN at the State Museum for Technology and Labour in Mannheim (Landesmuseum für Technik und Arbeit). It was planned to last for three months — from October 30, 1997 to February 1, 1998 — but was extended until March 1, 1998, on account of exceptionally large crowds. The range of opinions expressed even before the opening, and for some time afterwards, varied from enthusiastic agreement to forceful demands for it to be banned.

In this situation, Prof. Dr. Gunther von Hagens — creator of the exhibits, the novel anatomical specimens called plastinates — initiated a representative survey among the visitors. He wanted to obtain the most objective picture possible of their motives, expectations and fears before they had seen the exhibition, and their opinions afterwards. The public debate, which was greatly influenced by emotions, would, he hoped, be placed on a more factual basis when the opinions and experiences of those who were really informed became known.

After all, in the debate about KÖRPERWELTEN, before it had even been seen, representatives of the Church — supported by politicians from the conservative camp — had warned that large sections of the population could find their ethical and moral values offended by the sight of the exhibits. For their part, representatives of the medical profession had argued that such information and visual material about the human body was not suitable for the lay person; it was therefore extremely problematical to confront them with it.

Over a period of two and a half months, our team polled 2000 of the almost 780,000 visitors (500 in November and December 1997, respectively, and 1000 in January 1998). They were selected randomly. In addition, we ensured an even distribution of the samples over the days of the week and times of the day, in order to avoid possible distortions by polling only at weekends or at certain times during the week.

The first results of this survey were made public at a press conference in January 1998. They called many forecasts of adverse reactions from the public to KÖRPERWELTEN into question. However, the hope of rendering public opinion and discussion of this exhibition objective was not entirely fulfilled; in some cases at least, opinions were expressed that in the meantime had proved to be prejudices. In a television broadcast from Süddeutscher Rundfunk, the survey went unmentioned, although the reactions of the visitors were an important aspect of the contribution; instead, the editors selected only a few spectacular interviews, and suggested through the style of the feature that they were presenting an authentic reflection of the reaction — although the editor responsible for the programme was fully informed of the results of the representative survey.

Phases of Opinion Formation

Such surveys are nothing new. Nevertheless, they are difficult undertakings when they involve determining and understanding the effects of an exhibition as accurately as possible. In general, one satisfies oneself with a single questioning of people who have just seen the exhibits. However, such a strategy involves the risk of a confounding error, as it is called in statistics: in certain circumstances, a confusion (hence the expression) of the factors determining the answers is disregarded.

Visitors do not come to an exhibition unsuspectingly and by chance, but rather by intention. In general, they have familiarised themselves in advance to a greater or lesser extent — through the media and personal communications — and have developed specific expectations on the one hand about what they will see and experience, and, not rarely, on the other hand about the merits or demerits of what is on display. In psychology, the extent to which prior expectations and evaluations affect the actual judgement of an object or event has been adequately documented. If they are not determined before the visit to the exhibition, it cannot be decided whether and to what extent only the experiences during the visit are reflected in the opinions; in the interpretation of the answers the effect to be expected from prior opinions is then excluded. In contrast, our concept is based on two assumptions:

▪ The formation of individual opinions of an exhibition begins some time before it is visited;

▪ In this process a clear differentiation can be made between five phases (Figure 1).

Firstly (Phase 1) the potential public is informed from various sources. These may be media such as television, radio, newspapers, magazines and posters, or discussions within the family or with friends, acquaintances, or co-workers

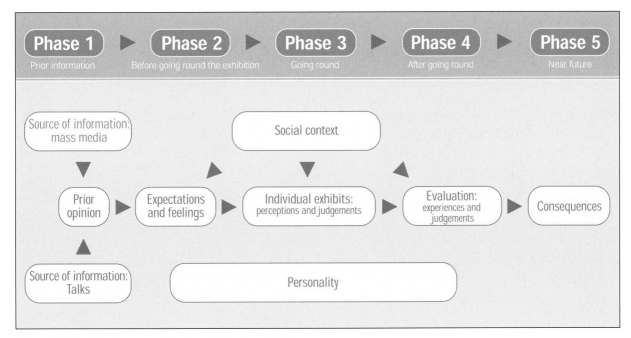

Figure 1: The five-phase model of a visit to the exhibition

Thus an initial opinion is formed. This phase is all the more important for the later personal experience and evaluation, the more controversially and intensively the exhibition is discussed in public and in private.

In the case of KÖRPERWELTEN, new press and television reports appeared repeatedly before and during the several-month exhibition in Mannheim. It must therefore be assumed that the discussions about it increased in intensity and frequency in broad sections of the population, that the level of information among potential visitors also increased, and consequently their initial prejudices and value judgements changed. A more accurate estimate of these chronological dynamics would be of great value for the overall evaluation of the event.

Those people who on the basis of their overall advance judgement have decided to visit the exhibition and in fact do so enter Phase 2. They come for a very wide variety of motives, with more or less distinct individual expectations and anticipations.

Only in Phase 3, which comprises the walk round, does the concrete experience of the exhibition take place. The visitors are faced with the individual exhibits, about which they now form their personal opinions on the basis of their previous opinions and direct impressions.

Immediately after their walk round (Phase 4) the visitors will form a summary of their observations and impressions, i.e. assess and evaluate the exhibition in its totality, they will review again what has particularly stayed in their memory, and examine their thoughts provoked by the experience.

Finally, a visit to an exhibition will have effects that last to a greater or lesser degree, possibly for a long time; very lively memories may even repeatedly occur (Phase 5). Precisely an exhibition like KÖRPERWELTEN, in which attention is drawn expressly to the complexity and frailty of the human body, is likely to give rise, in at least some of the visitors, to new thoughts and emotions, or even behavioural intentions that are not easy to work through or cannot rapidly be suppressed or forgotten.

However, this briefly outlined prototype course is formed by each visitor in his own way, so that specific impressions, experiences and evaluations result. The personality in question, his convictions and values, his age, sex and profession act — as one says in psychology — as filters in this process. People evaluate things and facts in accordance with their own values and experiences of life, and people with different values and experiences of life frequently evaluate the same facts very differently.

The concrete impressions, judgements and evaluations are also determined by whether the visitors go round the exhibition alone or in company — with relatives, friends or close acquaintances. This social context appeared to us to be of particular importance, precisely in the case of KÖRPERWELTEN.

Two Groups of Questions

The survey concerning the Mannheim exhibition of plastinates was based, in structure and content, on the five-phase model as far as possible. The visitors selected were therefore interviewed with the aid of two questionnaires, once (with regard to Phases 1 and 2) immediately before they had gone round the exhibition, and then (with regard to Phases 3, 4 and 5) immediately afterwards.

The first group of questions therefore concerned their indirect information about KÖRPERWELTEN and their prior opinions based on this. In addition to the age, sex and profession of those questioned, the essential sources of information that had induced them to visit the exhibition, their individual expectations and fears, their feelings at the time, and the social context of the planned visit (whether they were alone or in company) were therefore determined. In addition, several questions about their values and principles of life were asked. In the second group of questions, the same people were asked firstly about their impressions and opinions of individual exhibits, secondly about their overall opinion, i.e. their summary evaluation of various aspects, and thirdly about the longer-term behavioural intentions with which they left the exhibition.

Results

Firstly I should like to present the essential general findings. Then I consider in a more differentiated manner two groups of visitors: religious believers and members of the medical profession.*

Re Phase 1. The first question was: In the public, the opinions about this exhibition vary greatly. After all that you have previously seen and heard, are you now, before visiting the exhibition, more on the side of those who approve or on the

---

* Connections and differences between individual variables, which we have analysed with differing variants of the general linear model were only taken into consideration if there was at least a statistically mean effect. With a sample size of 2000, statistical significance measurements are without informative value, as even minimal differences and connections become highly significant on account of the logic of statistical interferences in such a large number of cases.

The following procedures were used: factor analyses, Guttman's scale reliability tests and multidimensional scalings if a summary of expectations, feelings and experiences regarding certain classes and scales was to be carried out, and also univariate and multivariate analyses of variance for testing differences in mean values between groups of visitors and regression analyses for determining the weights of individual variables for the achievement of certain judgements.

---

side of those who oppose this exhibition? Seventy eight per cent of those questioned before going round the exhibition described themselves as approving KÖRPERWELTEN

However, the advance judgements were influenced to differing degrees by the public reporting and the private discussions. In the first survey period (during the first and second weeks of November), 47 % indicated that they had obtained information exclusively through the mass media, only 22 % exclusively through conversations with friends and acquaintances, and 31 % named both sources. But already at the beginning of December the ratio was reversed: now more visitors had obtained information through friends and acquaintances than from the mass media; nor did this change during the third survey period. Those who had obtained prior information mainly from radio, television and the press generally had a more positive attitude towards KÖRPERWELTEN than those who had obtained it from conversations.

Re Phase 2. The visitors were shown nine statements about possible expectations, which we had derived from analyses of articles in the press about the exhibition. The answers were assigned to the three subject classes obtaining information, biological-medical insight and disturbing confrontation:

- 88 % of those questioned expected to learn more about the human body, and to see something new in general.
- As many as 90 % expected to feel reverence for the wonder of the human body and to gain encouragement for treating their own body in a healthy manner.
- In contrast, only 11 % expected to have disturbing negative experiences, be confronted by unpleasant things, and be inwardly disturbed or outraged.

In addition, eight questions were aimed at determining the momentary feelings of the visitors before they went round the exhibition. The self-estimates could be assigned to two scales of emotional state:

- 86 % had only positive feelings (curiosity, anticipation and expectant excitement)
- However, less than 2 % expressed only negative feelings (depression, anxiety, inner resistance or scepticism).
- The other 12 % entered the exhibition with mixed feelings.

The nature of these expectations and premonitions — positive or negative — was independent of whether the visitors had obtained prior information in private discussions or from the mass media. However, these sources of information did have an effect on the expectation horizon (Figure 2): at the beginning of the exhibition, reports and comments in the media encouraged differentiated expectations; later, dis-

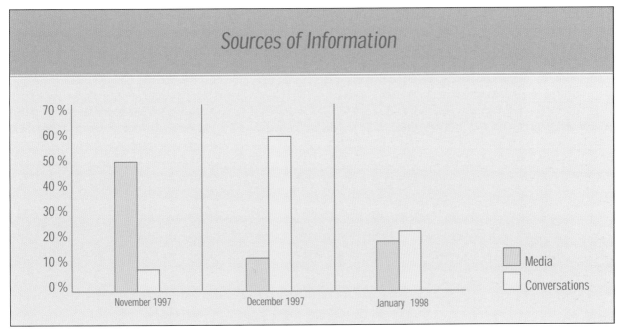

Figure 2: Differentiation of expectations depending on the sources of information

cussions and conversations among friends and acquaintances had the same effect; finally, opinion was again influenced by the media, however, only in a more exaggerated and greatly simplified manner.

Re Phase 3. After they had visited the exhibition the visitors were first questioned about their impressions of the various plastinates, their feelings when confronted with them, their assessments of individual groups of specimens (whole-body plastinates, isolated healthy and diseased organs, malformations, foetuses and body slices) and their opinion of their aesthetic qualities. Again the expressions of feelings could be classified into three groups:

- 64 % of those questioned had experienced exclusively positive information-related feelings (curiosity, amazement, fascination).
- 5 % reported exclusively feelings of rejection (having felt outrage, injured, revolted).
- 38 % reported general feelings of high intensity (either deeply moved or downcast).

A total of 92 % of the visitors were affected particularly positively by the whole-body plastinates, only 6 % rejected them. There was a similar ratio in the case of the organ specimens. The presentation of malformations found the least approval, with only 62 % of the visitors approving them.

The aesthetic impressions differed more greatly. As many as 60 % of the visitors found at least one exhibit particularly beautiful (most frequently mentioned were specimens from the blood vessel system). But 20 % were neverthe-

less of the opinion that there were also particularly ugly exhibits (the malformed foetuses in particular were mentioned); 28 % said that to exhibit such things publicly was brutal.

To the question whether their impressions and evaluations were also determined by the fact "that real bodies and parts of the body" were on display, 46 % answered "absolutely" and 38 % "yes, very strongly". To the question whether "an exhibition with deceptively genuine plastic models and vivid computer images would have had a similar effect", 14 % answered "yes, probably" and 33 % "perhaps", but 53 % "no, definitely not."

With a proven method of analysis, we attempted to filter out those aspects of exhibits that contributed in particular to positive or negative impressions in the Mannheim exhibition. These were primarily aesthetic qualities. Secondly, the fact that these were real anatomical specimens had an effect. Thirdly and finally, it is important that whole-body plastinates were on view.

It is not surprising that the initial attitudes to KÖRPER-WELTEN influenced the evaluation of these aspects. One likes to have one's opinion, once formed, confirmed. The more strongly the visitors were generally influenced negatively or expected to be confronted by morally outrageous exhibits, the more rarely did they then give a positive judgement (Figures 3 and 4). However, if the visitors came with the expectation of learning more about the human body, obtaining new motivations for treating their own body with an awareness of health, or feeling of reverence, they were with-

211

out exception also positively influenced by the individual exhibits. In contrast, whether those questioned had visited the exhibition alone or in company had no influence.

Re Phase 4. We determined the balance of the visitors by means of direct questions and from their comments on various statements about it that were shown to them. With regard to the presentation of plastinates overall, 88 % indicated complete acceptance of this idea; fewer than 1 % were outraged. When requested to summarise all impressions and thoughts, 1 % evaluated the exhibition as poor, 4 % as fair, 41 % as good, and as many as 54 % as very good.

As reasons for this exceptionally positive overall evaluation, our analyses (Figure 5) revealed: Obtaining knowledge about the human body was in first place; in second place the

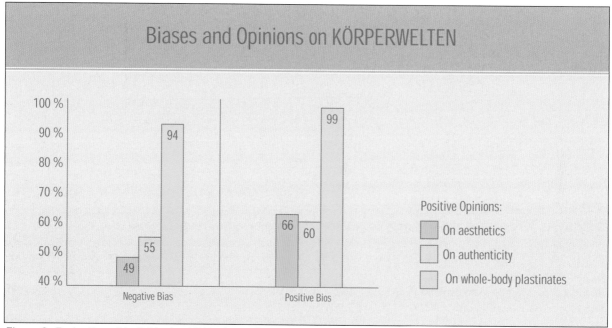

Figure 3: Evaluation of individual exhibits depending on prior judgements

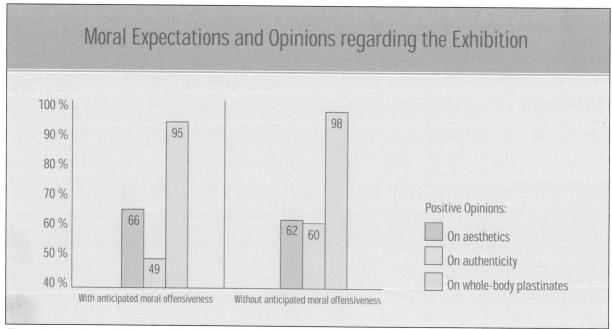

Figure 4: Moral expectations and opinions regarding individual exhibits

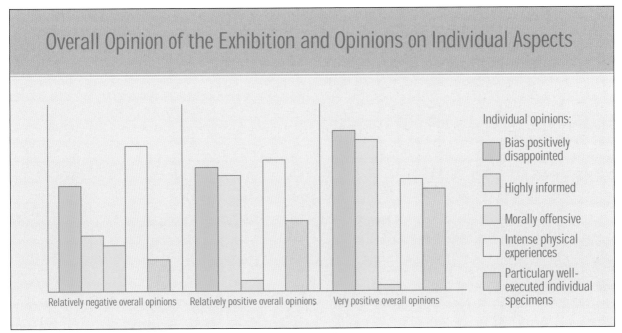

Overall Opinion of the Exhibition and Opinions on Individual Aspects

Individual opinions:

- Bias positively disappointed
- Highly informed
- Morally offensive
- Intense physical experiences
- Particulary well-executed individual specimens

Relatively negative overall opinions   Relatively positive overall opinions   Very positive overall opinions

Figure 5: Overall evaluation of the exhibition and reasons

particularly impressive encounter with individual specimens, followed by the pleasant surprise of a sceptical or critical prior judgement's not being fulfilled, and the confrontation with borderline experiences. In particular, the idea that human values were offended by KÖRPERWELTEN contributed to a negative evaluation.

Surprising at first view is the finding that visitors who went to the exhibition with negative or ambivalent, less pronounced, advance opinions, evaluated it particularly positively in their overall view — even more favourably than those with hopeful expectations. Apparently those questioned in the general balancing had thought about their previous opinions, and established, precisely because of that, that they — although many specimens met with their disapproval — found the exhibition as a whole far more impressive and positive than they had assumed before their visit.

In addition, the subjects were asked to summarise their concrete experiences. Seventy-four per cent stated that they were now better informed about the human body and more interested in it than before. Likewise, many mentioned as an enriching experience, that they had become more thoughtful about life and death, and more concerned about the vulnerability of their own body. Eighty-five per cent of the visitors left the exhibition with great respect for the nature of man, while only 7 % considered that human dignity had been infringed.

A comparison of individual expectations with the experiences in each case resulted in 22 % of those questioned being disappointed to a greater or lesser degree with regard to the

information obtained; a majority of 63 % experienced exactly what they had expected, and in 15 % their expectations were exceeded. In regard to fears, approx. 35 % of the visitors had them confirmed, while 65 % had expected something worse than what they actually saw and experienced.

Re Phase 5. We asked about possible long-term consequences of the visit to KÖRPERWELTEN from several points of view. Accordingly

- 59 % of the subjects had decided to pay more attention to their health in future;
- 21 % could well imagine donating their bodies for plastination, whereas 28 % by no means wanted to do this;
- 36 % of those who had not previously declared themselves as organ donors would do so after visiting this exhibition, and for 6 % this would now be less of a consideration; 50 % indicated that experiencing the exhibition would play no part in such a decision.

Also with regard to the consequences, it may be asked what further factors could influence them. According to our analyses, the intention of living in a more health-aware manner in future is most strongly determined by the impression of the vulnerability of their own body, especially as a result of the exhibition having awakened greater interest in their own body and respect for the nature of man. Prior information and prior attitudes had no detectable influence on this idea.

The intention of having their own body plastinated after death depends most strongly on the aesthetic qualities of the exhibits experienced, also on the conviction that KÖR-PERWELTEN contributes to human nature and the value of respect for man. The mass media also promote willingness for plastination. Whoever had a negative attitude before the exhibition tended to reject it after visiting the exhibition.

Finally, the willingness to donate organs was greater among those visitors who tended to consider the aesthetic dimension of the exhibition unimportant and had acquired prior information mainly from the mass media. In contrast, previous attitudes were of no importance.

The Religious Faithful and the Medical Profession

In the public discussions and debates about KÖRPER-WELTEN, reference was repeatedly made directly or indirectly to certain aspects of personality. Firstly, representatives of the Church had expressed extremely critical opinions with arguments drawn from moral theology; secondly, representatives of the medical profession had put forward considerable specialist objections to making plastinated anatomical specimens accessible to a lay public.

It is true that we obtained only little data on what determined the personality of the visitors to the exhibition. But on account of the topics that determined the general debate, in addition to age and sex we also asked about profession and values. Thus the attitudes and judgements of two particular groups of visitors could be considered more closely: those of religious believers and those of members of the medical and healing professions.

Twenty-seven per cent of those questioned described themselves as people for whom belief in life is particularly important. Those with such a belief who visited the Mannheim exhibition had fewer positive prior attitudes than non-believers. They had obtained prior information from the media less frequently, more in private discussions, came with fewer expectations of information but with greater expectations of reverence, had more pronounced negative prior feelings, and their expectation horizon was generally more differentiated.

When confronted with the individual exhibits, they also experienced stronger negative and — at the same time — more intense feelings than non-believers. In their judgement, they tended more than others to see human dignity infringed upon (9 compared with 2 %) but at the same time felt great respect for the nature of man. They did not differ from the other visitors in their overall evaluation of the exhibition, but they clearly differ in their future intentions: considerably fewer of them declared their willingness to release their bodies for organ donation or plastination after death.

According to the comparison of their data, the visit to the exhibition took a quite different course for the religious believers than for the non-believers. But fears of representatives of the Church that KÖRPERWELTEN could become a moral provocation and ethical interference for believers were not confirmed at all according to our observations.

The group of members of the medical and healing professions comprised 22 % of those questioned in Mannheim. Their prior opinions were more positive than those of people without medical knowledge.

They had exchanged more information about KÖRPER-WELTEN with colleagues, had fewer expectations of learning anything new about the human body, and their expectation profile was comparatively little differentiated. They visited the exhibition with fewer negative and fewer intensive feelings than others, paid more attention to the aesthetic qualities of the exhibits, and less frequently reported physical experiences. Their overall evaluation was more positive than that of other groups. They also said that they were more willing to accept plastination of their bodies, and the visit to the exhibition had increased their willingness to donate organs.

Moreover, there is no particularly critical attitude to the public display of plastinates manifest in the data on this medically trained group. In any case, the reservations and objections of some representatives of the medical profession would not appear to be supported.

Conclusion

The Mannheim exhibition KÖRPERWELTEN was the object of outspoken criticism as it will also be in future. However, this contribution was not concerned with continuing the public discussion from a general perspective, but letting the visitors themselves, as the real experts, express their opinions. Their exceptionally positive evaluation surprised not only the organisers.

The five-phase model of the formation of opinion that is presented has, we think, passed its first test as a heuristic strategy for the planning and execution of an exhibition survey. The findings summarised here reveal a broad picture of the conditions, factors and processes that are involved in the management of experiences and evaluations of various visitor groups.

In our opinion, analyses of this type can contribute decisively to a better understanding of unusual and totally novel exhibits. Thus the concepts of such exhibitions can also be optimised; under certain circumstances, experts would even have to accompany the visitors carefully.

Ernst-D Lantermann has been a Professor of Personality and Social Psychology since 1979 and since 1994 has also been the Director of the Scientific Centre for Environmental System Research at the Polytechnic University in Kassel. He studied psychology, history of art and German studies at the University of Bonn, obtained his doctorate in 1974 and qualified as a university lecturer in 1978 at the Rhine-Westphalian Technical University in Aachen. He has had guest professorships in Germany and abroad, and in 1994/95 chaired the Department of Global Change and Social Systems at the Potsdam Institute for Climatic Research. He has written approximately 80 articles and is the author or editor of numerous books on subjects of personality and environmental psychology and the psychology of art. The main focus of his current research is on the development of computerised training processes for complexity management in companies and educational institutions.

Axel W. Bauer

Plastinated Specimens and their Presentation in Museums — A Theoretical and Bioethical Retrospective on a Media Event

The Mannheim Exhibition KÖRPERWELTEN as a Magnet for the Public and a Media Happening

Between October 30, 1997, and March 1, 1998, within a space of only four months, nearly 780,000 people visited the special exhibition entitled KÖRPERWELTEN at the State Museum for Technology and Labour in Mannheim (Landesmuseum für Technik und Arbeit). After just a few weeks, there could be no more doubt that such a presentation of plastinated anatomical specimens was a singular undertaking and that there was just as singular a public and published resonance far beyond Germany.

The mass media contributed a great deal to making this — the most successful German exhibition of all time — world-famous. But it was also the media that could not resist the temptation to show the exhibits as well as their creator in a demonic light. Whether it was the flower lady reading "Baden's Latest News" at the weekly market in Karlsruhe or the post-modern TV gourmet on "Willemsen's Week" on Germany's Channel 2 (ZDF), the Crailsheim teacher who watched the "Lokaltermin" on regional TV channel 3 (SWF 3), a designated Protestant Regional Bishop, medical students and college instructors of anatomy and pathology, of law, theology and philosophy — all were suddenly talking about plastinated specimens, the plastinator and the moral provocation that he apparently had caused.

Elsewhere in Germany and abroad, the voices of the open-minded and the curious predominated. It was remarkable to see how the echo of the event grew so much more controversial and emotional, sometimes even shriller and more polemical the nearer one came to the Heidelberg/Mannheim area. It almost seemed as if one were entering the epicentre of a moral earthquake. This was how great the interest in the plastinated specimens was and how dramatic the debate that centred on the ethical defensibility of the entire exhibition or even of individual exhibits turned out to be.

For me, both as an author participating in this discourse and as a college lecturer on medical history, theory and ethics, there is considerable appeal from this retrospective vantage point to work again with the theoretical and bioethical aspects of anatomy in public and with the resonance during and after the Mannheim exhibition. This cannot be a matter of establishing one particular ethical standpoint — namely one's own — as the only legitimate and correct standard. This is not the purpose of medical ethics. Every concrete

ethical expert report is bound to its time and its people and is therefore of necessity subjective and thus contestable in a certain way; nevertheless, there is still a fair way of conducting a theoretical and bioethical discourse, which was nowhere to be found in the published contributions to the debate on KÖRPERWELTEN.

A Theoretical and Bioethical Perspective on Anatomy and the Public

A number of theoretical and bioethical questions has been raised, and in some cases discussed quite controversially in connection with the Mannheim exhibition, ranging from aesthetics to philosophical aspects to legal-ethical problems. Not least, a theological criticism that was harsh, but inconsistent in argumentation, opened up these topics before the exhibition.

In October 1997, the Mannheim Deans of the two major Christian Churches in Germany wrote a letter to the lord mayor of Mannheim and to the prime minister of Baden-Württemberg in which they asserted that the planned exhibition not only represented "excessive bad taste," but that the interaction with the dead practiced here also violated basic human dignity. The dead should not be degraded into exhibits, and the curious viewing of dissected dead people should not be stylized into a cultural event. The undertaking makes "no small contribution to the decline of moral values in our society"; thus it would be irresponsible to use taxpayers' money for it.

Those were strong accusations. Their tenor became more modulated in the weeks that followed due to the great public interest, but then the arguments started in a new direction. I will come back to that later. But first, I will take the phrase "decline of moral values" as the starting point for a theoretical digression, which will be important in clarifying terms.

Where Do Ethical Values and Standards Come From?

Does medicine require values? This could be the central question of the bioethics of the healing arts. Now someone may well answer spontaneously with "of course!" Whoever reacts this way generally has a fixed idea of timeless values and claims to know precisely how the concrete standards of attitude and action in medicine have to be set up.

But where do our ethical values and standards really come from? Were they always there? Are they unchanging? And how can we know for certain what they are? By asking these questions, we move into the realm of metaethics. In this realm, with all the diversity of individual approaches to the details, there are three groups of ideas of how moral values could be made and how they arise: cognitivism, emotivism and institutionalism. I would like to outline these theories briefly.

The cognitivist view holds that ethical statements have the same status as those statements with which we express empirical knowledge or logical conclusions. The constitutional postulate "The dignity of man is inviolable" in Article 1, Paragraph 1, of the German Federal Constitution would, according to this principle, be evaluated by the same standards as the statement "The cat's eyes are green" or the mathematical proposition "The sum of the angles of a triangle is 180 degrees."

The cognitivist theory has the advantage that it agrees with the syntactic rules of our language ("Property A of Object B has Form C."). Another advantage is that it also corresponds to everyday experience, which we gladly ascribe to commonsense. Most theologians, but also the majority of

philosophers from Plato (427–347 BC) and Aristotle (384–322 BC) to Immanuel Kant (1724–1804) to the English neo-realist George E. Moore (1873–1958), can be counted among the advocates of cognitivist positions. An ethical objectivism arises as a consequence: the content of moral statements is either unambiguously true or unambiguously false because it agrees with moral facts that for their part exist objectively in external (or metaphysical) reality.

However, two main difficulties have brought discredit to cognitivism. The first is the problem with the perception of moral facts. Man's physiological sensory organs are clearly unsuited for this; for this reason, the cognitivist must admit to the existence of a higher, so to speak, a metaphysical means of perception, namely intuition. But the important role of intuition contradicts the claim of objectivity, which is the basis of cognitivism.

The second difficulty is the derivation of normative rules from statements of fact. According to the law put forward by the Scottish philosopher David Hume (1711–1776), which states that what should be cannot be derived from what is, it is not permissible to base the deductive conclusion of a statement of fact on one of evaluation; the conclusion would then go beyond the content of the premises.

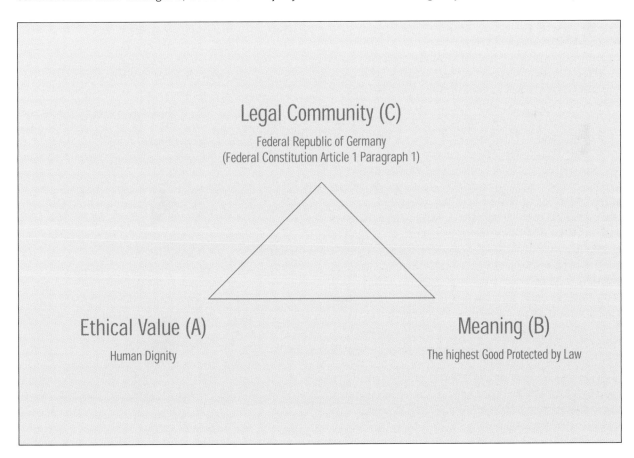

The structure of an institutional fact

In 1952, Englishman Richard M. Hare, who dealt extensively with metaphysics in his works and lectures at Balliol College of Oxford University, gave further support to this classical finding from a linguistic-philosophical perspective. The advocates of ethical cognitivism are consequently instructed to develop binding moral commandments or prohibitions from moral facts entirely in the sense of the deductive "facticistic" fallacy. (I explicitly note here that the deductive "facticistic" fallacy can occur not only in the form of the biologistic-naturalistic, but also in the varieties of the historical fallacy. There are just as few absolute moral standards for the present and future that derive from history as from biology.)

The followers of emotivism, among whom we find David Hume once again, draw a radical consequence from the aporias of cognitivism. For the emotivists, there are no objective moral statements. In their view, for example, the statement "The dignity of man is inviolable" does not describe any external reality ascertainable with reason; it is much more the literary résumé of a subjective feeling, an emotion.

Alfred J. Ayer, like Hare a professor at Oxford and one of the leading representatives of analytic philosophy, went a step further by saying, "It deserves to be mentioned that ethical terms not only serve to express feelings; they are also used to arouse feelings and thus to cause action." Hence, both descriptive emotivism with Hume and its appellative variations with Ayer cause a serious ethical discourse to appear nearly hopeless. If moral statements always reflect only subjective and individual feelings, then neither logical argument nor a generally valid standard of values or action can be derived from them.

Institutionalism offers a way around the dead ends of cognitivism and emotivism. Philosopher John R. Searle, who teaches at the University of California at Berkeley, introduced this way of thinking with the concept of the institutional fact and Swiss philosopher Rafael Ferber expanded it in the realm of moral facts. According to institutionalism, moral facts are not objective physical or metaphysical realities, as cognitivism claims. But neither are they purely subjective psychic phenomena, which can stimulate other persons to empathy or imitation, as emotivism maintains. Moral facts must rather be seen as social institutions created by people throughout history, which are inter-subjectively constituted, stabilized, handed down and modified according to certain rules within a cultural and linguistic community.

These rules follow the structure "A is regarded as B in the context of the community C" (see chart). It follows from this that the rules, according to which moral values develop, are always at the same time linguistic-semantic rules. Through these rules, the meaning B is assigned to the word A in the context of the linguistic community C. Since the words used for communication are symbols of a language, their asso-

ciation with concrete meanings can be characterized as a relatively flexible and, over time, changeable relationship. Institutional facts are thus interpreted as natural facts in a certain way; here the worlds of life and language enter into a certain normative union, which admittedly is neither rigid nor indissoluble.

Value Changes and Societal Consensus as Exemplified by Plastinated Specimens in Public

Values in medicine as well as in other areas of our lives are thus developed socio-culturally as institutional facts. They are not objectively predetermined by nature, but are created by man at particular times for particular purposes and interpreted by man in concrete situations. Since values are therefore unstable and changeable, they require a societal consensus to be valid. This first arises, however, in the course of a historical process, that is, in the framework of a public discussion.

Certainly now at the end of the 20th century, the course of such a struggle, especially when it is about total societal consensus, can no longer be manipulated solely by the calculated expediency of church duopolies or political parties. On the contrary, each individual citizen has a certain influence

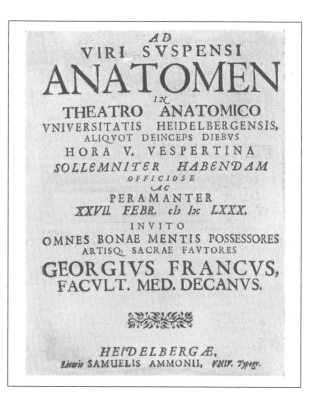

Invitation of the dean of the medical college in Heidelberg, Georg Franck von Franckenau (1644–1704), to the public autopsy of a hanged person on February 27, 1680.

on all future values and standards through his actions or inaction (which in a free democratic state based on the rule of law must at least remain within the limits of the constitution). The fact that this does not always please all of the parties interested in ethics should not stop us from taking note of it.

Why this relatively detailed digression into metaethical theory, when this article is specifically about an exhibition of plastinated human specimens in a public museum? The connection between theory and practice is quickly made: While more than 778,000 visitors have viewed and marvelled at KÖRPERWELTEN in Mannheim, just such a public discussion on bioethical questions arose just as the institutional theory describes and almost expects. Established values passed down over time were brought into the discussion, as were the most varied feelings as well as the desire to break taboos , and this chorus of heterogeneous voices was not very harmonious. This was exactly the situation that must always come about when we encounter something unfamiliar, for which we cannot make confident ethical and aesthetic judgments right from the very beginning due to a lack of relevant experience.

What can be said concretely about the course of this public discussion? In the first place there is the unexpectedly high number of visitors to the exhibition. The attendance represents people's "voting with their feet" (an expression I already used in the catalogue in November 1997, which opponents of the exhibition later often misinterpreted as the presumed relativization of human dignity): citizens of this country and those who travelled specially from afar, schoolchildren, university students, professionals and pensioners, healthy, sick and convalescents — all wanted to acquaint themselves with the structure of the human body by seeing the plastinated specimens with their own eyes. These visitors from all over Germany and the rest of Europe, and even from the US and Australia, who often waited in line for hours without complaint, were apparently of the opinion that viewing the interiors of human anatomy should no longer be the privilege of medical practitioners alone.

There could be multiple motives for visiting the exhibition; one important one was, without doubt, curiosity. Few — if any — cultural and civilized achievements would exist without this quality, and certainly no scientific discoveries. Thus it is absolutely unjustified to dismiss amazement at, and fascination with, the dissected and plastinated human bodies merely with negative terms such as "voyeurism" and "sensationalism" or to make the improper association of the motives of the visitors with "morbid curiosity at badly injured or dead people" at traffic accidents, as they did in a local newspaper interview published in November 1997.

The guest book of the Mannheim exhibition and letters to the editor in the regional press clearly demonstrate that even medical laypersons are capable of a sophisticated evaluation of KÖRPERWELTEN. A 52-year-old department manager stated, "Sometimes the thought shot through your head that this was a person. But I do not believe their dignity was violated." A 35-year-old physical therapist opined, "The insight into anatomy is incredibly interesting, you can see every muscle in practical detail. I think the churches' criticisms are excessive." A sixteen-year-old high school girl admitted readily, "I really liked it a lot. The criticisms of the churches are especially questionable to me. They also put their saints and relics on display."

This apparently addressed a sore point, since the theological campaign against the exhibition was later continued only by the Protestant side, even if more subtly than before. The saints and their relics protected the Catholic Church in a miraculous way from a public self-dismantling.

The objections of the then Dean of the Protestant church in Mannheim actually missed the point when he said that saints were only preserved in the Catholic Church "to remember them for their life as they were, not to use them artistically." A compelling counterexample is the Museo dei Padri Cappuccini in the church of Santa Maria della Concezione on the Via Veneto in Rome, in which one can admire candelabras and wall and ceiling decorations made of the bones of some 4000 monks, who died mainly in the Baroque period. Anyone who has visited it knows that here — as well as elsewhere — religion and art have come together in a close relationship, on the one hand for the glory of God, on the other hand for the benefit of the living. And though the Capuchins collect no admission charge to visit their bone museum, hardly any tourist could allow himself to dodge the unmistakable rattle made by the friars who offer the always well-filled collection plate on exiting. Only puritanical souls could object to this.

Warning! Art! A Threat to Human Dignity?

An objection to KÖRPERWELTEN that was obviously considered valid was presented in December 1997 by the then Dean of Mannheim, Ulrich Fischer, (now Regional Bishop of the Evangelical Regional Church in Baden): "The central point of my criticism is that with many exhibits the interest in scientific enlightenment has clearly taken a back seat to the artistic self-realization of the plastinator. Here, human beings have been made into aesthetically significant works of art. I reject such use of human beings."

Fischer had already spoken out against an "objectification of man" in a panel discussion presented on a local television programme on November 27, 1997, in which I also participated. There he introduced an ethical "slippery slope" argument: if a plastinator wanted to set himself up as God, dictating what may be done with human beings, we must then ask ourselves if one could then do anything at all with human beings and how we could recycle them. When human beings are objectified in the hands of a "human creator," then the dignity of man is in jeopardy.

Now that the spokesman of the Evangelical Church as well as other critics from the field of medicine and finally an expert in the field of medical law have addressed the concept of human dignity in this connection, some clarifying words on the different meanings of this essential philosophical and legal-ethical term must be introduced. As early as the Stoics, founded by Zeno of Kition (ca. 336–246 BC), and later the Roman statesman and proponent of Greek philosophy, Marcus Tullius Cicero (106–43 BC), a distinction was made between an equalizing form and a differentiating form of human dignity. The first is related to the species Homo sapiens as opposed to other forms of life. The second means the individual as a person with respect to other persons.

It was the Judeo-Christian ideas of man in the image of God, which are related to the equalizing form of human dignity, that the humanistic scholars of the Italian Renaissance and the later Spanish Scholastics and the theologians of the German Reformation took up and developed further as the Middle Ages turned into the early Modern era. With the anthropological turn of the 18th century, the concept was finally secularized; human dignity now found its basis in the unique quality of reason, which the protagonists of the Enlightenment held to be a typical characteristic of humankind.

Immanuel Kant interpreted dignity as a sign of that which "is sublime above any price, for which therefore no equivalent suffices." For Kant and his successors, only man could not be instrumentalized and was thus the sole possessor of dignity, because of his reason — the prerequisite for free self-determination. This was the basis and justification for the absolute rule of man over animate and inanimate — in the Kantian sense "worthless" — nature, during the last two centuries. Animal and plant protection and any ecological thinking did not lie in the field of vision of an equalizing interpretation of human dignity.

The second or the differentiating interpretation follows a political tradition. Historically concrete civil rights, which individual persons could make valid with respect to others or with respect to the state and its organs, first appeared in important legal documents. In particular, basic texts of constitutional standing from Western European and American history emphasized group-specific civil rights, from the English Magna Carta (1215) to the Act of Habeus Corpus

Lymphatic Vessel Man by Paulo Mascagni (1755–1815)

(1679), the British Bill of Rights (1689), the American Bill of Rights (1776) and the French *Déclaration des droits de l'homme et du citoyen* (1789) to the Constitution of the Federal Republic of Germany (1949), in whose first 19 Articles — the basic rights — human and civil rights are closely interconnected with one another: Article 1, Clause 1 of the German Constitution makes it explicit that the dignity of man is inviolable. To respect and protect it is the duty of all state authority; this highest value in our free democracy finds its historical explanation in that terrible experience as those in power trampled on every conceivable form of human dignity during the Nazi dictatorship.

The differentiating form of human dignity is in effect in the United Nations Universal Declaration of Human Rights of 1948 and in the constitutions of those countries that use the term as "innate," or given to each person by nature, independent of ancestry, character and life development. It is a widely recognized, anthropological basic value, a fundamental standard of modern structures based on the rule of law, even when in reality it is often violated.

If a representative of the Evangelical Church in connection with the Mannheim exhibition KÖRPERWELTEN was worried about endangering human dignity, we must make it clear to ourselves that he has in mind the traditional, equalizing form in the sense of man made in the image of God. The human dignity in Article 1, Clause 1 of the German Basic Law, which originates from the autonomy of the individual citizen, is however in no way identical with this Christian interpretation of the term. In a country, in which according to Article 4, Clause 1 of the same Basic Law the freedom of conscience, of belief as well as the religious and ideological confession is just as inviolable, the church version cannot be legally or ethically binding in any case.

Legal-Ethical Critique

Shortly thereafter, another even weightier critique of the Mannheim exhibition was articulated, which was expressly based on the concept of human dignity as anchored in the civil rights of the German Constitution. This argument by the Mannheim pathologist Uwe Bleyl was carefully considered, brilliantly formulated and so significant in content that it deserves a detailed discussion. This was really the legal-ethical core of the problem.

Bleyl analyzed the situation approximately as follows: human dignity is a personal legal value in the constitutional law of the FRG and is the basis of the idea of man as an individual related to and bound up with the community, which is based on free self-determination. An individual must always remain a purpose unto himself. The bearer of human dignity is the individual as a person, i.e. as a being equipped with a spiritual nature, gifted with awareness of self, self-determination, free will and freedom of choice.

The Federal Constitutional Court has placed the dead under the protection of human dignity as well, which it has defined as a right to self-determination of the living that persists beyond death. Of necessity, the result of this is that treatment of the dead is subject to the same ethical standards as treatment of the living. This also means that violations of the dignity of the living and the dead are to be viewed as such even if they occur by consent of the living or the dead.

In this principle, an anatomist is included as a plastinator in the responsibility for medical education and training — still Bleyl — so that no ethical considerations could apply against plastination and its practice on volunteer donors, as long as it was being performed exclusively for educational purposes. However, ethical reservations arise where aesthetic or aestheticizing manipulations come to the foreground and human handling of human remains is motivated by aestheticizing heteronomy and the creative self-realization of others.

So much for this sound and critical argumentation. The heteronomy of the body to be plastinated was seen as an objective violation of human dignity due to the plastinator's artistic urge to form — a heteronomy that may not be viewed as allowable even if the body donor had given a prior written declaration of intent. Legally then, it could be assumed that under certain circumstances donating one's body in one's will could be postulated as partially illegal according to Para. 138, Clause 1 of the German Civil Code. However, before we turn to the question whether the artistic presentation of plastinated specimens really conclusively represents a violation of human dignity and by what criteria one could objectively evaluate such an artistic arrangement, it should be shown how much even that legal term of "good morals," from which that indirect reference was taken, requires interpretation.

The Supreme Administrative Court in Berlin dealt with this term in 1990 in a decision on the questionable morality of peep shows. The court at that time considered peep shows immoral because the human dignity of the women placed on display there was damaged in that they were presented as "objects," the consent of the women in question notwithstanding.

The court explained at the time: "According to the jurisdiction of the Senate, the concept of good morals is an undefined legal term that requires greater clarification, whose application in its full extent is subject to court examination. With it, the law refers to the social-ethical values that are subject to historical development, which are recognized in the legal community as prerequisites for order. Thus the feelings of small minorities are not to be emphasized. On the other hand, it is not necessary — and practically impossible — for the values of all members of the legal community to be represented. The important thing is rather the prevailing social-ethical convictions. These neither have to express themselves vociferously — in public protests — nor must they be accompanied by the demand never and nowhere to tolerate phenomena considered unworthy in the eyes of a social-ethical judgment. Even when the legal community disapproves socio-ethically of a particular occurrence and thus views it as an offence against good morals, it can have reasons to accept the occurrence within certain limits."[1]

One sees that the Supreme Administrative Court implicitly followed an institutional metaethic here, in that it emphasized the historical change of that which is considered morally acceptable in a particular society at a particular time and which disturbs the social consensus too much. Without doubt, there is only a minimal consensus in our society and in our time, as a survey conducted by *Der Spiegel* magazine in December 1997 showed: to the question "Who do you think is important in the transmission of values?" 37 per cent of the Germans interviewed named the churches, 38 per cent Greenpeace, and at least 43 per cent believed the political parties played an important role. However, the police were clearly at the top of the scale of possible vehicles for transmitting values at 51 per cent. We must conclude therefore that a majority of the German people identify ethical values with monitoring the observance of state laws and punishment of violations.

This result is a high and presumably well-deserved honour for our police. But at the same time it is a rather alarming sign for our society as a whole. Nevertheless, according to

---

1 Ruling dated January 30, 1990, 1 C 26/87.in: NVwZ 1990, pp 668–670.

the American bioethicist H. Tristram Engelhardt, in a pluralistic, secular state with a Western character, a different result could hardly be expected.

In a case concluded in 1980 between the Baden-Württemberg SPD party head at the time, Erhard Eppler, and the then head of the regional CDU, the Federal Constitutional Court took a different, more civil rights-oriented position than the Supreme Administrative Court did ten years later regarding peep shows, in light of the right of personality protected by Article 2, Clause 1 in connection with Article 1, Clause 1 of the Constitution. The protection of the right of personality, the Constitutional Court explained, is based on the idea of self-determination. Therefore, only the individual person himself can determine what should make up his social claim to validity; in this respect, "the content of the general right of personality [is] primarily influenced by the self-image of its bearer."[2]

Also in a very detailed legal analysis on the permissibility of plastination published in autumn of 1998, the Heidelberg medical-legal expert Brigitte Tag, who had been interviewed on the television programme "heute-journal" on January 23, 1998, by ZDF journalist Alexander Niemetz, made reference to the relevant statement by the Federal Constitutional Court, in which it can be regarded as a violation of human dignity if the concrete person is reduced to an object, to a mere means, to an acceptable extent. In taking advantage of the aesthetic latitude opened up by the process of plastination, Brigitte Tag explained, the human dignity to which the dead are also entitled is not violated so long as they do not become an object of artistic alienation; and under our legal system, the moral and legal claim can be raised that such a strictly personal decision on body donation after death should also be respected after death.

In connection with these differentiated legal situations, the two concrete questions which could arise from the above-referenced legal-ethical objections against the exhibition KÖRPERWELTEN should now be formulated. They appear to be:

- Does an artistic presentation of plastinated specimens necessarily constitute a violation of human dignity?
- By what criteria can one objectively evaluate the artistic presentation of a plastination?

At this point, we now come to the problems in detail. Without doubt, a certain aestheticizing heteronomy and creative self-realization on the part of the dissector of the anatomical specimens is connected with plastination — although not with plastination alone. If we think of aesthetic, plastic

[2] Ruling dated January 30, 1990, 1 C 26/87.in: NVwZ 1990, pp 668–670.

and restorative surgery, it quickly becomes apparent that even there the patient does not have full autonomy over the result. As an example, the plastic surgeon Michel Pfulg of Monteux recounted in an article in *Der Spiegel* in December 1997 that he works "artistically" with all body parts whose appearance is a source of concern for his patients. The face, which should be made to look younger and more beautiful, must nevertheless "retain its own expression." Of course, what "its own expression" really means after such intervention is determined by the skill and creativity of the surgeon in the end.

Now it can be argued that the patient's partial loss of autonomy can at least be balanced out by a subjectively better quality of life, by joy about the beautification of his own body. This is the reason for the legal justification of the current boom in cosmetic surgery.

Here, although this may surprise some readers, we can draw a perfect parallel to plastination: the self-esteem of a — non-religious — person in our society could very well rise if he knew during his lifetime that his body would remain in a transformed state after death that is not only useful for medical education but is also attractive. Such emotions have nothing to do with "being perpetuated," as the former Dean of Mannheim Fischer suspected, but rather with post-mortem aesthetics. More and more people find it rather depressing that their bodies will one day be slowly given over to microbial and chemical decomposition in an expensive oak coffin (to which many cemetery ordinances pay no attention, releasing the graves for new occupation after a relatively short time). The idea that the dead body as an anatomical specimen could undergo the shaping freedom of a plastinator, clearly alarmed a Heidelberg medical student — like me and many others — much less than the idea of what happens after burial: in an interview in the *Süddeutsche Zeitung* on January 17, 1998, he stated that at age 27 he had signed a form to donate his body.

The question of whether the artistic presentation of plastinated specimens necessarily constitutes a violation of human dignity can thus not be answered in the affirmative. At the same time, it cannot be ruled out that in some cases it could be otherwise. That would depend in the first place on how it was done and then one would have to remember the statement of the Federal Administrative Court on the time- and context-dependent "good morals."

At this point, we are entering highly sensitive terrain. By what criteria can one objectively evaluate the artistic presentation of a plastination? In other words: what is art and who is an artist?

The ancient Greeks dealt much more simply with the concept of art than we do today in the ostensible post-modern age: they spoke of téchne; and the specialist who practiced it was called the technites. Plastination would undoubted-ly have fulfilled the criteria for téchne, as do medicine, rhetoric and architecture. For we must understand téchne in its premodern sense. This refers most likely to a store of knowledge of a certain complexity that is defined by a set of rules and is teachable in this form, which requires considerable effort and patience to learn. Thus all romantic and post-romantic associations such as spontaneity, creativity and genius fade away in this old concept of art; here science would be just as out of place.

It appears as if the plastinator Gunther von Hagens is taking up this old concept of téchne, and as if he may actually be a technites in the classical sense. I at least interpret his self-assessment that dissection and plastination are handicrafts, and the result of his efforts is — he coined the term himself — anatomy art.

We can also agree with his statement that art is in the eye of the beholder. Our modern concept of art is open. It is no longer only intentional, or seen in relation to the intentions of the artist, and also no longer strictly bound to certain topics suitable for art — for example religion — as was the case in the Middle Ages; instead, it is mainly reception-oriented, that is, it is seen in relation to the observer. Our concept of art, like our concept of morality, is understood institutionally: a particular object is a work of art in the context of a particular culture and language community, without a completely undisputed ultimate classification ever being possible or even necessary. Problems of evaluation and of judgment arise here.

If the plastinator assures us that his works should "neither be art, nor impart science, but rather enlighten," we must believe that this is his intention. Any other explorations of conscience would be out of the question with regard to human dignity — in this case that of the plastinator. The intentional concept of art thus does not further the debate in this connection.

On the other hand, should courts of law in future really rule on what constitutes art— and thus on what is permissible and not permissible? Should a glass eye used in a whole-body plastination really tip the scale in this complex and subtle context? You are herewith expressly warned of this. Whoever supports the presentation of plastinated specimens in accordance with human dignity may not force anatomical dissection techniques and creative craftsmanship to contradict each other over content. The anatomical institutions of the world have more than enough collections of jars with aesthetically unattractive, if not repulsive, specimens floating in formaldehyde, which are certainly not commensurate with the dignity of the dead.

Plastinated Specimens –Originals, Structural Models or Real Virtualities?

An important question that we keep coming back to in the dispute over KÖRPERWELTEN is what the actual ontological status of a plastinated specimen is, particularly that of a whole-body specimen. Is it a person, is it a cadaver, or is it an object of a particular type, since it could not have existed at all before Plastination was developed? Another question is: where does the soul of a body donor reside?

This complex of themes is much too difficult for us to handle thoroughly here. For this reason, I would like to outline roughly my current, thoroughly contestable opinion on the subject: a dead human body neither houses a soul in the theological sense nor can the mind, the consciousness or even the historical-biographical personality of the deceased emerge from the brain function in the bio-philosophical sense. Like the living, cadavers still have substance and form — in the Aristotelian sense of causa materialis and causa formalis. They can thus be interpreted as a natural material and structural model of man, at least with reference to the goals of scientific discovery pursued by anatomists.

In the catalogue for the exhibition "The Power of Age" in the autumn of 1998, the art theorist and cultural critic Bazon Brock called Plastination an "educational science" and plastinated anatomical specimens "real virtualities," whose reality content is demonstrated by their authenticity. This is also a very apt characterization, this time from an artistic-aesthetic perspective.

If a cadaver now becomes the object of anatomical dissection, another characteristic appears: due to the basic anonymity of the anatomically dissected body, which in this respect establishes a distinction between the process with pathological-anatomical dissections and forensic autopsies, the historical-biographical personality of the deceased is effectively protected from unauthorized exposure; it is not infringed upon. Our grief or sympathetic thoughts do not go out to the lifeless body or even the specimen infused with plastics, but rather to the dead person whose fate we remember and to whose personality legal protection should be assigned.

A personal aspect does not play a role in anatomical dissection, and for good reason: unlike the clinical subjects pathology and forensic medicine, the research and teaching objectives of anatomy consist not in finding out the medical history of a particular patient or to determine his cause of death. Anatomists are more interested in the structure and the resulting functions of a healthy human organism. This is basically a scientific construct, which arises only virtually in the imagination of the observer, beyond the individual specimens. Dead bodies are individually and distinctively formed; they are unique; we regard them nevertheless as real virtualities, not as biographical-historical personalities. We can also see this distinction emotionally, in that anatomical specimens, both plastinated and unplastinated, command the respect of the observer, but do not arouse fear.

What natural and institutional relationship do plastinated specimens have to the person of body donors? They are nearly identical in form, but not in the chemical composition of the material, since nearly 70 per cent of the body material, specifically the water of the tissue fluids, was replaced with plastic in a technical process. Plastinated specimens are thus natural structural models of the cadavers; their relationship to the person of the body donor is a two-step modelling.

I am quite conscious of the fact that not only the critics of the Mannheim exhibition KÖRPERWELTEN see this point differently, but also many of those who were enthusiastic about it. For them, the plastinated specimens were simply human originals. The supporters of the ex-

hibition found this fascinating because of the authenticity, while the opponents found that it was not permissible.

Most people involved saw the gradual transformation of a living person to a cadaver to a plastinated specimen as a graduated practice of ethical attitudes. Thus for most viewers, it was quite unproblematic when Gunther von Hagens laid a plastinated plastination slice down on the table next to his water glass after his presenting it on the ZDF television program "Willemsen's Week" on December 5, 1997; conversely, it would certainly not have been as easy to reach an ethical consensus had he used it as a coaster for the glass. It was interesting for me to observe how such practices occurred without having to be debated.

Plastinated specimens are not just any material. They are rather a natural structural model of the human body that make use of some of the material of the original. This is a correct description of the facts, and this is where ethical attitudes towards plastinated specimens also seem to orient themselves. The question of what relationship this has to the cultural and aesthetic assessment of plastinated specimens as real virtualities is beyond the competencies

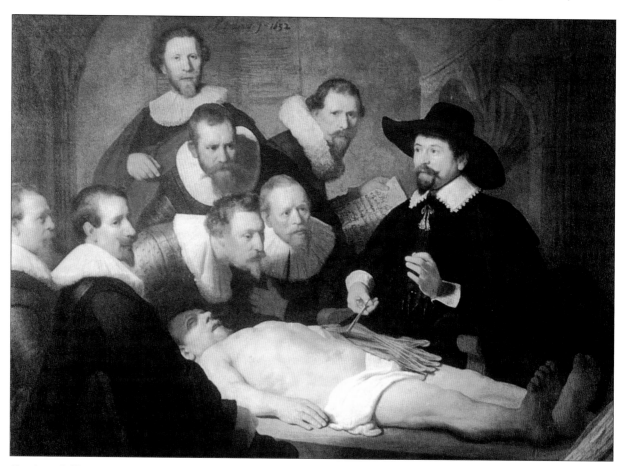

Rembrandt Harmenszoon van Rijn (1606–1669) The Anatomy Lesson of Dr. Nicolaas Tulp (1593–1674) Painted 1632, The Hague, Mauritiushuis

of a bioethicist. Aesthetics as a discipline must seek an answer to this question, and in the meantime, it appears as if it is going to accept this challenge.

Plastinated Specimens and the Physicality of the Observer

Are there other reasons to fear that the human dignity of the observer could be violated even with the impeccable aesthetic presentation of plastinated specimens? Are there some natural facts about the human organism that the light of public display should shy away from? Does the "Story under the skin," as the University of Hanover historian Barbara Duden called her book on gynaecology in the 18th century, have a dangerous or subversive secret that may only be brought to light by doctors for doctors? Is there cause to worry that this will contribute to the fall of moral values in our society?

None of this seems to be the case. The true facts of the matter are even more tragic: many people today know their way astoundingly well under the bonnets of their cars or within the programmes on their computers, but know practically nothing about the inner structure of their own bodies. On the other hand, ca. 70 per cent of our fellow citizens have been cultivating a more or less public sympathy for alternative methods of treatment, i.e., forms of therapy whose effectiveness has never been proven or whose ineffectiveness has even been shown. More than just a whisper of paradoxical neo-mysticism must be registered in our supposedly enlightened time in the field of medicine and its environment.

What could be more helpful in such a situation than an uninhibited and unbiased look at the natural facts of our bodies, at their complicated biological structures, which would make it obvious in a cogent way that health, illness and healing cannot be explained or even manipulated with a couple of comforting platitudes and easy to understand patient remedies? The overwhelming interest of the public in such natural facts, which manifested itself in the onslaught of visitors to the Mannheim presentation of KÖRPER-WELTEN, speaks much for the idea that there is an untapped demand for more solid information that could be the basis for a genuine ethical justification for this exhibition under the aspect of bearing responsibility for our own health. The sensory awareness of plastinated specimens through direct visual contact and the comprehending touch of the hand offered a unique quality of experiential gain that was utilized as an opportunity by medical laypersons and not rejected as a risk.

Even this well noted democratization of what Bazon Brock called "educational science" already provoked some concern in the sensitive contact zones of academic and public spheres before, during and still several months after the Mannheim event. This worry produced all kinds of remarkable arabesques with the energetic assistance of the reputable media.

The Real Virtualities of the Plastinator in the Funhouse Mirror of Virtual Media Reality

The more visitors that streamed into the Mannheim exhibition, which remained open around the clock in the end, the softer the often aggressive railing in the press of the Rhine-Neckar region became. Thus the local press did not report at all at first about a lecture I gave on January 7, 1998, in the State Museum for Technology and Labour (and from which this article ultimately emerged), while "KÖR-PERWELTEN" made positive headlines on the same day in the New York Times: "An Exhibit of Human Anatomy in Mannheim Has Upset Some Clerics" read the dry commentary of Edmund L. Andrews under a small map of Germany, on which an arrow pointed out "Mannheim" to the American reader. Apparently under the influence of the unusual success of this exhibition, the majority of the German print media finally agreed by the end of February 1998 that those among their readership who were interested in the plastinated anatomical specimens were perhaps not simply sensationalist voyeurs.

At the same time, however, next to the museum, in the Mannheim studio of the South German Radio (SDR), which was only a few months away from its merger with Southwest Radio (SWF), the planning, and shortly thereafter, the filming of a television programme was beginning, which would be broadcast all over Germany late in the evening on April 16, 1998, on Channel 1 of German public television (ARD). Walter Sucher and Harold Woetzel called their 45-minute collaboration "The Cadaver Show: An Exhibition Becomes a Sensation," which would also be shown numerous times on the regional channels of the ARD as well as the tri-national cultural station 3SAT in early summer 1998.

Anyone who saw the Mannheim exhibition and the fascinated but always attentive and thoughtful visitors could hardly believe his eyes: the way in which this film presented the exhibits in short, choppy sequences really conveyed the impression of the Last Judgment. Aside from the visual frenzy, the background music that had been selected with nearly diabolical perfection contributed to this impression. The pieces selected by the producers, "Pictures at an Exhibition" by Modest Mussorgski in Maurice Ravel's dramatic orchestration and "Fossils" from the "Carnival of the Animals" by Camille Saint-Saëns, instrumentalized in the truest sense of the word — the former to elicit goosebumps in the viewers and the latter to characterize the action of the plastinator at least acoustically as a macabre perversion.

Excerpts from statements by several academic experts in philosophy, medical ethics, anatomy, law, art and other fields were used in a biased manner. In the same way, the journalists used suggestive questions to steer interviews with visitors to the exhibition, from whom criticism of the plastinated specimens still could generally be coaxed out only with the greatest effort. The scientists were granted more broadcast time depending on how obvious or polemical their negative opinion turned out to be. The supporters of Plastination, on the other hand, hardly got a word in; all that remained of the approximately half-hour interview that I gave the SDR team on March 13, 1998, was no more than 10 seconds of picture and 25 seconds of sound, and all of my statements of any substance were cut out.

Do ethics not have something to do with truth and credibility above all else — before any concrete and possibly controversial individual approach to a problem? This is not the least of the questions that should be put to those involved in that regrettable farce broadcast on public television.

Despite all of their efforts, they were still unsuccessful in using the fun-house mirrors of virtual media reality to destroy the anatomical and aesthetic fascination, which emanated from the real virtualities of the plastinated bodies to the interested and thoughtful observers. Directly confronting the authentic structural models of educational science we hear softly, but unmistakably, the reminder handed down by the moralist and founder of Latin-Christian literature, Quintus Septimus Horens Tertullian (ca. 160–220 AD), to a victorious Roman hero returning home in triumph: Respice post te, hominem te esse memento (Look around you, remember that even you are only human).

Literature

Edmund L. Andrews: "Anatomy on Display, and It's All Too Human." The New York Times, January 7, 1998, pp. A1 and A4.

Alfred J. Ayer: Language, Truth and Logic. 17th Edition. London 1967.

Klaus Bartels: Veni, vidi, vici. Geflügelte Worte aus dem Griechischen und Lateinischen. Munich 1992.
[Veni, vidi, vici. Familiar Words from Greek and Latin.]

Axel W. Bauer: "Die Anwendung zeichentheoretischer Methoden auf Geschichte und Gegenwart der Medizin."
["The Application of Semiotic Methods on the History and the Present of Medicine."]
In: Axel Bauer (Editor): Theorie der Medizin. Dialoge zwischen Grundlagenfächern und Klinik. (Medizin im Dialog) Heidelberg, Leipzig 1995, pp. 141–153.
[Theory of Medicine. Dialogues Between Basic Fields and Clinic. (Medicine in Dialogue)]

Axel W. Bauer: "Braucht die Medizin Werte? Reflexionen über methodologische Probleme in der Bioethik."
["Does Medicine Require Values? Reflections on Methodological Problems in Bioethics."]
In: Axel W. Bauer (Editor): Medizinische Ethik am Beginn des 21. Jahrunderts. Theoretische Konzepte, Klinische Probleme, Ärztliches Handeln. (Medizin im Dialog) Heidelberg, Leipzig 1998, pp. 1–18.
[Medical Ethics at the Beginning of the 21st Century. Theoretical Concepts, Clinical Problems, Physicians' Practices. (Medicine in Dialogue)]

Uwe Bleyl: "And what we are, you will be, too."On the Dignity and Inviolability of the Dead."
Editorial. Der Pathologe, Issue 19 (1998), pp. 171–175.

Bazon Brock: "Bildende Wissenschaft."
[Educational Science.]
In: Die Macht des Alters. Strategien der Meisterschaft. Herausgegeben von Bazon Brock im Auftrag der Stiftung für Kunst und Kultur e.V. Cologne 1998, pp. 142–145.
[The Power of Age. Strategies of Mastery. Edited by Bazon Brock on Behalf of the Foundation for Art and Culture, a non-profit organisation.]

"Das Gesicht als Schlachtfeld. Weil Frauen und Männer vom Drang besessen sind, jünger und besser auszusehen, boomt die Schöhneitschirugie." Der Spiegel 52/1997, pp. 150–155. ["The Face as a Battlefield. Because Women and Men are Obsessed with the Desire to Look Younger and Better, Plastic Surgery is Booming"]

"Das ist ein ergreifender Eindruck". Rhein-Neckar-Zeitung befragte Besucher der umstrittenen Ausstellung KÖRPER-WELTEN – Alle waren fasziniert – Großer Andrang. Rhein-Neckar-Zeitung. October 31, 1997, p. 15.
["A really moving impression" Rhein-Neckar-Zeitung Interviewed Visitors to the Controversial Exhibition KÖRPER-WELTEN – All Were Fascinated – Big Crowd.]

"Die Toten nicht der Neugier preisgeben." Heidelberger Anatomie-Professor Dr. Klaus Unsicker kritisiert von Hagens' Ausstellung KÖRPERWELTEN – RNZ-Gespräch. Rhein-Neckar-Zeitung. November 18, 1997, p. 13.
["Do Not Expose the Dead to Curiosity." Heidelberg Anatomy Professor Dr. Klaus Unsicker Criticises von Hagens' Exhibition KÖRPERWELTEN – Interview in Rhein-Neckar-Zeitung.]

Günter Dietz: "Menschenwürde bei Homer."
["Human Dignity in Homer"]
In: Bismarck-Gymnasium Karlsruhe, Jahresbericht 1996/97. Karlsruhe 1997, pp. 91–101.
[Yearbook of the Bismarck Gymnasium, Karlsruhe]

"Drei Fragen an den Mannheimer Dekan Ulrich Fischer." Badischer Neueste Nachrichten, December 17, 1997.
["Three Questions for Mannheim Dean Ulrich Fischer."]

H. Tristram Engelhardt, Jr.: The Foundations of Bioethics. Second Edition. Oxford University Press, New York, Oxford 1996.

Rafael Ferber: "Moralische Urteile als Beschreibung institutioneller Tatsachen." Archiv für Rechts- und Sozialphilosophie 79 (1993), pp. 372–392. ["Moral Judgments to Describe Institutional Facts."]

Rafael Ferber: "Metaethik des moralisch Guten." ["Metaethics of the Morally Good."] In: Rafael Ferber: Philosophische Grundbegriffe. Eine Einführung. 6th Edition, Munich 1999, pp. 162–179.
[Basic Philosophical Concepts. An Introduction]

"Finger weg von der Wissenschaft! Zur Ausstellung KÖRPERWELTEN in Mannheim."
Ketzerbriefe 77 (1997), pp. 5–15.
["Fingers Away from Science! On the KÖRPERWELTEN Exhibition in Mannheim."]

Gunther von Hagens: "Der plastinierte Mensch." ["The Plastinated Man."]
In: KÖRPERWELTEN. Einblicke in den menschlichen Körper. October 30, 1997 to February 1, 1998. [KÖRPERWELTEN: Insights into the Human Body]
Exhibition catalogue. Published by the Landesmuseum für Technik und Arbeit in Mannheim and by the Institut für Plastination, Heidelberg. 2nd Edition. Mannheim 1997, pp. 201–217.

Richard M. Hare: The Language of Morals. Oxford 1952. (German: Die Sprache der Moral. Translated by Petra von Morstein. Frankfurt am Main 1983).

Reinhard Hildebrand: "Ein menschliches Bild vom Menschen? Prolegomenon zum Wandel des Menschenbildes in der Anatomie." Sudhoffs Archiv, Vol. 78 (1994) pp. 129–153.
["A Humane Image of Humans? Prolegomenon on the Change of the Image of Man in Anatomy."]

Wolfgang Huber: "Menschenrechte/Menschenwürde."
["Human Rights/Human Dignity."]
In: Theologische Realenzyklopädie, Vol. 22, published by Gerhard Müller. Berlin, New York 1992, pp. 577–602.
[Theological Encyclopedia]

David Hume: A Treatise of Human Nature, Being an Attempt to Introduce the Experimental Method of Reasoning into Moral Subjects. London 1739/40. Cited per the edition of L.A. Selby-Bigge. Oxford 1888. Second Edition with text revised and variant readings by P.H. Nidditch. Oxford 1978.

"Interview with Professor Gunther von Hagens." Ketzerbriefe 77 (1997), pp. 16–41.

George Edward Moore: Principia Ethica. Cambridge 1903.

Bodo Pieroth und Bernhard Schlink: Grundrechte. Staatsrecht II. 13th Edition. Heidelberg 1997.

Pressewelten: "Einsichten in die deutsche Medienlandschaft. Eine Nachlese zur KÖRPERWELTEN-Ausstellung in Mannheim." Ketzerbriefe 81 (1998), pp. 47–65.
[Press World: "Insights into the German Media Landscape. Selections on the KÖRPERWELTEN Exhibition."]

Dieter Schmidtchen: "Markt und Wettbewerb in Gottes Welt. Religiosität fußt auf Rationalkalkül. Kirchen als Mehrproduktunternehmen. Das staatlich geschützte Duopol der Glaubensgemeinschaften ist ordnungspolitisch bedenklich." Frankfurter Allgemeine Zeitung, November 1, 1997, p. 17.
["Market and Competition in God's World. Religiousness based on Rational Calculation. Churches as Purveyors of Multiple Products. The State-Supported Duopoly of Religions is Politically Questionable."]

John R. Searle: Speech Acts. An Essay in the Philosophy of Language. Cambridge University Press 1969. (German: Sprechakte. Ein sprachphilosophischer Essay. Übersetzt von

R. und R. Wiggershaus. 6th Edition. Frankfurt am Main 1994).

John R. Searle: Die Wiederentdeckung des Geistes. From the American by Harvey P. Gavagai. Frankfurt am Main 1996.
[The Rediscovery of the Spirit]

Brigitte Tag: "Zum Umgang mit der Leiche. Rechtliche Aspekte der dauernden Konservierung menschlicher Körper und Körperteile durch die Plastination." Medizinrecht, Vol. 16 (1998), pp. 387–394.
["Proper Handling of Corpses. Legal Aspects of Using Plastination for the Long-Term Preservation of Human Corpses and Body Parts."]

Gerhard Vollmer: "Sein und Sollen. Möglichkeiten und Grenzen einer Evolutionären Ethik."
["To Be and Should Be. Possibilities and Limits of an Evolutionary Ethic."]
In: Gerhard Vollmer: Biophilosophie. With a Preface by Ernst Mayr. Stuttgart 1995, pp. 162–192.
[Biophilosophy]

Harald Weinrich: Lethe: Kunst und Kritik des Vergessens. Munich 1997.
[Lethe: The Art and Critique of Forgetting.]

"Wertevermittlung: 'Wen halten Sie bei der Vermittlung von Werten für wichtig?'" Der Spiegel 52/1997, p. 68.
["Value Transmission: 'Who Do You Think Is Important in the Transmission of Values?' "]

Zwischenfrage: "Warum verschenken Sie Ihren Körper, Herr Alsfasser?" Süddeutsche Zeitung. January 17/18, 1998 p. 33.
[Supplementary Question: "Why are you donating your body, Mr. Alsfasser?"]

Axel W. Bauer studied medicine at the University of Freiburg and received his doctorate in 1980. Since 1981, he has been working at the Institute for the History of Medicine at the University of Heidelberg. He was first a college assistant and, after completing his credentials for a professorship (Habilitation) in 1986, a lecturer and acting director of the institute. He became a college docent in 1989 and in 1992 an extraordinary professor. Since 1999, he has worked as a research project leader at the clinic of the University of Heidelberg. In addition, since 1994, he has been a lecturer in medical history, theory and ethics at the faculty for clinical medicine at the Mannheim branch of the University of Heidelberg. Since 1998, he has been a docent for ethics and medicine in the postgraduate curriculum on "Health Management" at the Academy for Further Education at the Universities of Mannheim and Heidelberg. Bauer has been a member of the Academy for Ethics in Medicine in Göttingen since 1996. His research has focused on the history of pathology and pathological anatomy, the development of scientific medicine and the institutionalization of the medical disciplines in the 19th and 20th centuries as well as scientific theory and scholarliness in medicine, semiotics and medicine, medical ethics and bioethics, and sociobiology as they relate to evolutionary epistemology.

Ulrich Fischer

When Death Goes on Display

The story of the 1997/1998 KÖRPERWELTEN exhibition in Mannheim and the response on the part of the Churches was a story about learning for me. I was startled by the sensationalized reports published in news magazines prior to the opening of the exhibition, and, as dean of the Lutheran Church of Mannheim, I felt compelled to voice my concerns (as did the Roman Catholic dean of the district of Mannheim) to the responsible authorities at the State Museum of Technology and Labour (Landesmuseum für Technik und Arbeit), the premier of the State of Baden-Württemberg and the mayor of the City of Mannheim. We did not want to prevent this exhibition; instead we wanted to prevent the fears aroused by media portrayals of both the exhibits and their creator from becoming a reality.

In these early reports, the guiding force behind the exhibition, namely Dr. Gunther von Hagens, appeared over and over again as someone whose scientific interest was combined with a demeanour clearly reminiscent of that of action artist Joseph Beuys (1921–1986). This made us suspect that KÖRPERWELTEN would be a sensationalistic display of human corpses that had been artistically dissected and processed, which is the reason that we felt we had to act. Our efforts did at least bear some fruit in that the State Museum acknowledged the concerns put forth by the Churches and reacted to them quite sensitively: children not accompanied by a parent or guardian were denied admittance to the exhibition; a sign indicating the potential for offending religious sensibilities was placed outside the museum entrance; and signing consent forms for donating one's body to plastination was prohibited on museum grounds.

Our efforts were at times misconstrued by the public to mean that the Churches were acting on an anti-progressive impulse and attempting to prevent public access to the medical knowledge of our time. That was never our intent; far more at issue was the preliminary media coverage, which did not make it clear that the primary aim of this exhibition really would be to impart the insights of medical science.

In fact, many of the concerns that we expressed did not turn out as might have been expected. Public reaction was quite evidently serious, at least during the initial weeks of the exhibition: many visitors expressed fascination at the "miracle of the human body"; others even felt strengthened in their belief in God, the Creator; and one person included a quote from Psalm 8 in the guest book, thereby professing a faith in God and His miraculous creation of the human body.

Even during my own many visits to the exhibition, I became aware of a discrepancy between what I had feared and what I was actually being shown. My objection to KÖRPERWELTEN, however, came at the temporary end of a learning process, which not only focussed my concerns significantly — it also significantly reinforced them. This learning process came as a result of my numerous television and radio commentaries on the subject of KÖRPERWELTEN, my many meetings with the artist, the variety of reactions within both the Lutheran and Catholic Churches of Mannheim and most of all as a result of the zealous interest on the part of journalists regarding the critical stance taken by the Church.

Two objections were raised over and over again: the Church had no business getting involved in matters that did not concern it, and the large number of people visiting the exhibition was in and of itself an important argument against the criticism of the Church. The man behind the exhibition even went so far as to say, "Majority rules on issues of morality."

Were we simply to leave formation of ethical judgments and decisions on morality up to the democratic process, however, capital punishment and public executions would no doubt be part of our reality once again. Twentieth century German history more than adequately shows how very little majority opinion can protect us from immoral behavior. This is also why I would like to outline in more detail why the Church has become involved in the discussion on KÖRPERWELTEN and why it cannot simply leave decisions of morality up to the majority or to a public voting with its feet.

On the Educational Aims of the Exhibition

The indisputable educational motives driving the exhibition's creator has been stressed over and over again: democratizing science, sharing anatomical knowledge, providing a glimpse of the body's interiors, improving our understanding of the human body and of human life — that was to be the purpose of exhibiting his plastinated specimens or plastinates. Yet no small number of critics, many of them outside of the Church, energetically disputed those aims, accusing him of "shredding" the dead and of nothing short of perverting enlightened thinking.

In fact, some of the whole-body exhibits left no room for doubt that von Hagens' artistic ambitions had displaced the interests of scientific enlightenment. These included the following:

The exhibit entitled "Runner," a photo of which promoted the exhibition on posters all over the country,

The "Fragmented Man" from Kirgizskaya, which was not shown on television until the end of the exhibition,

- The plastinated individual holding out his internal organs in his hands,
- The person whose skin is draped over one arm
- And the exhibit in which all of the individual parts of the human body are shown hanging on nylon threads and are thus fashioned into a mobile.

Yet other exhibits as well — such as the plastinated body which had been cut into cross sections, the three-dimensional foetus within a whole-body cross section, and the body used to demonstrate all of the possible orthopaedic operations — suggested that either the interests of scientific enlightenment were not really at the heart of the exhibition or that such interests could just as easily have been demonstrated with models of the human body. It cannot be denied, on the other hand, that certain exhibits were extremely informative on a scientific level, such as the lungs of the smoker and the plastinated nervous and circulatory systems.

When criticizing KÖRPERWELTEN, it certainly cannot be said that none of the exhibits served the purpose of scientific enlightenment. Keeping that qualifying statement in mind, however, it must be pointed out all the more clearly how this exhibition has combined scientific enlightenment and the artistic presentation of human corpses in ways that, in many instances, are highly questionable and insensitive to human feelings.

If von Hagens has indicated that the public has a "right to view bodies," then this may certainly be accepted in the sense that the public has a right to share in the insights of the natural sciences. This " right to view bodies," however, can easily be perverted to a presumed right to satisfy voyeuristic curiosity — and, given the massive onslaught of visitors towards the end of the exhibition, that is certainly what happened. This is especially true in a social setting in which voyeurism is permeating and threatening our public life, and in which many no longer recognize or respect the bounds of human curiosity. Intimate secrets are exposed on talk shows; there would no longer seem to be any reserve whatsoever with respect to the private sphere. The voyeurism surrounding the death of Princess Diana was a particularly horrifying example of this. A society hallmarked by voyeurism, a society of gawkers, onlookers, and of curious people who want to dig up all of the intimate details, such a society can seriously harm our human culture, which has always been characterized by a balance between intimacy and publicity.

On top of this, an inevitable effect of the display of corpses at the KÖRPERWELTEN exhibition is to depersonalize human beings. The person, the corpse, is presented as an inanimate object, similar to the way in which our media frequently portrays corpses as objects rather than as dead persons. In this respect, the term "whole-body exhibits" is highly suspicious, as it suggests that these are not people who lived their own unique lives, but rather objects to be processed in a matter-of-fact way and without emotion. There is, of course, nothing objectionable about the free, natural attitude towards the body that those responsible for the exhibition have asked of their visitors again and again; yet wherever the "right to view bodies" suddenly changes into a right both to reveal the "human object" at all costs and to blend that revelation with special effects, the line separating a free, natural attitude towards the body from prostitution becomes very thin.

This is not about criticizing breaches of taboos simply because they reflect a lack of respect. There can be no doubt that breaking taboos — often at the prompting of science — has at times benefited life and served to advance human culture. This insight, however, should not cause us to hide the fact that humanity and the quality of life have at other times suffered, and that the dignity of a culture has been destroyed by breaking taboos.

For this reason, I find it extremely pressing that the question be discussed as to whether the breach of taboos represented by the KÖRPERWELTEN exhibition is really one that can be described as serving humanity. When I compare this case to others where life's boundaries have been destigmatized, called into question and ultimately exposed to human manipulation, the explosiveness of this issue is unmistakable: when taboos along life's boundaries have been broken, has it not led in the end to man's assuming power over human life in ways that our limited human abilities should preclude?

On Corpses as Works of Art

As I mentioned earlier, the Mannheim exhibition of plastinates prompted me to embark on a learning process; one of the central issues that came out of that process is the problem of attaching aesthetic value to death and to the dead. When I heard over and over that these corpses could be viewed without horror or revulsion, when I heard the words "attractive corpses" and "odourless specimens," when I call to mind how artistic the photos were in brochures and posters for the exhibition, and, finally, especially when I am reminded of the artistic disposition of the exhibition's creator, I cannot escape the conclusion that these corpses were to be displayed as works of art.

This longing for "attractive corpses" feeds into a trend in society that one might well describe as an unhealthy preoccupation with appearances. The media repeatedly sends out images of the beautiful in such a way that, in the minds of average people, beauty becomes equated with successful human life. It is not out of the question to suspect that, in the end, the desire on the part of exhibition visitors to be plastinated after their deaths only serves to satisfy their own personal vanity. When a body donor explains that he would like to erect a monument to himself, and not just any monument, but one that is aesthetically perfect and attractive to look at, when body donors offer themselves to the artist and trust that they will be transformed by his hands into works of art, then the human experiment has taken on a whole new dimension: no longer is man a creature with flaws and short-comings, scars and wounds; he is now a perfect work of art, created by an artist — a work of art whose vanity has been satisfied.

Does this correspond to Judeo-Christian teachings of creation? In the near future, such works of art could conceivably be made available not only to museums but also to private individuals; in other words, loved ones could essentially be displayed in the family room as works of art or they could accompany future generations as plastinated knick-knacks. If this prospect does not remain outside of the realm of possibility, the perverting of humanity will be complete.

Judeo-Christian beliefs concerning creation hold that we private do not belong to ourselves, but rather that we are God's handiwork; our bodies are likewise not our property, but instead a "temple of the Holy Spirit" (1 Corinthians 6:19). Beliefs in creation as it is described in the Bible affirm man's status as a created being, which also encompasses his transience and his imperfection; these beliefs reflect an understanding of man's existence as a physical manifestation of God's creative act in this world. Everything that forms a basis for both human self-awareness as well as human limitations is lost when human beings become works of art in the hands of artists. The death of a human being does not end his or her status as a person; even a corpse is a person, with all of the features of a created being. Contributing these concerns to a critical discussion of the KÖRPERWELTEN exhibition is the responsibility of the Church and an expression of our Judeo-Christian beliefs.

On Dealing with Death and Dying

It has been remarked that the objects of the KÖRPERWEL-TEN exhibition are not corpses; they are whole-body exhibits or whole-body specimens. They are not objects of respect; they are the objects of study. They are not to be mourned; they are odourless specimens. Reading between the lines of sentences such as these reveals the pride taken in an unemotional attitude towards death — a pride that ties in with Gunther von Hagens' audacious theory that mourning is an obstacle to the learning process. Conversely, religious asso-ciations were unmistakable in this exhibition, such as when plastination was referred to as an "act of resurrection" or that plastinates had been "preserved for all eternity."

It would not be reading too much into such formulations to see in them a longing for immortality that interacts in an unusual way with the artist's dreams of omnipotence. Longings for immortality and dreams of omnipotence are both hallmarks of a society which is increasingly incapable of dealing with death and dying, and whose funeral culture — developed over centuries — is continually eroding. The "hygienic disposal" of corpses, such as when one has no grave site, is taking the place of a funeral culture, in which phrases such as "ashes to ashes, dust to dust" express man's oneness with creation.

The plastination technique meets this need for "hygienic disposal," assimilating both the longing for immortality on the part of plastination donors as well as the desire to have no grave site and thus to leave no traces on this earth. As a number of discussions have demonstrated — among them a conversation with the daughter of one of those whose remains had been plastinated — the very decision to donate one's body for plastination means that the donor has withdrawn himself or herself from a dying and grieving process in which all take part, thereby depriving those persons in his or her social environment of the grieving process. Consequently, this raises the question as to whether what becomes of me after my death is really my decision and my decision alone, or whether those people with whom I shared my life should also have a voice in the process.

Could it be that deciding to have oneself plastinated after death also has something to do with denying the knowledge that our time on earth is limited, that there are boundaries and limitations to our lives, that we will not simply continue to exist beyond death? Doesn't that mean that deciding to be plastinated after death is equivalent to avoiding the question of how we can find meaning in view of the limitations on our lives?

And does plastination not separate the body from the person in an unacceptable manner, as if the person weren't an integrated whole? In fact, the science of psychosomatics teaches that the separation of reason and emotion, of body and soul, which had not been a concept before modern times, has brought with it mental schisms that promote human sickness. Man is a person with body and soul; as such a person he is a creature of relationships, whose relationship with God does not end with death.

Is the body really just a shell and the resurrected soul something else? Christians who know something of the incarnation of Christ, who know that God Himself became flesh and blood and that He revealed Himself in the person of Jesus Christ, will not be able to answer that question in a way that relegates post mortem physical existence to irrelevancy. Statements made by the Apostle Paul in 1 Corinthians, Chapter 15, are certainly difficult and, in many cases, not at all easy to identify with today. (Take, for instance, verse 44: "It is sown a physical body, it is raised a spiritual body. If there is a physical body, there is also a spiritual body.") Yet his struggles with the question of how the resurrected body is to be understood do make one point clear: human existence beyond death cannot, at any rate, be separated from the question of the physical form which that existence may be expected to take.

For this reason bodies cannot be disposed of, nor can they be hygienically processed without damaging the human existence of the persons involved. Dead bodies must be treated with at least a faint degree of respect, and so the theory that mourning is an obstacle to the learning process must be rejected. Instead, grief, emotions and the resulting reverence for the person are what actually liberates the learning process. Learning without respecting man leads us to hold him in contempt. Learning without reverence for human existence incites us to think and act in a way that reduces others to inanimate objects and as such they can be misused.

On Discretionary Control over Human Dignity

This describes the final and most important consideration to be brought forth in the discussion surrounding the KÖRPERWELTEN exhibition. It has been emphasised repeatedly that a plastinated person made the decision to be plastinated on his or her own, and that self-determination on the part of that person may be taken as a given. Plastination of one's own body has been viewed as nothing short of an expression of that individual's personal dignity.

Assessing people in this way, however, only sees them as mere individuals without considering their intrinsic role in humanity as a whole. This begs the question as to whether a person's discretionary control over his or her own dignity may really be viewed as extending beyond the grave, or whether it should instead be limited. We should be asking whether human dignity is to be defined merely as an individual's personal right or whether that dignity might be violated when individual actions taken within the framework of personal accountability form an integral part of a larger, undignified event. Even if individual body donors see their dignity as preserved, as plastinated human beings they are an intrinsic part of a larger, voyeuristic event, which violates human dignity.

Certainly in the final weeks of the Mannheim exhibition, voyeurism won out over the more scientific interests of the visitors. During a televised discussion towards the beginning of the exhibition, Gunther von Hagens himself said,

"People who are really interested will come early on; after that you'll see the crocheting clubs and the punks." The initial public reaction was generally characterized by scientific curiosity; yet going to see KÖRPERWELTEN gradually became a mass movement; it became a huge spectator event. Anyone who had not been to see the corpses of Mannheim had nothing to contribute at parties; he or she was just out of it. This is how a spectacle can devaluate life, and life itself can become a spectacle. In the end, we feel that we have been entertained, perhaps even informed, but human dignity has suffered.

If this has indeed been the case, the blame cannot necessarily be attributed to the exhibition's creator, as we may assume that the motivation for the exhibition was certainly one of scientific enlightenment. One question, however, remains: Was it not inevitable, in a media age and in a society with voyeuristic tendencies, that the scientific, educational interest of such an exhibition would be displaced by other motives — motives that would end up perverting what had perhaps been well intended?

For this reason, my overall conclusion regarding the KÖRPERWELTEN exhibition is extremely negative: when death goes on display, human beings have no chance of retaining their human dignity.

Ulrich Fischer was made dean of the Lutheran Church of Mannheim in January of 1996 and has been the regional bishop of the Lutheran Church of Baden since April 1, 1998. He decided to study theology while completing his compulsory military service, and went on to study at the Universities of Göttingen and Heidelberg, completing State ecclesiastical exams in Hanover in 1973. Over the next two years he worked in the area of New Testament research at the Theology Department of the University of Heidelberg, initially providing research support and then as an official research assistant. A recipient of a scholarship from the Studienstiftung des Deutschen Volkes, he was awarded his Ph.D. in 1975 and completed the second round of theological exams in Karlsruhe in 1977. After serving as curate in Sandhausen near Heidelberg, he became the pastor of the Blumhardt congregation in Heidelberg-Kirchheim from 1979 to 1989. Dr. Fischer then went on to work as regional youth minister for the Baden Lutheran Church until 1995, and also chaired the Lutheran Youth Association of Germany from 1993 to 1996.

Transparent body slice

Franz Josef Wetz

The Dignity of Man

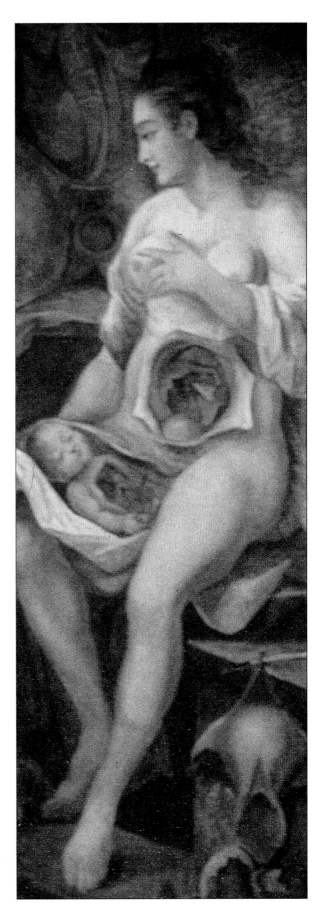

Man is something worth looking at: he presents a picture full of sublimity and dignity. At least, that is what the Renaissance philosophers thought. They one-sidedly emphasised the outstanding importance and sovereignty of this living creature that had the gift of language, and which had already once in its history — in the sculptures of classical Western antiquity — depicted itself, or at least its gods and heroes, as the ideal. With such a self-confident way of looking at themselves, numerous thinkers and artists between the 14th and 16th centuries clearly rejected the dismal medieval image, which, in contrast to the glorious Christian after-life, frequently depicted the misery of existence here on Earth, its wretchedness and worthlessness.

owever, what is truly special about the humanistic revaluation of man lies not merely in the emphasis of his worth, but above all in recognition of his beauty. It was as though it was only then that their unique upright posture enabled the inhabitants of Earth to gain an objective view of themselves, as it were. Not only at that time was the scope of what the world contained studied, comprehended and painted as an unending landscape as never before — for the Renaissance masters the body of the mortal man itself, in ancient times often called the grave of the soul, had become proof of God's existence. Now it was said that the human body had been designed so superbly in order for it to form a worthy vessel for the immortal soul. The heavenly perfection promised by the Church was given an aesthetic earthly counterpart.

It was therefore not by chance that anatomy reached a peak for the first time during the Renaissance and was connected with the art of the time: as countless portraits of the period — realistic even to the extent of dirt under the fingernails — show, man had become convinced that he could be seen as an individual; and he began systematically to discover the inner as well as the outer features of his form.

Since the Renaissance, artists' representations of the human body have been based on anatomical studies, and from then onwards representations of anatomy, which was only founded as a medical discipline in that period, for a long time followed aesthetic rules and motifs taken from art. The "Dissected woman with opened abdomen and foetus" by the French medical illustrator Jacques-Fabien Gautier (1711–1785), a pioneer in four-colour printing, was painted in 1746.

However, to be looked at also means that we offer a target. For however highly developed we may be, we still remain vulnerable creatures, and frail ones at that. It is precisely our vulnerability in many respects and our great and different sensitivities that cause us to perceive our own visibility as a danger; we therefore conceal ourselves in clothing and housing, and even hide ourselves when we by no means need to shun the light.

Thus on the one hand we consider ourselves worth looking at, do not want to be overlooked, and even seek publicity from time to time, but on the other hand we are also aware of our vulnerability. Ultimately possessing little security, most people are confronted with the need to shape their arduous and worrisome existence themselves throughout their lives. Those who are happy at most experience episodes of a care-free, unworried life.

This recognition of the greatness and misery of man raises the fundamental question of whether the individual also possesses a value that differentiates him from nature. Is he not ultimately only one transient being among others — a naked, narrow-nosed mammal with an overweight head on a spinal column that is rather unsuitable for his upright posture?

Precisely our neediness, imperfection and shortcomings, our insignificance in the boundless universe, and our mortality repeatedly raise doubts today about the dignity of man in general, the latter of which, against this sobering background, appears to be a ridiculous presumption. Nevertheless, innate human dignity is a slogan of our time; sadly, however, it is burdened with an unbearable vagueness. Virtually nobody is able to provide clear information on the significance of, and justification for, this great idea. However, everybody uses the expression as if it were obvious. Thus one often hears and reads about the lack of dignity throughout the world, that this or that regime totally disregards human dignity, that something is beneath someone's dignity, even that the dead have a sacrosanct dignity. Except that what that all really means is generally impossible to find out.

The pathos that is always discernible in the expression all too easily masks its vagueness and openness. Instead of being inviolable, dignity appears to be elusive. One only needs to say the word "dignity" out loud to be shocked by its hollow ring. Like many big words, this one too has largely worn thin today.

This is worrying if one considers the value that should be given to human dignity throughout the world.

All of the United Nations' fundamental documents acknowledge this, and demand that it be recognised by all states and citizens. Accordingly, Article 1 of the Universal Declaration of Human Rights from 1948 begins with the sentence:

Marcus Tullius Cicero, the most famous orator in ancient Rome, was the first to proclaim the idea of general human dignity — to be understood both as a distinctive characteristic of each individual as well as a way of individually shaping one's life

"All people are born free and equal in dignity and rights." But these declarations say nothing about what the expression implies, nor do the numerous state constitutions, into which it has been incorporated.

An explanation is therefore urgently needed, especially as many people regard the expression "dignity" more as an empty phrase than a pure introductory word, as a commonplace word to be used in Sunday sermons, that — like edifying words intended as comfort — merely contributes to satisfying the need for general harmony. People like to refer to dignity, because this word still sounds good, and the fact that it is easy to remember gives the impression that it has a definition.

The fact that in truth it does not have one at all was proven by the examples to be found in the debates about the first major exhibition of plastinated whole-body specimens or plastinates in Germany. Like an all-purpose weapon, it was used against every reasonably justified argument, and was even ideologised. In debates like this, the reference to dignity — or rather to the lack of dignity — was often misused as a rhetorical phrase, either in order to silence unpleasant opponents or in order to help gain general recognition for one's personal interests and ideals associated with the traditional term. Who, by dissenting, would like to give rise to the suspicion that they supported infringements of human dignity? This explains why, in differences of ideological opinion, it can often be played as the joker, and why supporters of the widest range of opinions frequently like to refer to it.

Because dignity was one of the most widely used expressions in the controversy about KÖRPERWELTEN shown in Mannheim in 1997/98, I shall discuss here in more detail its significance and justification in four general sections and in a fifth section the dignity of the dead.

Sketches from Cultural History

All highly advanced cultures maintain that they respect and protect human dignity. But the expression, if one looks more closely, is mainly of Western origin. In this traditional environment, it is almost always used in two ways.

Firstly, it is used to describe an innate quality. Accordingly, as a result of his humanity, the individual possesses a special dignity as an essential characteristic peculiar only to him, irrespective of his behaviour and the social conditions in which he lives: one comes into the world equipped with it in the same way as with arms and legs.

Secondly, dignity is a question of how to achieve it. Accordingly, it depends on us humans ourselves, on our lifestyle and manners, whether and to what extent we acquire and possess dignity. In this connection, it is sometimes considered more as an individual achievement, and sometimes more as a social skill.

In Western history, both views have almost always been connected with each other. It was said that man should satisfy his innate dignity — the natural characteristic — in his life through his thoughts and actions, i.e., prove himself worthy in accordance with what is required. But only the idea of dignity as a concrete task permeates the whole of Western culture, not its understanding as a natural basic condition and determination of being.

For the ancient Athenians and Romans, the idea that all human beings possessed dignity from birth onwards was foreign. At that time, it was considered to be solely the result of individual achievement and social recognition. Dignity was dependent on the ability and effort made to

conquer passions and control feelings. A dignified personality observed the correct moderation and lived according to reason; he bore unhappiness, which did not unduly distress him, in just the same relaxed way as the happiness that he did not allow to result in excessive high spirits. In addition, he displayed dignity in his behaviour, his expressions and gestures, his body care and clothing, and in the calmness that he radiated. Such a person never spoke too loudly, and always walked circumspectly and gracefully. Social esteem, from which dignity could also grow, was bestowed by the general public either on aristocrats or persons with a particular social rank, who — as persons with dignity — generally occupied a high political office.

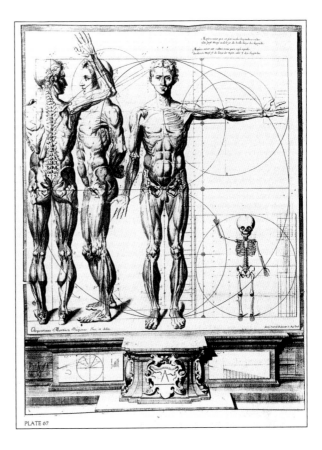

With the fundamental change in Western philosophy at the beginning of the modern era, a humanistic view of man began to take hold, who now began to investigate both his interiors and exteriors at the same time. Beauty was understood not merely as a superficial quality, but was attributed to internal structures and harmonious proportions. The drawing "Skeleton and muscle figures to illustrate proportions" by the Spaniard Cristomo Martinez (1638–1694), based on related studies by Renaissance artists such as Leonardo da Vinci and Albrecht Dürer, appeared in print in 1689 in Fontainebleau and in 1692 in Frankfurt and Leipzig.

As far as is known, however, the Roman philosopher and politician Marcus Tullius Cicero (106–43 BC) was the first to express in his writings the idea of general human dignity, describing it both as an unmistakable characteristic as well as a requirement, which he attributed to all men; he based this kind of dignity, on which every individual should base his life, on human rationality. However, Cicero's wider understanding did not gain immediate acceptance; only Christianity brought his ideas to maturity.

If we combine the viewpoints of Christian teaching and of philosophy, the result is the following picture: according to these ideas, the dignity of man is based on the biblical God having created man in His image and allowing him to share His reason and might. As God's special creation, man has an absolute value, as a result of which he differs from all other creatures. In contrast to the natural world, he occupies the centre of the universe, which was created for him and for his sake. In addition, according to Christian opinion, the superior worth of man can also be seen in his upright posture, his personality, free will, his immortal soul, and from the reason that enables him to recognise the world and God. In particular, however, it appears through God's becoming man — the Almighty becoming flesh — and through the redemption by Christ through His death and resurrection.

In all of these conceptions, human dignity is always seen as an essential characteristic possessed by each one of us, and which is not due solely to an elevated position, aristocratic origins or an impeccable life-style. It must be respected by every individual and all social institutions up to the State itself; all must protect and preserve it.

From the innate worth of man in this respect, however, an obligation is also derived, namely to live in an honest and God-fearing manner and to treat oneself and others kindly. People were convinced that although no-one can destroy the dignity innate in all men, the individual can nevertheless harm himself by allowing himself to revolt against God in sin and disobedience, and by being governed by his inclinations and unbridled egoism — instead of living a thoughtful, virtuous, considerate life.

Unlike the Middle Ages, from the 17th century onwards the dignity of man ceased to be attached to his being the image of God and to his position as the highest being in the world. Knowledge of the immensity of the universe had gradually become widespread, and even today this has the disturbing effect of making man aware of his minuteness and triviality. As a result of rational views, by the beginning of the modern age it had become impossible to deduce further the particular quality of man from his position in the world. Consequently, the fact that the stars do not revolve around man became ever less essential for determining his importance. Man's overriding dignity was seen in the human abil-

According to mediaeval Christian thinking, the dignity of man resulted from his being made in the image of God. In contrast, Immanual Kant, a philosopher of the Enlightenment (shown above in a miniature portrait painted in 1795), based the value of man that he considered unique on man's intellectual gifts.

ity to recognise nature and goodness. Thus, the French philosopher and mathematician Blaise Pascal (1623–1662) confirmed that although man was only one being among others, and as such was of only slight significance, he was a rational being — and as such he was far superior to all other creatures as far as dignity and rank were concerned.

The thinkers of the Enlightenment also speculated that only man possesses self-awareness, freedom, moral standards and reason. Their most important protagonist, Immanuel Kant (1724–1804), based the dignity of man exclusively on his particular intellectual gifts, on his capacity for self-contemplation and moral self-determination. On the one hand, Kant was convinced that man is a transitory part of nature; on the other hand he considered him as a person standing out from nature with a particular, indeed absolute, dignity. By this, Kant meant an absolute, incomparable value, higher than any price; having a price meant having only an external value, and thus capable of being bought, being exchangeable. Conversely, man as a rational being has an intrinsic value — dignity — and is therefore just as irreplaceable as he is unique. As an intellectual and morally rational being, he justly has the right to the respect of his peers, and conversely is obliged to heed others. In addition, the individual also has the same obligations towards himself, and these include never grovelling voluntarily to others. Whoever obsequiously bends the knee in search of favour is insulting himself. Whoever creeps to others should not be surprised if he gets kicked. Only a life in mutual acknowledgement and honest self-respect permits walking tall as the only physical and mental bearing appropriate for man.

According to Kant, the capacity for moral self-determination is expressed above all in the ability of the individual to free himself from his own desires, drives and instincts, and to decide on moral behaviour. One should always ask oneself what would happen if everyone acted like oneself, and then behave in such a manner that everyone in fact could act in the same way as oneself, without its resulting in chaos, injustice or pain.

For Kant, man was master, but not owner of himself. As a rational being with moral standards, the individual does indeed have power over himself, but he should not misuse this power to rid himself of it (that is why the sober thinker was also against intoxicants). Just as the respect-worthy value of the free man forbids his being treated simply as an object or tool, he as a person — that is, as a rational being bound to moral standards — must also never use himself merely as a means to an end or as an object; his dignity therefore forbids him from mistreating, selling or even killing himself. For Kant, human dignity as the embodiment of moral freedom is also a characteristic of man's being and form.

The following is clear: in the modern age, the idea of human dignity has detached itself from old religious bonds, but, as the one innate quality, it has continued to exist and has now found its ultimate foundation in rationality and morality.

In the Labyrinth of Legal History

As rich as cultural history is in opinions on this idea — remarkably, the term human dignity still did not play any part in any European declarations and constitutions of the 18th and 19th centuries. Its value in law therefore has a fairly brief history.

Today, human dignity and human rights are usually mentioned in the same breath, and are always associated with each other. It is said that human rights are based on the idea of human dignity, which is the ultimate basis on which they are determined. Yet the fact that the two terms

originally did not belong together is often overlooked.

A declaration by the State concerning human dignity is found for the first time, albeit more or less in passing, in Article 151 of the democratic German constitution drawn up in 1919 by the Weimar National Assembly. Then it is not found again until, strangely, in the corporate-fascist Portuguese constitution of 1933, later in 1937 in that of Ireland, then, above all, in the UN Charter of 1945, further in the Universal Declaration of Human Rights of 1948, and finally in the Constitution of the Federal Republic of Germany of 1949, in numerous later declarations and conventions, and in the Greek, Italian, Spanish, Swedish, Canadian, Swiss and former East German constitutions, but not in that of the United States. This inevitably gives rise to the question why it was specifically in the 20th century that the dignity of man became the highest standard. The answer is simple: the reason lies mainly in the terrible atrocities of the Second World War. But neither the Universal Declaration of Human Rights nor the German Constitution gives a clear definition of what human dignity actually is, and on what it is ultimately based — although during the consultations on a constitution for Germany (the legal successor to the so-called Third Reich after all) the term had been discussed many times from different points of view.

On August 10, 1948, 23 State lawyers and constitutional experts met on the island of Herrenchiemsee (women were not represented) in order to draw up a first draft of the Constitution in the seclusion of the so-called Altes Schloss. In the debate about what basic rights were to be considered, on August 18, Hans Nawiasky proposed the "dignity of the human personality" after having succeeded in having this phrase accepted in the discussions about the Bavarian constitution, which had come into force on December 8, 1946; in that, even the preamble demanded "respect for the dignity of man," and Article 100 states: "The dignity of the human personality must be respected in legislation, government and in the administration of justice." The formulation is linked to the United Nations Charter of June 25, 1945, in which right at the beginning the world community at the time had acknowledged the "dignity and value of the human personality."

Nevertheless, the constitutional convention initially planned a religious clause as the beginning for the Constitution: "Man is created by God, but the State is made by man." However, the state lawyer and SPD politician, Carlo Schmid, achieved the avoidance of any reference to God in Article 1. His last Herrenchiemsee version states: "(1) The State exists for the people, not the people for the State. (2) The dignity of the human personality is inviolable. The authority of the State in all its forms is obliged to respect and protect human dignity." The small word "inviolable" included in this draft was already included in Article 3 of the Hessian constitu-

Der Parlamentarische Rat hat das vorstehende Grundgesetz für die Bundesrepublik Deutschland in öffentlicher Sitzung am 8. Mai des Jahres Eintausendneunhundertneunundvierzig mit dreiundfünfzig gegen zwölf Stimmen beschlossen. Zu Urkunde dessen haben sämtliche Mitglieder des Parlamentarischen Rates die vorliegende Urschrift des Grundgesetzes eigenhändig unterzeichnet.

BONN AM RHEIN, den 23. Mai des Jahres Eintausendneunhundertneunundvierzig.

[signature]

PRÄSIDENT DES PARLAMENTARISCHEN RATES

[signature]

I. VIZEPRÄSIDENT DES PARLAMENTARISCHEN RATES

[signature]

II. VIZEPRÄSIDENT DES PARLAMENTARISCHEN RATES

The concept of human dignity occupies the most important position in the Constitution of the Federal Republic. However, both the constitutional convention and the Parliamentary Council had debated whether it should be included at all — and if so, in what form and in what context. The photograph above shows Ernst Reuter, then Mayor of West Berlin, at the signing of the Constitution, whose passing and recording was documented by the Presidium of the Parliamentary Council (below).

tion of December 1, 1946, where it is stated: "The life and health, honour and dignity of man are inviolable." The constitutional convention completed its work on August 24, 1948.

Just one week later, on September 1, 1948, the opening session of the Parliamentary Council — the actual constituent assembly of Germany — took place in Bonn. By May 8, 1949, its 65 members, including four women, under the leadership of the future Federal Chancellor Konrad Adenauer, had drawn up the Constitution, which came into force on May 24, 1949.

The Parliamentary Council had particularly lively discussions about human dignity. On several occasions, it was concerned with the question of whether the words "God-given" should be added to the wording concerning dignity. But as a result of numerous objections, in particular from Theodor Heuss, later the Federal President, all applications for this were rejected by a majority — albeit a narrow one. His proposal to assign absolute force to the highest value, but initially to leave it uninterpreted, was accepted. Heuss put forward the opinion that it was not so important to justify dignity theologically, philosophically or in any way ethically; the main thing was that it should be respected. The final wording of Article 1, Paragraph 1 of the German Constitution: "The dignity of man is inviolable. It is the obligation of all authorities of the State to respect and protect it" had already been settled on December 13, 1948; however, it took some weeks before it met with general approval in the Parliamentary Council.

According to Article 79, Paragraph 3 of the Constitution, respect for human dignity is absolutely binding and is exempt from any democratic resolution — as stated in Article 79, it may not be affected by any change to the Constitution. Strangely, however, what this great idea means, and on what it is based, was — as mentioned — not stated. Apparently the founders of the German Constitution, even just after the period of National Socialism, had confidence in the plausibility of the idea that, irrespective of the strength and weakness of the individual, there must be respect for man as such: for his ideal essence, which may be destroyed neither by the authority of the State nor by anyone else, and therefore should be established in law.

However, the German Federal Constitutional Court has not been able to refrain from a closer description and justification of dignity. That is not surprising, because every condemnation of an event as infringing dignity presupposes a concept of what it is to be human and thus a clear understanding of dignity as the criterion.

The jurisprudence expert Hans Dürig had a particular influence on this in 1952, with a discourse on the concept of man in the Constitution, according to which the individual is a "person by virtue of his intellect," which differentiates him from impersonal nature and makes him capable of achieving self-awareness and shaping himself by virtue of his own decision. From then on, the Federal Constitutional Court took this interpretation as a basis by considering human dignity as residing in the person of the individual, thus as deriving from his membership of the human species, i.e., as a result of his being a rational being. Since then, various fundamental judgements from the Federal Constitutional Court have consistently stressed that the idea of dignity is based on the concept of man as an intellectual and moral being who is able to practice self-determination and develop in freedom, not as an isolated and autocratic individual, but as an individual who is part of the community.

From this it follows that neither the State nor any other body can grant man his dignity; the State merely has the task of ensuring that it be respected and protected. To be precise, the sentence "The dignity of man is inviolable" says two things: both that as a natural inherent quality it cannot be infringed — cannot be destroyed — and also that as an ethical matter it may not be infringed — may not be violated. The expression 'inviolability' therefore covers the traditional double definition of dignity as a characteristic of man's being and form.

In the opinion of the highest court, human dignity is infringed if the individual is condemned to be a mere agent, is reduced to the level of an object, or if his very own area of privacy is disregarded, his honour is offended in a humiliating fashion or his life is condemned to one of mere vegetation. It has been repeatedly said that making someone merely an object contravenes human dignity. Admittedly, this so-called object formulation does not exclude making people a means to an end, and in modern society this would also be completely unrealistic; for example, the bus driver is a means to an end for the passenger, the lady on the check-out is a means to an end for the shopper, the teacher is a means to an end for the student. The dignity of the individual is not harmed as long as his fellow-citizens and the State still see and respect the person in him. However, opinions as to when a person simply becomes an object for others greatly differ.

Looking more closely, behind the Federal Constitutional Court's definition and justification of dignity, one can recognise Kant's philosophy of reason; it is its real source in the history of ideas. Conversely, in judgements from other courts, the Christian image of man still appears more clearly. In any event, human dignity is regarded today as the greatest earthly good and as the highest value in the social order.

Uncertain Ideological Viewpoints

In the meantime, however, major doubts about both traditional and official understanding of the term have arisen: doubts about man occupying a special position in nature — whether as a result of his being in the image of God or as a result of his reason. Many reject this superiority over the animal and plant world and the resultant devaluation of all other beings as being doubtful, if not presumptuous or even unworthy. Doubts of a quite different nature weigh even more heavily.

It is still occasionally maintained that the political-legal idea of human dignity is inconceivable without religious assumptions. However, this is countered not only by the fact that in the secular, pluralistic society Christian beliefs have become incomprehensible for many people; the anchoring of human dignity in religion is in contradiction of the constitutionally guaranteed neutrality of liberal communities and of the ideological openness of the United Nations. Accordingly, neither the individual State nor the world community may stipulate an ideology for people — which would, however, be the case if the idea of human dignity were made generally subject to the Christian image of mankind. The liberal constitutional State and the world community should therefore take a neutral stance not only with regard to people's decision to adopt or reject a religion, but should also restrict itself to imparting only ideologically neutral values that are indispensable for the well-being of the individual and the peaceful co-existence of all. The idea of innate dignity based on the ideal of man as being in the image of God does not belong to this.

This is not to say that innate human dignity does not exist. State and law should merely act as though it did not exist, because no one should impose acknowledgement of one particular ideology on another. It should be pointed out, however, that the requirement of neutrality affects only the State and its citizens in their political-legal role; conversely, no one should be denied the right to advocate his religious-ideological opinions in his private and social sphere, or the right to live in accordance with these.

The same objections that oppose a Christian interpretation of human dignity can also be put forward against the rational-philosophical view. The human concept on which it is based is just as invalid universally. The idea of man as a rational being with an absolute value that is distinct from nature is almost as ideologically secure as a religious belief. Hence, the rational-philosophical interpretation of dignity contradicts the constitutionally guaranteed neutrality of our State and the ideological openness of the United Nations; it becomes incompatible with a liberal community and a pluralistic world public as soon as it becomes applicable and binding for all.

However, this does not prevent the individual from having good reasons for being convinced of the truth of a particular ideology. But he should not want to force it onto his neighbour, the State not onto its citizens, and the world community not onto its member states. Only ideologically neutral moral concepts can be asked of anyone and acknowledged by everyone.

However, an ideologically completely neutral interpretation of the concept of innate human dignity is not possible; any such attempt must fail as a result of ideological controversies, because the ideas represented cannot be generalised. Consequently, in principle there can be no generally valid interpretation. It would either be definite with regard

The practice of stargazing, one of the oldest sciences known to man, developed from the 15th century into modern astronomy, and broke with traditional mystical ideas. In particular, the knowledge gained only 80 years ago, that even our familiar Milky Way system with its billions of suns, is only one of countless galaxies in the immeasur- *able universe, made the planet Earth, and thus mankind, into just a fleeting cosmic peripheral phenomenon. The photograph shows a highly active area of star formation in the Rosetta nebula, whose dark clouds will probably also compress and finally collapse to form new stars.*

to ideology or vague with regard to content, for without ideological background assumptions, the assumption of dignity as an innate characteristic remains incomprehensible and empty.

Admittedly one can go one step further. As stated, the need for ideological neutrality merely requires the political institutions to act as if innate human dignity did not exist; modern natural sciences suggest, however, that in fact it does not exist.

Thus modern cosmology can at least teach modesty to the citizens of Earth: our planet is only one of nine in the solar system, our central star only one average star out of a good two hundred thousand million in the galaxy, and the latter only one of more than a hundred million such galaxies, which in turn form groups and super-groups with immense empty spaces between. Similarly, the knowledge that humanity is a chance result of undirected and often crisis-like biological evolution can place our proud self-awareness in proportion. For example, for about 150 million years of the earth's middle age, reptiles — the dinosaurs — were the predominant creatures living on land; the anatomically modern Homo sapiens has only existed for about 100,000 years. Moreover, according to modern genetics and the neurosciences, our behaviour and intellectual life are determined by hereditary factors and unknown cerebral processes to a greater degree than was previously assumed.

Apparently there are no signs in nature that man could point to himself as an indication of his dignity. On the contrary, he is a transitory part of nature, concerned with himself in a world that is not concerned with him. The earliest known traces of hominoids who walked upright were found in a forested area in Tanzania, the Laetoli. These footprints are more than 3.5 million years old. Like the already very human-like primates, who left these behind, we human beings — the last representatives of the species Homo — will at some point have disappeared from the surface of the earth.

There is no victory over the briefness of time. The many ruined walls, the weather-beaten columns and the torso sculptures from bygone phases of the very short — measured by geological ages — era of civilisation very clearly bear witness to this. What is existentially important is not what the Roman Forum and the Acropolis once were, but what they are today: ruins and piles of rubble, which impressively remind us of the transient nature of everything human. In the nearer or more distant future nothing and no-one with the knowledge that there was once life on earth that claimed a particular value for itself will any longer exist. It requires no excessive pessimism, rather a sober realism, to recognise that man and all his works of intellectual culture have ultimately been condemned to disappear without a trace.

Self-Assertion of Dignity

We shall neither want to accept nor be able to come to terms with complete rejection of the idea of innate dignity, even though it cannot be generalised, and will possibly prove to be merely a fantasy. The excess of suffering, oppression and injustice in the world makes such a rejection appear nothing less than irresponsible; rather, it calls for respect for this idea in everyday practice and for its preservation in philosophical theory. We therefore cannot escape the question of how, despite all reservations, it can be saved.

This question can never be disregarded when humanitarian principles are infringed. This means that our vulnerability and sensitivity in many respects, but also our longing for a successful life, self-determination in freedom and undisturbed self-development, reveal a need for help and protection in which an ideologically neutral right to dignified

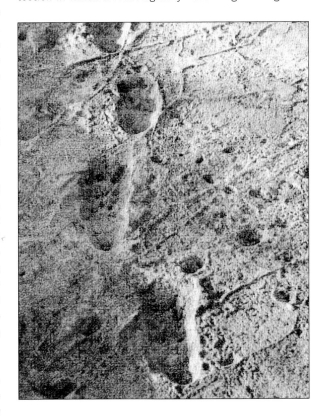

Biologically modern man appears late in the evolution of organisms, and is the last hominoid. Anatomically, we are for the most part the heirs of earlier species of our genus; for example, fossilised footprints discovered in Tanzania confirm that as early as approximately 3.5 million years ago human-like beings were walking upright. Like its ancestors, humanity will not last forever despite all of its achievements in terms of civilisation; the end of all life as we know it will come at the latest when the sun inflates into a red giant, and then our planetary system will be destroyed.

treatment is established. Consequently, the expression 'dignity' has a meaning for as long as we can still imagine anything in terms of human degradation and humiliation. The trembling body — ever a symbol of elementary vulnerability and need for protection — stands for such a need for respect, recognition and assistance. One can call this the self-assertion of human dignity as a result of becoming aware of it possibly and actually being disregarded.

This knowledge by no means contradicts the view that man is only one part of transitory nature, only one being among others. For in accordance with the same existentialist premise that each of us is condemned to shaping his needy and worried existence himself, oppression and injustice are perceived as distressingly cruel; nature by no means eliminates the difference between a successful and unsuccessful life.

However, one thing is no longer possible — adhering to the idea of innate human dignity. It is not only difficult to reconcile it with the natural scientific philosophy of our time — it already stands in contradiction to the fundamental principles of our liberal community and of those of the multicultural world community.

Only dignity as an aim can be generalised. Understood in this way, it is less given to us than imposed on us, not a general sign of nobility, but a particular identification of that imperfect being — man. Yet it denotes an ethical ideal and the concrete task of preventing and eliminating intellectual oppression, material need and social injustice. The basis for this is the mutual respect of humans as vulnerable beings concerned for themselves and for others. Considered from the ideologically neutral point of view — that is from the radically secular viewpoint — dignity is not naturally a part of us, but results only from the individual's dealings with himself and his equals, and the dealings of the State with its citizens.

However, if dignity is only a matter of shaping the conditions under which we live, it becomes possible to think that humans have none. Whenever someone is brutally degraded or loses his self-respect, his dignity disappears — albeit not the ethical right to it.

In order to avoid misunderstandings: no-one should be stripped of his dignity; but on the basis of the existence of those who lead, or who are forced to lead, a wretched life without self-respect, one can no longer sensibly say that it has dignity if innate dignity is absent. But even if this existed, it would be of no help to those affected, for such a nobility of being could not give any consolation to them about their undignified conditions anyway. If, therefore, dignity in the religious or rational philosophical sense does not exist, it in no way means that it should no longer be respected as an objective to be striven for. The contrary is the case:

Human dignity should be respected precisely when it does not exist as the one so that it exists as the other.

In this ideologically neutral assessment, the rational philosophical principle, which the adherents of religious opinions also share, namely that no one may merely be misused as a means to an end or as an object, continues to be maintained. Such a demand is sensible and ethically justified even if we no longer regard man as a being in God's image or as an intellectual being removed from nature, but merely as a transitory part of nature concerned with himself.

Dignity as an ethical right is one thing, but its guarantee in law is another. In view of the general tendency of man to indifference, egoism and violence, in view of the fact that we cannot be gods creating perfection and general happiness, but are rather animals, the special protection of human dignity in the community — as in Germany as a result of Article 1, Paragraph 1 of the federal Constitution — appears to be absolutely justified. This arrangement is sensible even without ideological background assumptions.

The Dignity of the Dead

According to general opinion, the right to the protection of dignity also applies to those who have died. In this connection one talks of its continued influence and effect even beyond death. In the debate about KÖRPERWELTEN in Mannheim, the dignity of the dead has become a key concept on which the questions, opinions, assertions and arguments concerning the permissibility and responsibility of the public exhibition of whole-body plastinates are focused.

The Inevitability of Death

Lifelessness is the norm in the cosmos, not a special circumstance; life, in contrast, is a borderline case. What is most natural for us humans — our own existence — is the great exception to which death is the rule.

If the whole of reality were full of life, death would have to remain a puzzle because in that case it would not fit into the world. However, the real puzzle is life, because ever since the big bang the universe has consisted mainly of a field of inanimate particles and forces. Measured against the universe's dimensions of time and space, the entire history of organisms known to us is a fleeting episode restricted to a tiny concentration of matter — the planet Earth.

This applies all the more so for the Homo sapiens phase: just as it was by chance that our species appeared in the biotic evolution characterised by erratic mutations and selection (also as a result of catastrophic mass death), the end of humanity is just as certain; and this will not have to wait for the annihilation of our planet when the sun explodes into a Red Giant in about five thousand million years time.

Like the death of life in general, the death of the individual human being is neither mysterious nor profound. It is the end of a natural course. Admittedly, we can try to postpone this biological actuality with the aid of modern medicine and a healthy life-style, but we cannot avoid it. Our death is as natural as the ageing and decline of the human body, in the course of which nerves and muscle cells die, the skeleton becomes more brittle and the hair less rich in pigment, eyesight and heart and brain functions deteriorate, and dark spots develop on sagging skin. For one thing, all these processes are due to the wear and tear to which tissues and cells are exposed in the everyday performance of their tasks; for another, ageing follows a genetic programme that determines the life of the individual cells, organs and the entire body. Harbingers of the end of life are age-related illnesses, which often considerably reduce the quality of life. When, finally, the supply of oxygen to the body breaks down, the person who was alive a moment ago is now dead.

Ambiguity of the Dead

But who are the dead after all? Without necessarily having to go into the medical question of definite signs of death, on closer consideration the term itself proves to be ambig - uous. On the one hand, we understand the dead to mean the dead body, while on the other hand we mean the deceased.

The deceased is commemorated; the body is disposed of. Nowadays, and in this country at least, it is either buried in a coffin or cremated and its ashes placed in an urn and interred or scattered at sea. Graves can be anonymous or furnished with names.

However, funeral practices, some of which are very old and carefully handed down, are as diverse as cultures. The ancient Egyptians, who for some of their Pharaohs built the pyramids that subsequently came to be considered wonders of the world, and provided them with costly gifts for the afterlife, were generally buried in a linen cloth. The Parsees placed their dead, naked, on the towers of silence for the vultures. In many tribes, ritual cannibalism took place right up to modern times. The atheist Communist Party of the Soviet Union embalmed their first dictator Vladimir Ilyich Lenin and placed him on show. The Catholic Church allows bones and other physical relics of its martyrs and saints to be revered as relics. Meanwhile, not only plagues, but above all wars and systematic murder like the fascistic genocide of the European Jews have also filled numerous mass graves.

How a culture treats a body is one expression of the instinctive rejection of the idea that, with death, the definitive end of life has come. The other manifests itself in that, according to general opinion, the wishes of the deceased should remain valid even after death; thus wills that are valid in law must be adhered to by the surviving heirs. The specific instructions of a person concerning the fate of his body after death — such as how it is to be buried and how the grave is to be designed, or whether it is to be donated for anatomical purposes, plastination or transplantation surgery — are also always the provisions of the deceased; they cannot be those of the body. Although we associate the term "the dead" with both the deceased and with the body, the two expressions do not mean the same thing. How otherwise could one sensibly talk about the "body of the deceased?"

Etymologically, the term "body" refers to the (dead) physical shell. The expression, which is perceived to be more considerate, is often used instead of "corpse"; and this latter word in its turn had already supplanted the Old and Middle High German words hreo and re with their blunt meaning of "cadaver." Yet one also talks about mortal remains, about the part of a human that can decay. The body, which after the death of the individual still retains its form for some time in silent motionlessness, showing features of its personality, is called a corpse until the flesh has disappeared from the bones, and any connection with the former unmistakable whole no longer exists as a result of natural decay or other form of decomposition.

The corpse is no longer a person; its ego ceased to exist at the latest after brain death. The corpse as a physical thing or object reveals itself to the unprejudiced view as what it actually is — a possible object for decay or cremation, organ removal, anatomy or plastination. On death, the person comes to an end; he is no longer in this world. He has thus lost his subjective quality and has become an object.

Since time immemorial, man, needing not only direction about reality, but also reassurance about it, has invented symbols and stories in order to cope with death. These make it clear that our need for realism is limited. Glossing over the harshness of reality, even now one talks about peaceful sleep or the resting of the dead, and includes in this picture the body, which, lying on its back with eyes closed and hands folded, is laid out and placed in the coffin. Yet the terms rest, peace and sleep, when related to the body, say less about death itself than about life — its restlessness, restless effort and exhausting difficulty.

Yet the popular image of peace in death is also connected to religious ideas, especially those of the Christians, because they expect re-awakening and resurrection. This concept was often transferred to the body, which is the reason that the Catholic Church forbade cremation for many hundreds of years; the prohibition was only lifted in 1963.

However, if such religious expectations are not, or are no longer, convincing, many people suffer an existential trauma or fear such a trauma. Admittedly, even a religious person cannot seriously believe that a body rests and sleeps. Even though one usually does not wish to know what happens so precisely: a dead person does not rest, he decays; he does not sleep, he decomposes and disintegrates to dust or is burned to ashes The disintegration of his body into organic and inorganic molecules is inevitable, until, in accordance with the old Latin proverb terra tegit terram, earth again only covers earth.

Possibly the dead person remains an object of mourning the whole time. However, this, too, like respecting the last wishes, relates not to the body, but only to the deceased. The body is a lifeless object in appearance, but the deceased is a living subject in memory. Even the visible grave into which the body was lowered, and which those left behind visit, care for and decorate as a place of particularly intensive memories, almost always evokes for them the image of the person who once was, as they knew him, not the image of decaying flesh and disintegrating bones. Not least because this idea is difficult to bear, more and more people are deciding on cremation nowadays, and many are allowing their bodies to be used after death for the living — through transplant surgery, for anatomical purposes or for plastination.

Nameless gardens of rest and communal graves for ashes are a further sign of an absence of illusions in our society. History no longer grows on these grassy areas in many cemeteries. Like the graveyards without individual names that were common in earlier phases of European history, they are

in advance of their time, for at some point all graves will reach this state of anonymity and inconspicuousness, and the bodies buried in them will have disappeared without a trace. Even the stone monuments and mausoleums disintegrate if they are not cleared away beforehand.

Memories are of even shorter duration. The mourning for the death of a person cannot hurt forever. The memory of his or her life pales, and finally the once inconsolable ones left behind die themselves; we cannot stop the past from slipping into nothingness. Finally, a veil of forgetfulness covers us all, and even this forgetting is ultimately forgotten.

The Dignity of Plastinates

It should always be made clear in what sense — religious, rational philosophical or ideologically neutral — the word dignity, which can be interpreted in different ways, is being used. If one must apply the word to the dead, in light of all that has been mentioned above, a strict differentiation must be made between the dignity of a body and that of the deceased.

This is not easy. One might think that the word refers only to the body, not to the deceased, since the highest value cannot logically be attributed to something that does not physically exist, that only lives on in memory, which, moreover, gradually pales. However, it is also feasible that dignity apply only to the deceased, but not to the body or even its ashes and the dust, into which it disintegrates, since, with death, the person is extinguished and has lost his subjective quality.

In the debate about plastination and the Mannheim exhibition of plastinates, there was much talk about infringe-

Burying corpses or burning them and placing the ashes in an urn are merely cultural conventions — and by no means the only ones, and not the ones that are always adhered to in modern Europe. For example, the Capuchin

tomb in Palermo is the largest cellar of mummies in the world. The picture on the left shows a young woman and her godfather, the one on the right the so-called corridor of scholars.

The Christian religious ideas of resurrection are expressed in concrete terms in the traditional picture of the peace of death. Accordingly, the Catholic Church has dressed up relics and whole bodies of saints — here Marie-Bernarde Soubirous (1844–1879), known as Bernadette, in the chapel of the convent of St. Gildard in Nevers. The religious visions that she had at the age of 14 formed the basis for the pilgrimages to Lourdes; she was canonised by Pope Pius XI in 1933.

ment of human dignity — that the dignity of the dead, that of their closest relatives, even that of the general public, if not the whole of humanity, had been disregarded. This criticism was expressed by representatives of both Christian churches, who knew that they had the support of politicians from different camps, and also by doctors; and many journalists made themselves the mouthpieces of these
accusations.

It was striking, however, that mostly one only heard or read that human dignity had been infringed, rarely to the extent to which it was supposed to have been. Apparently the critics were confident that those who refer to dignity are correct from the outset, without a precise justification and closer definition of what is meant. Thus the very different questions that arise in this connection, and which I shall discuss below, remained largely disregarded:

- Does the individual infringe his own dignity if he makes his dead body available for plastination?
- For its part, does this type of anatomical dissection and preservation of the donated body infringe human dignity?
- In particular, does the aesthetic form of a plastinated body, and possibly its conversion into a work of art, jeopardise the dignity of the dead?
- Can public exhibitions of plastinates, which are acknowledged to be aesthetically attractive, offend human dignity?

- And to what extent would charging entrance fees for visiting such exhibitions and providing plastinates for scientific and educational purposes in return for money be compatible with the dignity of man?

Limits of Self-Determination

The supporters of the most varied of ideas of dignity are largely agreed that self-determination is one of its essential characteristics. Whether they represent a religious, rational philosophical or radically secular viewpoint — they are all convinced that one of the freedoms of man is being able to make binding arrangements about his estate for the time after death.
Furthermore, it is then often simply maintained that the dignity of a person continues after death and even extends to the dead person.

However, on closer examination, this quite common argument proves to be extremely problematical. For it gives the impression that the dignity of a person can outlive the person himself. However, that is nonsensical, to some extent a misunderstanding of logic: such use of language presupposes that the deceased, although he no longer exists, must nevertheless continue to be regarded as existent; for only something that exists can have properties such as human dignity. But an existent non-existent is a contradiction in itself.

Respect for the dignity of someone who has died can therefore only mean respect for the dignity that the person had when he was still alive. That therefore means respect not for something that is present, but merely for something that is past. To have this respect is obviously possible, just as the arrangements made by a deceased regarding what he leaves behind can remain binding for the survivors after his death.

The question is, however, where does this obligation come from? It is mainly a social agreement that can be justified both by the wish of the citizens to take decisions that are binding beyond death, and also by their right to self-determination and by the dignity that they can normally demand when they are still alive.

There are nevertheless generally acknowledged limits to the free development of the individual personality. Heading these is the freedom of the person in question. To illustrate the point: the right to swing his arm ends at just the point where somebody else's nose begins. For a similar reason, in some circumstances — despite the right of self-determination — personal disposition over one's body must be withdrawn.

According to religious opinion, man may not dispose of his body in any way that he wishes, because the body, as the image of God, is also God's property; even a corpse has dignity. According to rational philosophical thinking, man may be master of himself, but he is not the owner of himself; accordingly, the individual may not take an entirely free decision about his dead body, because as a former bearer of reason it is given a particular dignity. In contrast, according to radically secular understanding, the mortal remains of a person, considered by themselves, have no dignity whatsoever; only to the extent to which the body is respected and honoured is it given a certain dignity.

Does it follow from these three ideas that while the individual is alive he may not decide on the fate of his later dead body? If that were really the case, the dignity of the body would be in direct conflict with the dignity of the person who has died — his former right to self-determination.

Let us disregard the fact that in major natural disasters and epidemics, and in wars, when the living count for virtually nothing and the corpses buried in mass graves count for nothing at all, and let us also disregard the numerous anonymous communal graves from former times that also lack special respect for the dignity of the corpses. Whether influenced by this or not — in the meantime man has come to the decision that the dignity of the deceased, i.e. his right to self-determination when he was alive, should be valued over the dignity of his dead body. It is said that the freedom of man includes being allowed to make arrangements about the fate of his mortal remains. Thus what has been said about its not being permissible to decide what is to happen to the corpse has already been partially countered.

Moreover, anyone who can decide between the different methods of disposal after death must decide on one possibility, and as a result of this situation he is inevitably master of his own corpse. Then, however, instead of burial or cremation of his body, he can stipulate that it be given to an anatomical institute for educational and research purposes, or to transplantation surgery for the removal of certain organs, organ parts and tissues in order to save the lives of others; and in view of these long-established possibilities, it would be absurd and inconsistent to forbid individuals from donating their own bodies for the relatively new procedure of plastination.

There is also another aspect. The authorities responsible may only approve a cremation if all suspicion of murder or manslaughter can be ruled out. In order to be sure of this, it is sometimes necessary to perform an autopsy; likewise the legal authorities can order an autopsy and the exhumation of a body that has already been buried — without the consent of the deceased and his relatives — in order to solve a crime. Not only the supporters of the radically secular understanding of dignity are in agreement with this, but usually also those who hold religious and rational philosophical views. However, by doing this, they also forfeit the idea of the unavailability of the human corpse. For apparently the fact that this is considered to be the property of God or a former bearer of reason, and the fact that relatives, friends and the general public would like to honour the person in the same way as they perceived him at the time of his death, apparently counts for less than the deceased's right to self-determination and the requirements of public safety.

This does not prevent religious or rational philosophical dignity from being conferred on the decaying body, the ashes of a cremated body, the anatomical dissection, the transplantation-surgery organs or a plastinate. It is merely that — as stated above — ideological opinions, which cannot be generalised, may not be imposed on anybody. The liberal State must therefore evaluate the concept "corpse" only from neutral and generally valid points of view, and not from points of view that are bound up with religious allegiance or intellectual history. However, the dignity of the corpse independent of all religious and rational philosophical convictions does not exist. Seen from an ideological point of view, the dignity of a corpse only arises when living persons are handling it; this also includes the respect for the last wishes of the deceased with regard to his mortal remains, as long as public order and health would not be affected by this decision.

Accordingly, with regard to the criticism of plastination and KÖRPERWELTEN, it must be concluded that whoever, while he is alive and in full possession of his mental faculties, voluntarily and after comprehensive information makes his body available for this procedure, and gives his consent to exhibition of the denaturised and transformed dissection resulting from it, is not offending the dignity of his body. In contrast, whoever forbids such a donation of a body is infringing the dignity of the deceased — unless public order and health would be jeopardised.

Objectification of a Dead Body as a Result of Plastination?

The object principle put forward in connection with the supreme court's definition and establishment of human dignity has recently also been applied to plastination. There was talk of degrading conversion of the dead into mere objects by making them into organ and whole-body specimens, of demeaning the dignity of their bodies by making them simply objects or things.

This accusation is untenable. It is untenable for the simple reason that while they were alive, the donors contractually agreed to plastination of their bodies after death and because plastination does not indicate contempt for the dead. Above all, the accusation is unjustified because a corpse, as the impermanent remains of a deceased person, is already an object or a thing. It becomes a thing before it comes under the hands of the plastinator. Consequently, the object principle can only relate to living persons, not to dead bodies, as these no longer have a subject quality.

Admittedly, considering the body as an exception to the 'either-or' classes of persons and objects has become established in law. However, this cannot seriously mean that the corpse is still somehow a person, rather that, being the mortal remains of a person who once was, possibly it should not be treated in the same way as other lifeless objects. It can be the object of respect and mourning; and for religious and ideological reasons, out of consideration for the wishes of the deceased and consideration of our own moral feelings, but also, with an eye to public order, we are obliged to treat it with respect. However, none of that would change anything with regard to the status of a corpse as an object. Otherwise in principle, it could not be used for the removal of organs and tissues for transplants or used for anatomical purposes, and it could not even be burned or left to decay in the ground.

According to Gunther von Hagens, the inventor of plastination, during its conversion into a whole-body specimen, a corpse goes through three stages: firstly it becomes anonymous. Then it is turned into a durable specimen, physically and chemically denatured through and through, which can no longer be identified with the former person. Finally it becomes an object of scientific information. It is simply absurd to consider the rendering of a dead body anonymous (by its not being given the name of the deceased) to be degrading, and to see degradation in the subsequent elimination of its physiognomical individuality (as a result of the anatomical dissection). The person bearing the name did indeed have his own individual life and sickness history; but this is not taken away from the deceased as such, and thus nor is his dignity, whereas the corpse was an object even before plastination.

In this respect, the only thing that is new, and thus unfamiliar, about the otherwise truly revolutionary procedure is that its results, instead of showing the mere frailness and transitoriness of life as anatomical specimens preserved in the usual way do, show the human body in a state that is no longer alive but not yet decayed for a virtually unlimited period of time. In addition to the amazing functionality of our body, its inner beauty can also be revealed if the plastinator is sensitive to this and proceeds with sufficient skill.

Improper Aesthetisisation of Plastinates?

As described at the beginning, anatomy blossomed for the first time in the Renaissance, and entered into an alliance with art. At that time, and for a long time afterwards, reproductions of medical discoveries and aesthetic depictions of the human body in paintings and sculptures were very closely connected.

Plastination, as Gunther von Hagens practises it, is in this tradition. A plastinate, if it is to fulfil the task of general enlightenment that is the aim, must be given an appropriate form, which could by no means be achieved with traditional methods of dissection and preservation. If the senses as well as the intellect are to be appealed to, aesthetically attractive solutions to the problem of form almost inevitably result.

However, von Hagens seems to have gone a step further when he oriented the shape of some of his whole-body plastinates on paintings and sculptures. Indeed, the opinion could arise that great works of art had served as models for him: the "Prototypes of Movement in Space" by the Italian futurist painter Umberto Boccioni (1882–1916) for the Runner; the "Anthropomorphic Cabinet" by Spanish surrealist Salvador Dali (1904–1989) for the Fragmented Man; the figure of Bartholomew in the Sistine Chapel by the Renaissance genius Michaelangelo Buonarroti (1475–1564) for the Muscle Man with his skin draped over his arm; and "The Doll" by German-French graphic artist and sculptor Hans Bellmer (1902–1975) for the Fencer. However, these similarities came about purely by chance, as Gunther von Hagens did not yet know of these works of art when he conceived these plastinates. Although this may indeed seem astounding, there is nonetheless no doubt about the aesthetic, virtually artistic presentation of his anatomical themes.

Various groups have protested vigorously against this ambitious structural transformation of anatomical specimens. In particular, they maintain that the plastinator is to some degree blasphemously making himself the Creator; in reality he is not concerned with passing on knowledge, but in self-expression. In the process, he is degrading the bodies of the dead in a demeaning manner into mere objects of art that allow the fact that they consist of parts of real bodies to be forgotten. The dead person serves him only as the means for an aesthetic purpose.

In addition, this criticism describes consequences that are to be expected after the supposed taboo has been broken. This leads to the question of how far one wants to go with the treatment of dead bodies. For if the fashioning of corpses so that they can be displayed in museums of art and galleries were once to be allowed, it would only be a small step to transforming dead men and women into armchairs, skeletons into hall-stands, skulls into soup bowls — most definitely infringements of dignity showing contempt for mankind.

The religiously biased accusation that the plastinator is playing the Creator with his whole-body specimens carries as little weight as the suspicion that the workers in a crematorium are behaving like the assistants of the Old Testament's God of Wrath or mythical idols when they push the dead into large incinerators. If one were to argue in this way, one would have to ask whether every surgical procedure performed on humans — whether for health or aesthetic reasons — would not have to be condemned as pride and an offence against the omnipotence of God. Apart from the members of certain sects, the vast majority of people obviously consider this absurd.

Moreover, the criticism of the aesthetic quality of plastinates misses the point here insofar as it is claimed that they are clearly identifiable as objects of art. In principle, however, no object can stipulate how the human mind must perceive it; whether it is perceived as a work of art depends mainly on the eye and judgement of the beholder (although the difficult question of what art or beauty is can be ignored here).

According to what Gunther von Hagens himself says, he makes no claim to be a genuine artist. However, he by no means denies an intended affinity of his works with sculptures — in the same ways as was attempted for the first time with the anatomical portrayals of the Renaissance, and was realised with three-dimensional anatomical models that later became famous. It was for this reason that he even coined the term KÖRPERWELTEN. He can, of course, give his reasons for this: firstly he owes it to the body donors to give their cadavers an aesthetic form. Secondly, in addition to the functional aspect of the human body, his aim was to reveal the natural beauty of its inner structures. Finally, since traditional anatomy has become increasingly isolated from the public, his plastinates were intended to provide general enlightenment; therefore, among the non-medical lay public, he is trying to prevent the natural fear of death and the horror and revulsion that the usual anatomical specimens can provoke.

In the opinion of almost all the visitors to the KÖRPERWELTEN exhibitions here and abroad up to now, he has, in fact, succeeded in this. Apparently, with his plastinates, many people can be shown things that would otherwise cause existential trepidation and could stir up the emotions, something that, in a natural realistic form, i.e., a form left unaesthetic either through thoughtlessness or by intention, they would not be willing to look at, even if it were to interest them.

The critical observation that this aestheticisation is simply a means to an end that is superficial for, and alien to, a dead body is doubtlessly correct. However, to interpret

At an early stage in the modern era, anatomy and art joined forces, and medical knowledge was depicted in aesthetic images of the human body. The sculpture "Scorticato" (The flayed one) by Lodovici Cigali (1559–1613) is in the Italian National Museum in the Bargello Palace in Florence, one of the most important collections of works of Tuscan sculptors of the 14th–16th centuries.

aestheticisation as an infringement of dignity is nevertheless wrong. Firstly, this reproach does not hold water, because the intentions pursued — dispelling revulsion and creating beauty — are not in themselves offensive, and are fully in accord with the interests of the body donors, who expect their dead bodies to be preserved as perfectly as possible and to be made presentable for lay persons. They would certainly never have agreed to the degradation of their bodies. Secondly, this attack also misses its target because it implies, without explicitly stating it, that the inherently true purpose of a corpse is to be burned or to decay, and that to be plastinated in an aesthetic manner is missing its real purpose. If that were true, it would have to follow that every anatomical or legally ordered autopsy, and even the removal of organs for transplant purposes, would merely be a means to an end that is superficial for, and alien to the true purpose of the body and thus would infringe its dignity. To take that to its ultimate conclusion: the same argument could be used to object to any type of disposal of a body. The reason is that with hygienic disposal of bodies, one is pursuing the remaining superficial remaining purpose of preventing harm to health that would result from their decaying in the proximity of the living — not to mention the intolerability of the appearance and the smell. None of these ways of treating a body can be regarded as an infringement of dignity, because a corpse is no longer a subject and thus there is no purpose inherent to it that could be disregarded.

Does this imply carte blanche to use the dead for any purpose whatsoever? If it is permitted to transform them into aesthetic objects, why not into useful objects — chairs, hall-stands or bowls? After all, in the 17th and 18th centuries in France and Germany, corpses were used for supposedly very effective remedies; soldiers believed that carrying the finger of a fallen comrade would bring them luck, and candles made from human tallow were considered to be helpful when seeking treasure. Furthermore, in the Capuchin church in Rome, one can still admire pillars made from skulls, arch supports made from shinbones and chandeliers made from vertebrae, produced by an old monk.

To what extent does a plastinate differ from these? In principle, they do differ: firstly, these products made from human remains were truly only in fact a means to an end (even though they did not fulfil any rationally comprehensible end). Above all, however, they depicted something that was not human. In order to be truly clear about this attribute, it is necessary to differentiate between relative unfamiliarity with a body and absolute alienation from it: plastinated whole-body plastinates such as Gunther von Hagens offers to the public depict the human organism as such in order to educate the individual observer about the inside of his own body. In doing so, he uses anatomical specimens rendered durable through unusual techniques — but only relatively, because they still bear the image of man. Conversely, to transform bodies or parts of bodies into bowls or clothes-stands would mean totally alienating the dead bodies, because they would then no longer appear to be anything human.

Nowadays, using bodies or parts of bodies for the wrong purpose would conflict not only with ideological opinions of dignity. Public opinion is almost unanimous in believing that the importance of a body as the remains of a person who has died and respect for his memory would be incompatible in such cases. Even if the deceased, when he was alive, had agreed in his will to his body's being used for useful purposes, or had even demanded this, in the opinion of most people compliance with this wish would not be possible for reasons of observing the established social order and because it would generally be too excessive to be acceptable.

Conversely, the relative (mental) recycling of a body for purposes of serving life, maintaining order and providing education — such as removing organs and tissues for transplantation surgery, performing autopsies for forensic medical purposes or for pathological clarification of the causes of death and dissections for anatomical research and instruction — is basically compatible with any and all ideas of dignity. Plastination, as just expounded, is a relative recycling in the same sense; why then has criticism been sparked by the public exhibition of plastinates?

Offensive Visibility of Plastinates?

Covering dead bodies is a cultural-historical phenomenon of particular importance. Many people find it difficult to bear, or even refuse to look at them. This is an expression of reluctance to face one's own death and the death of others, but also of the need to keep the physical picture of the deceased, whom one has known and loved, intact in one's memory — and possibly of the fear of being reminded of the future decay of one's own body.

This defensive attitude is particularly striking in highly civilised societies. A cloth is placed as soon as possible over the face of the person who has died. The catafalque is covered with flowers and wreaths. In the Federal Republic of Germany, even being waked in an open coffin requires a permit from the authorities.

However, it was not long ago that death was perceived to be natural to a far greater degree than it is today, and dealing with the dead was far more relaxed. Piles of bones and skulls can still be seen in ossuaries, and mummy cemeteries — as in Rome and Palermo — and can still be visited. Unlike Northern Europe, in many places in the Mediterranean countries, it is still the custom to leave the coffin half open until burial so that the immediate family as well as the relatives and friends who have travelled some distance, and all other members of the deceased's community can have a parting look.

In our artificial world, we are rather more inclined to suppress natural facts — the inevitable end of life and the physical disintegration of the body. Confrontation with anatomically dissected and preserved bodies is all the more confusing for many people. Many others, however, want to have them consigned to invisibility, so to speak; thus, in order to deter other interested parties from visiting the KÖRPERWELTEN exhibition, attempts were made to prevent it from opening in Mannheim, with the objection that it lacked dignity; and when that failed, the public was accused of pure voyeurism, of seeking sensation, and of having a tasteless thirst for horror. Just as the Jesuits at one time condemned Galileo Galilei because the knowledge that he had obtained

In the not too distant past, dealings with the dead were far more uninhibited than they are today, as ossuaries in many places show. In these, skulls and bones from opened graves were stacked on top of each other. From time to time, however, the limits of piety were considerably exceeded, as in the Capuchin church in the Via Veneto in Rome, where a monk used human bones to make abstruse room decorations.

by looking at the sky through one of the first telescopes threatened their traditional conception of the world, our contemporaries were now to be denied views of the human body that were not possible before the invention and development of plastination, or which, in a different and far less attractive manner were reserved exclusively for members of the medical profession.

There is no doubt that a particular attraction lies in the authenticity and originality of the plastinates. An exhibition of anatomical models that looked confusingly genuine would certainly not have had such enormous success or lasting impact as KÖRPERWELTEN in Mannheim in 1997/98. Certainly many visitors came simply out of curiosity and with the expectation of ambivalent feelings — stunned oppressiveness as well as excited fascination. Yet a representative survey revealed that, instead of these feelings, almost all the visitors had an objective interest in, and concerned thoughtfulness for, the exhibits. The majority proved only to be interested in the structure of the human body, and at the same time recognised its greatness and misery, the physical quality and frailness of the interiors of their own bodies.

What had already been confirmed in the article entitled "Anatomy" published by Denis Diderot and Jean le Rond d'Alembert in the great French Encyclopédie that appeared from 1751–1780 all of a sudden became a happening: "Knowledge of oneself requires knowledge of one's body, and knowledge of the body presumes knowledge of such a wonderful chain of causes and effects that one can say that none leads more directly to the concept of an omniscient and omnipotent God; it is, so to speak, the foundation of natural

theology." And further: "In addition to such an important motive, there is a benefit that cannot be disregarded, namely that of being informed of the means by which one feels well, by which one can prolong one's life, which explain the sites and symptoms of disease when one is ill…Knowledge of anatomy is important for everyone."

However, the question remains as to whether the use of plastinates in a way that provides an opportunity for emotional experiences and factual knowledge is generally compatible with the dignity of man. That would certainly not be the case if the public exhibition of anatomical objects were equivalent to a debasing heteronomy of the dead. No one is being debased; and nor is there any heteronomy, as a corpse does not possess any self-determination of purpose. Despite this, those representing a very wide range of ideas of what dignity is or should be are agreed that a body, as the remains of a person who has died, may never be used merely as a means to an end. However, this merely means that one should approach the specimens with a certain respect, and not that the right to view them must be reserved exclusively for the medical profession and should be refused to non-medical lay people.

Unseemly Exploitation of Plastinates?

Whoever respects the dignity of man respects his neighbour for his own sake and does not regard him merely as a replaceable object. Supporters of religious and radically secular viewpoints also share this rational philosophical principle of Immanuel Kant. Can it also be applied to plastinates?

Many people maintain that selling them (the only possible purchasers are research and teaching institutions and natural history museums) or charging admission to attend an exhibition of them is an infringement of dignity. But even if one concedes that the corpse as a mere thing should be given a certain degree of respect because it is the dead body of someone who has died, that does not apply to payment for a plastinate — considered with reference to Kant's idea regarding goods.

The practices of the Institute for Plastination do not permit any doubt whatsoever on this matter, because they already fulfil the strictest conditions: firstly, the Institute requires that the donation of the body carry no reward; and secondly, it is committed to the principle of never to charging for a plastinate itself, only for the costs of producing it — i.e., the cost of dissection and preservation.

Thus the Heidelberg Institute is clearly a service-provider, just like the undertaker who transfers the body to the mortuary and sells the surviving relatives a coffin or urn, the newspaper that accepts death notices, the florist who supplies wreaths, the restaurant owner who prepares the funeral meal, the municipal authority that maintains the cemetery, and the layman who speaks at the graveside — but it is also like the Church, which is paid for providing spiritual support at the graveside through the church tax.

Conclusion

All in all, it should have become clear that plastination and all of the activities connected with it do not infringe human dignity. These activities are not only compatible with the radically secular understanding of the concept, which as a result of its ideological neutrality can be generalised; but also those who hold an opinion connected with an ideology — religious or rational philosophical — which mainly belongs to the private sphere of the people, do not necessarily have to regard the plastination process or the exhibition of plastinates as an infringement of dignity.

The words "human dignity" weigh heavily, even though they trip off the tongue so lightly. Precisely for that reason, they should also in future be used more judiciously and with greater circumspection in all respects with regard to plastination.

Franz Josef Wetz has been a Professor of Philosophy at the College of Education in Schwäbisch Gmünd since 1994. He studied philosophy, German and theology, and graduated from the University of Giessen, where he did his doctorate and won a prize for his dissertation in 1989. He was employed there at the Centre for Philosophy and Principles of Science from 1981 to 1993, latterly as scientific assistant to Prof. Dr. Odo Marquard. Wetz took up deputy chairs in Erfurt and Giessen, and a guest professorship in Warsaw. Since he obtained his postdoctoral lecturing qualification in 1992, he has also been an independent lecturer at the Thüringen Institute for Teacher Training and Curriculum Development. His main areas of work are hermeneutics, ethics, and cultural and natural philosophy. Up to now he has published ten books and edited an additional three, broadcast several times on radio and television and written numerous scientific articles.

Readers with a deeper interest will find a detailed discussion of the intellectual, political and legal history of the concept of dignity and a systematic analysis of the image of dignity in modern culture in Franz Josef Wetz's book *Die Würde der Menschen ist antastbar* (*The Dignity of Man is Violable*) Klett-Cotta, Stuttgart, 1998.

Brigitte Tag

Legal Considerations regarding Body Donations, Plastination and Human Dignity*

The prospect of viewing plastinated human specimens have attracted spectacular numbers of visitors to the KÖRPER-WELTEN exhibitions in Vienna, Basel, Cologne and Ober-hausen. Even before the individual exhibitions opened, and particularly as the tide of visitors rose, this exhibition received an extraordinary amount of attention from the media, the political establishment, the religious community, and the general public, as well. Harsh criticism of the exhibition, which was polemically described as a "corpse show," was silenced or became more sober in view of the repeated success of the exhibition.

The more detailed the bioethical, moral, theological, and social questions pertaining to these two exhibitions become, the clearer the need will be to dignify these controversial events by considering their legal ramifications. Never before has it been possible to reveal both human anatomy as well as the logic underlying the body's functions as naturally as plastination allows, and never before has the question of legal limitations on the use of human corpses been as urgent as it is when considering plastinated bodies[1].

The Legal Situation

Being displayed as a plastinated specimen: for some, this idea arouses feelings ranging from disapproval to disgust. At times emotionally upset yet still making an effort to remain calm and objective, critics reject plastination as a "de-personalisation of human beings"[2] and a violation of "human dignity and inalienable human rights[3]." For others, it is time to destigmatize the use of corpses within the framework of the science of anatomy. The inner face of man should be made visible[4], they claim, and use should be made of the dead for the living.

This raises a number of questions. Up to this point, the discussion concerning the proper use of a corpse has focused primarily on organ transplants; the major issues involved here have been the debate on brain death and on finding solutions to problems of consent, i.e. when objections are raised to a given donation. This controversy did not end even when the Organ Transplantation Act went into effect in Germany. Still less of a social or legal consensus exists with respect to other uses of human corpses.

If we look to the law for security or clarity on this issue, if, in other words, we are looking for unambiguous guidelines for legal action or for laws and prohibitions complete with penalties to ensure their enforcement, then it rapidly becomes evident that what exists is a loose web of norms that are by no means definitive. This does not necessarily have to be a disadvantage, however. Both the tremendous advances in many areas of research and the applied sciences, as well as shifts in values and opinions demonstrate that our legal framework has to openly face these new challenges. Otherwise, it would run the risk of imposing traditional patterns of behaviour as an inflexible model of acceptable conduct while at the same time ignoring any new developments, without taking account of changes in legal reality. With this in mind, lawmakers' tendency to let social, ethical, moral and theological arguments act as guiding factors for society's use of corpses should most definitely be seen as wise, cautious reserve. In the meantime, it remains open whether this discourse will be the end of the issue or whether it will result in the demand for legislative action. This having been said by way of introduction, the following pages will go into more detail on issues of body donation, plastination, and human dignity.

Whose corpse is it?

Before KÖRPERWELTEN there had never been a debate this controversial and far-reaching concerning whether and to what extent anatomical specimens of human origin should be accessible for viewing not only to doctors and medical students, but also to lay persons. Legal considerations on this issue must begin by exploring the legal status of a corpse as a basis for plastinated specimens.

The question as to who owns the corpse is assessed on the basis of property or disposition rights applying to the human corpse. These rights require as a conditio sine qua non a legal relationship between the holder of the right and the

* This article is based in part on a publication of mine entitled "Proper Handling of Corpses: Legal Aspects of Using Plastination for the Long-Term Preservation of Human Corpses and Body Parts" which appeared in the 1998 issue of *Medizinrecht,* p. 387.
Superscript Roman numerals indicate annotations and source references included at the end of this article for those readers wishing further information on certain topics.

corpse. This statement may appear simple and obvious at first glance; upon closer inspection, however, it proves to be highly complex, because written law is only just beginning to regulate the legal status of the corpse. The result is a whole host of problems of fundamental importance, beginning with a preliminary question: how are we to understand the relationship between a living human and his or her body?

A living human being, functioning in its natural state as a single, holistic organism, is granted unique legal protection on the basis of the unity of body, soul and spirit. This distinctive feature is what sets humans apart not only from plants and animals, but also - and this is critical in the context at hand - from inanimate objects in the truest sense[5], attributing to us both human dignity[6] and the right to privacy. The commonly heard statement "man belongs to himself" does not mean that people have discretionary power over their bodies as they would have over inanimate objects. Instead, the relationship between a living human being and his or her body should be understood purely in terms of the right to privacy. "Being a body" is granted the same status as "having a body[7]." The statement "man belongs to himself" reflects the self-evident conviction of modern man that we lead a self-determined life and assume responsibility for our actions

This legal assessment changes with the last breath we take. If a person's life is extinguished, his or her remains are what initially determine the nature of the legal object now under consideration. The current state of affairs would indicate that one's mortal remains have come to be viewed as an object.

Defining the status of a corpse purely in terms of property laws, however, is not convincing when addressing the issue of ownership of a human corpse. On the one hand, this would result in unlimited ownership and marketing rights over the corpse; this is not acceptable, however, given that the mortal remains were once a human being. On the other hand, property ownership carries with it the rights of owners to do with their property as they see fit - selling or improving it, for instance - and to exclude others from having any influence so long as this violates neither the law nor the rights of third parties. The law also allows for the purchase of movable goods in good faith, provided they have been neither lost nor stolen. Were all of these legal provisions to be applied to human corpses, the consequences would be intolerable in view of their human origin.

For this reason, numerous regulations argue in favour of extending rights to individual privacy, and thus against the unlimited application of property laws to corpses. In light of this, decisions made by the deceased regarding the type and location of his or her funeral become important[8], and the Organ Transplantation Act[9] makes organ donation de-

pendent primarily upon the consent of the deceased. If no consent has been expressed, the consent of survivors or of other persons whom the deceased has so authorized is required. The presumed will of the deceased must, however, be taken into consideration, insofar as it is known. The law of succession also clearly shows that the wishes of the testator extend beyond his or her death[10]. Furthermore, Article 22 of the Copyright Law pertaining to works of art *(Kunsturhebergesetz)* guarantees a person the right to images of himself or herself for a period of 10 years following his or her death. During this time, photographs of the deceased may only be used with the permission of survivors, in which case the wishes of the deceased take priority, insofar as they are known.

The basis for decisions such as these is the interpretation of Germany's Constitution to mean that the inviolable human dignity guaranteed in Article 1, Section 1, remains in effect even after one's death. This would imply that the testamentary dispositions of the deceased remain valid[11]. As a result of these unique aspects of the law, while a corpse may be an object, making use of that object is subject primarily to regulations concerning the right to privacy of individuals.

The following is therefore clear: the human origins of a corpse last beyond the death of the former bearer of legal rights[12]. The continuity of human dignity beyond the grave means that while corpses and/or body parts are, according to prevailing[13] albeit controversial views, objects, they are not generally considered property. In keeping with this, heirs inherit neither property rights nor acquisition rights to the corpse of the deceased. Instead, the corpse is, as a rule, not owned by anyone and falls to the custody of those survivors charged with caring for the dead.

Permissible Discretionary Rights over Corpses

Legal constraints regarding proper use of a corpse are limited to a few selective statements. Unlike regulatory authority over organ donations, the authority to regulate dissection and body donations made to anatomical institutions does not fall under federal jurisdiction[14]. For this reason, individual states in Germany not only have their own funeral laws; they may also have their own laws governing dissection - or they may have none at all on this subject. Germany has no unified, definitive regulations concerning the proper use of corpses. As a result, dealing with this issue means having to fall back on general regulations and principles as a supplement to existing laws.

Nevertheless, the legal principle involved is clear: within the bounds of current law, every individual has the right to determine what will be done with his or her mortal remains. If the deceased made no use of that right while alive, it is incumbent upon the survivors to exercise their rights as next of kin and take the required steps. They may not, however, act in any way they wish; the posthumous right to privacy dictates that they must instead take the wishes of the deceased into consideration.

The right of an individual to determine the fate of his or her corpse for the time after his or her death results from the Constitution. The universal personal right protected by Article 2, Section 1 in conjunction with Article 1, Section 1 of Germany's Constitution constitutes the legal basis hereto. As the human dignity guaranteed in Article 1, Section 1 of Germany's Constitution remains in effect even after one's death, dispositions regarding body donations remain valid postmortem. Testamentary dispositions do not have an expiration date saying: "Valid until death".

The right of an individual to determine the fate of his or her corpse is not limited simply to a choice between the usual types of funerals, however. Arranging to have one's body donated to an anatomical institution following one's death has always been recognized. This view is reflected in several state funeral laws[15] and in the law on dissection of the State of Berlin[16]. In addition, long-term preservation of corpses and parts of corpses for anatomical purposes as well as for use in natural science museums is not unusual and is accepted by the legal community. Neither should we forget the numerous institutions where mummies, corpses or parts of corpses preserved in formalin as well as deformities and malformations can be viewed by the public. The very fact that these specimens have been on public display for years and decades proves that not every corpse is interred. The legally recognized use of corpses for diverse purposes outside the narrow guidelines of the funeral laws demonstrates that the obligatory interment[17] demanded by the opponents of the exhibition is and never was valid in absolute terms. In addition, the standardized provisions of State law pertaining to the use of corpses are subordinate to the principle of proportionality. When interpreting these issues in keeping with Germany's Constitution, obligatory interment has to be regarded in the light of the superior Constitution, which can restrict simple laws. However, should the body donation for anatomical purposes and therefore also for long-term preservation by using traditional methods, and the retention of the specimens in universities and natural science museums be in accordance with human dignity and obligatory interment, the purely rational conclusion can be drawn that this is in principal also valid for self-determined body donations for plastination purposes.

A significant aspect of anatomical science lies in dissecting and preserving dead human bodies[18]. The use of corpses is, of course, not limited solely to the education of medical students. They are also used for experiments in the area of basic and applied research[19], and as preserved exhibits for, inter alia, anatomical and other natural science museums. Also relevant in this context is the issue that human body parts and products of human metabolism are used in ways that do not necessarily benefit the donor. Medications, for example, have long been produced from blood, blood serum and plasma, bones, skin and glands, and, as mentioned above, donating and removing human organs, parts of organs and tissues for use in other human beings has recently been regulated by the Organ Transplantation Act[20].

In conclusion, it is clear that traditional use of a corpse has generally consisted of interring the dead. Nevertheless, our legal system does have provisions for other, perfectly common uses of corpses. Objections to plastination that stem from ethical and moral considerations are therefore not shared by the law to the extent that discretionary rights to donate corpses for these purposes would inherently be viewed as a violation of moral codes and thus as null and void.

Advantages of the Plastination Process

The discretionary right to donate one's body to plastination is a continuation of the tradition of donating bodies to anatomical institutions. The use of plastinated specimens, however, is not limited to training and further education of medical professionals, especially since bodies can now be preserved for more than just a limited time and their appearance is more than just a little aesthetically appealing from the perspective of lay persons. The goal of the new technique is to transform dead bodies into durable, three-dimensional visual aids; as such the technique offers a great deal more freedom of action, in that specimens can remain for a while in a "pre-plastination" state. In this state, body cells have already been saturated with plastic, which denatures the body both physically and chemically; yet as long as the plastic has not polymerized and thus cured, specimens can be subtly shaped in keeping with anatomical as well as aesthetic objectives. This is the basis for making the interior of the human body accessible not only to experts, but also to lay persons having an interest in the field of medicine. With previous preservation techniques, this was either impossible or could only be done to a limited degree.

Testamentary Dispositions and Body Donations

No small number of people have expressly consented to donate their corpses for these purposes. As of January 28, 1999, the Heidelberg Institute of Plastination had received 873 such declarations. For others, the thought of having their own body plastinated after their deaths and subjected to the scrutiny of the public is either difficult to imagine or unbearable.

The basis for any decision, whether in favour of or against plastination, is the right to discretionary freedom regarding one's own body, which the German Constitution grants each individual both by virtue of his or her mere existence as well as for the sake of the right of self-determination. As a result, the ultimate decisionmaking authority is generally the individual involved. Just as organ donors, body donors bear the consequences of their decision, and only they understand their own personal priorities and values.

This self-determination extending beyond the grave puts in concrete terms both individual values as well as a discretionary interest in one's own body. On the one hand, it is a tangible act that empowers anatomists to intervene in the postmortem legal orbit of the body donor. Accordingly, a donation disposition is not a declaration of intent in a contractual sense, but is instead another kind of legal act. Unlike a contractual declaration of intent, a donation disposition declares whether and in what capacity the body donor currently has discretionary rights over the object of legal protection (in this case his or her own body). This precludes any obligations attached to the disposition from extending into the future. The disposition is non-binding with respect to motives or time periods and as such may be revoked at any time.

A body donation disposition is only legally binding if it does not violate any overriding laws. It must also be proven - before the death of the individual - to be a true act of self-determination. For it to be legally binding, the individual must therefore be of sound mind and capable of expressing his or her consent. This capability is not to be confused with competence as defined by civil law, nor with the ability to stand trial as defined by criminal law, nor with the age limits associated with this ability. Instead, it determines among other things whether the donor is in possession of the presence of mind and sound judgment required for comprehending the meaning and scope of both the donation and the lasting conservation of the body via plastination. Judgment and presence of mind can only be evaluated on an individual basis.

Plastination does, of course, present several unique issues with respect to traditional uses of corpses: the procedure makes it possible to fashion full and partial-body specimens in a huge variety of anatomical arrangements. Specimens can also be preserved for a very long time. Finally, some specimens are exhibited, and - although anonymity is strictly maintained - this means they are subjected to the scrutiny of countless interested persons. Such actions severely encroach upon the privacy rights of the deceased.

When considering the dignified use of a corpse, it is therefore not enough that the donor has volunteered his or her body for the plastination process; he or she must also be aware of the consequences associated with such a donation. For a disposition to be legally binding, the individual in question must as a result be informed in advance and in detail of the potential uses of the corpse. Individual aspects of this fundamental statement have by no means been clarified definitively, however, which is a problem affecting, for instance, the scope of the information provided. Most certainly, information must be fully truthful, and questions must be answered in a concrete and appropriate manner. Apart from that, certain distinctions must be made; the need for information must as a result be tailored to the donor's prior level of understanding, which may already have been influenced on certain points by the media or medical literature.

The right to self-determination does not, however, automatically lead to an obligation to self-determination. The flip side of the right to information is therefore the right of an individual to decide what information - regarding both plastination and those uses of a corpse which are associated with plastination - he or she deems necessary for deciding either in favour of or against donation.

Donating Bodies for Plastination and Human Dignity

In addition to requiring a legally binding donation disposition, the legal system also places other objective limits on plastination and on exhibiting plastinated specimens. When considering the proper use of a corpse, the most important limitation is the premise outlined in Article 1, Section 1 of the Constitution of Germany, which states that the duty of all public authorities is to respect and protect the inviolable dignity of man[21].

There have always been differing opinions as to what the term dignity means. Yet despite the fact that this term, anchored as it is in our constitutional law, has been influenced by widely disparate views within the history of German thought, these views alone do not determine its interpretation. The human dignity described in the Constitution expresses the highest value of our liberal democracy; this is especially evident in light of the historical context of past totalitarian regimes under which the crassest violations of human dignity were committed[22].

Nevertheless, people are generally united in the view that the concrete meaning of dignity depends on the situation at hand. One and the same process can be a violation of human dignity when ordered by the state, and yet be compatible with human dignity if one submits to it voluntarily. This is true because, within certain parameters, the concept of dignity includes the idea that dignity not be forced upon anyone[23]. The Federal Constitutional Court considers it to be a violation of human dignity whenever the person involved has been degraded to a mere object, to a means to an end, to a quantity that can be replaced at random[24]. The individual must, however, conform to the legal system and is, as a result, confronted with third-party rights. For this reason, the foregoing negative definition of a violation of dignity is only valid if the principle of man's inherent rights under the law has been challenged or if human dignity has, in a specific case, been arbitrarily disregarded[25].

The starting point for considering the compatibility of plastination and human dignity is the definition of object according to the Federal Constitutional Court. Only with great care and reservation can this definition be applied to the posthumous dignity of the deceased, because, despite the fact that an individual's right to privacy extends beyond death, a corpse is still a thing - the material nature of a corpse alone makes it an object. Anyone viewing the issue solely in terms of the right to privacy ignores this fact and is confronted with the problem that an individual's status as an entity under the law ends when that person dies.

Unless we turn to ancient Germanic mysticism, this dilemma could only be solved by granting rights to a non-existent entity or by recognizing that the dead are partially capable of acquiring and holding rights and duties. Under privacy laws, however, the link between the individual and the law excludes the possibility of granting rights to a non-existent entity; and the partial capacity to acquire and hold rights and duties would be in conflict with Article 1922, Paragraph 1 of the German Civil Code, which states that upon a person's death, ownership of his or her entire estate is transferred to one or more persons. This leads us to conclude that the capacity to acquire and hold rights and duties ends with death.

The question as to whether plastination jeopardizes posthumous human dignity should therefore focus on whether a corpse can be treated as merely an object. One could argue in favour of intervening on behalf of posthumous human dignity, were the specific use of a corpse to disregard an individual's right to privacy, which is legally binding even after death, and were this use to express contempt for the regard to which that person was entitled while alive. A judgment in this case would be determined both by objective factors as well as by the subjective purpose to which the corpse is to be used.

One of the central obligations arising from the posthumous right to privacy is that testamentary dispositions of the deceased be honoured. This places the authority to decide the fate of a dead body directly with the individual involved. The discretionary right to donate one's body for plastination does not challenge a person's status as a legal entity, but rather underscores it.
There is also the argument that body donation does not con-

stitute a common form of interment, but is instead aimed at preserving the body for long periods of time. The attempt to dispute the legally binding nature of a donation disposition must likewise fail, as this would mean guaranteeing human dignity as objective property at the expense of an individual's freedom to donate his or her body; as a result either abstract ideals divorced from social reality or even governmental claims to power would override an individual's wishes without consideration being given to his or her motives.

In addition, long-term preservation of corpses and parts of corpses as a means of advancing anatomical science and for use in natural science museums is not unusual[26] and is considered legal by prevailing opinion. The predominant view represented in legal writings exceeds this, even going so far as to view corpses used by anatomical institutions and museums as marketable objects[27]. Given that the legal community has not only accepted but also welcomed body donation as a laudable service to anatomical science, thus accepting complete dismemberment and long-term preservation by traditional means, this view and no other can apply to plastination for the time being.

Anatomy and Aesthetics, Art and Ability

Nevertheless, that plastination allows others to fashion human bodies in artistic ways is viewed by many critics as specific evidence of the undignified use of corpses. This raises two questions: during the plastination process, does the body of the deceased become an object of artistic creativity? If yes, is this permissible?

According to the decision of the Federal Constitutional Court regarding the freedom of artistic expression guaranteed in Article 5, Paragraph 3 of the Constitution, it must be assumed that defining the term "art" contradicts our current understanding of what art is. Because the administration of the law nevertheless requires that a distinction be made between this and other uses of the word, its meaning can be paraphrased as "the free creative process, in which a specific medium is used as a vehicle for making the impressions, experiences, and insights of the artist accessible for contemplation[28]." As such, art as it is meant in Article 5 section 3 of the Constitution is to be understood as a creative activity transcending that which can be learned or reproduced.

A distinction therefore exists between this usage of the word "art" and the usage referring to "ability". This meaning is used often enough in a medical context, in such expressions as "the art of medicine" or lege artis (according to the rules of the art of medicine), and is synonymous with knowledge, capability, readiness and thus highly developed manual skills.

To be sure, the term referring to art as protected under the German Constitution must be broadly defined, and the line between creative art and "ability" art is fuzzy. Still, there are starting points for differentiating between both uses of the word. Evidence of creative art, for example, would be if the artist views his or her work as a work of art, and if third parties well-versed in issues of art likewise feel that the work in question could justifiably be described as art.

Yet another criterion for a work of art ought to be that it allow for new interpretations each time it is contemplated. It should be remarked at this point, however, that there are very few human activities, accomplishments and works that cannot be interpreted in various ways. A supplemental distinguishing criteria must therefore be that creative art, unlike "ability" art, is not subject to any code of rules that could be used to gauge its quality - this would directly contradict the meaning of art. Unlike "ability" art, creative art is its own justification.

Even though each individual case would have to be considered separately, classifying plastination as art would appear to be questionable. This can be said because the educational intent of the procedure justifies it, provided this type of dissection and preservation is performed with the aim of displaying the body in a manner faithful to human anatomy in its natural state, thus making it accessible to the lay person and prompting observers to reflect upon themselves and their own physical nature. This remains true, even if persons with little or no medical training only understand the anatomical relationships after receiving appropriate guidance and explanations.

To see plastination as an artistic distortion of the human body which potentially degrades it to a mere object would mean that a specimen is not be viewed as an educational tool for understanding human anatomy, but rather as an object that serves as its own justification and which should be so understood. The human dignity of the donor has not been violated, however, if the sense and purpose of a given specimen is to serve humans for their own sake by making the complexity of the human body and the interaction of individual body components easier to understand, and if the aesthetic presentation of the specimens helps to educate people about their bodies. In addition, it should be noted that aesthetic means are essential to ensuring that the dignity of the donor is preserved. Only when the dissection, form and preservation of a specimen have been perfected is it possible to maintain the body and its components for future generations in such a way that lay persons can understand them and look upon them without horror, thereby preserving the body for posterity and maintaining its dignity beyond the life of the individual[29].

This makes it clear that art in the sense of ability is not identical to art as it is understood in its constitutionally protected sense. This holds true, even though the prerequisite for creating aesthetic and anatomically correct specimens includes skills that unite perfect ability with intuition. For this reason plastination most definitely withstands a qualitative comparison to the creative activities of art in a modern sense.

Despite these conclusions, admonishing objections to the at times controversial display of plastinated human bodies and body parts cannot simply be dismissed; the reason for this is that, as mentioned earlier, the line between art and ability has always been thin. If corpses were being fashioned into objects of art, and were as a result - not as a necessary result but certainly as a potential result - used for purposes where highlighting and providing information on the functions of internal structures were not the primary motivation, then a new legal assessment would be required. However, as long as plastinated specimens are used solely for conserving bodies and/or body parts in a manner that is instructive yet in keeping with anatomy in its natural state, it would not appear that human dignity has been violated. These guidelines are also appropriate for gauging the use of aesthetic aids.

Reverence and the Autonomy of Donors

Critics who denounce the fabrication and exhibition of plastinated specimens as unacceptable, regardless of the decision of a body donor, generally back up their arguments by referring to the right to care for the dead, and to feelings of reverence on the part of both survivors and the general public.

The right to care for the dead is a fiduciary right normally reserved for the next of kin. Its purpose is to ensure that all laws applying to the care of the corpse will be observed, to exclude unauthorized intervention of third parties, and to observe the wishes of the deceased as expressed during his or her lifetime. The term reverence acts as a legal principle of general application, combining respect for the peace of the dead (the corpse should not be desecrated in other words) with the memory of the deceased, i.e., the feeling of oneness with that person, even after his or her death. This legally protected interest belongs primarily to survivors, as it draws upon a bond with the deceased that has grown within the framework of a lifelong relationship. The sense of reverence of the general public, however, generally merits legal protection when interpreted in the sense of respect for the peace of the dead.

Thus we have on the one hand the right to care for the dead and the sense of reverence on the part of both survivors and the general public; on the other hand we have a wilful decision on the part of the body donor. Defusing this strained relationship means ensuring that survivors be obliged, either despite or in fact because of the fiduciary aspects of the right to care for the dead, to respect the testamentary decisions of the deceased and thus not be able to do with the corpse as they see fit. This likewise holds true for the decision to donate one's body; the posthumous right of self-determination makes such a decision legally binding even after death. While living, the individual has the right to determine the fate of his or her future corpse independently and without taking the sensibilities of either survivors or third parties into account. It follows that there is no clear legal reason why the feelings of reverence of these people should have a legally binding effect on a person after his or her death. In addition to this, the effect of anatomical specimens, their preservation and the act of fashioning pre-plastinated specimens is to make the corpses anonymous. This procedure first displaces the personality of the deceased and then suppresses it entirely, and as personal features fade, so does the obligation to reverence. Viewed in this way, it does not make sense to take the laudable decision of an individual to donate his or her body to science for the purpose of educating the public and thus contributing to public welfare, and subordinate it to a third-party concern for reverence.

Exhibiting Plastinated Specimens

Even though staying within the limits described above means that neither body donation dispositions nor plastination of corpses is at variance with the concept of human dignity, the constitutionality of displaying plastinated specimens for the general public needs to be reviewed.

Public encounters with plastination[30], although based on voluntary visits to the exhibition, are themselves not sufficient for establishing a violation of human dignity. Just as in the case of corpses and specimens that have been preserved for the purpose of educating medical personnel in the subject of anatomy, the intent of displaying plastinated specimens is not to express contempt for the regard to which the body is entitled simply by virtue of its having originally been a human being.

Instead, the purpose of the exhibition - as explained in the exhibition catalogue for KÖRPERWELTEN - lies in presenting both the unique nature of the human body, as well as the body's internal structures and the logic underlying their functions. The public will hopefully receive authentic information on the human body, and visitors will better understand how their bodies work. The preserved originals are meant to prompt visitors to reflect on their own physical nature and as a result raise their level of health consciousness[31].

Long before the invention of plastination, museums dedicated to pathology and anatomy set for themselves the goal of generating public discourse on healthy and pathological functions of the human body, and on how to recognize and take seriously the body's signals even though specimens preserved through traditional means were less instructive for lay persons[32]. Educating the public on human anatomy and on the logic underlying bodily functions is also part of the significant task of our public health system to make persons interested in medicine familiar with the human body in a vivid and comprehensible manner, thereby inspiring them to adjust their behaviour in ways that promote good health.

Insofar as exhibiting plastinated specimens furthers this goal, and as long as the exhibition takes place in a manner in keeping with the posthumous dignity of the donors, it is not in conflict with any existing regulations. Reserving plastinated specimens solely for medical personnel and science students would encroach upon the right of the open-minded, responsible citizen to self-determination as the term applies to issues of health and the body.

Selling Plastinated Specimens

Admission to exhibitions such as KÖRPERWELTEN is not, after all, free. Plastinated specimens are also sold to teaching and research institutions and to museums. On condition that this field of potential buyers does not expand, and that the potential for improper use of the specimens has been ruled out[33], the objection that remains to be discussed is whether deriving economic gain from plastination indicates a potential violation of accepted moral standards.

The phrase "accepted moral standards" is taken from civil law. According to Article 138 of the German Civil Code, a legal transaction is null and void if it violates "accepted moral standards." Any conduct constitutes such a violation if it runs counter to the sense of decency of all just and fair-minded individuals[34]. This is geared towards average sensibilities and not towards the subjective sensibilities of an individual. Furthermore, the phrase "accepted moral standards" does not refer to morality in an ethical sense, but rather to a minimum of moral conduct with respect to the procedure at hand. What constitutes a minimum of moral conduct should be inferred as much as possible from the prevailing legal system. When this fails to provide a concrete legal definition, the recognized moral and ethical values of society should be used as a guide[35]. It must, however, be noted that the prevailing moral values of society can only be determined within a narrow context, and as such yield very few points from which to consider the use of plastinated specimens. The reason for this is that judicial means are all but insufficient for characterizing such concepts as decency, moral sensitivity, respectful consideration for survivors, and a sense of tact regarding corpses, particularly when a donor has decided not to inter his or her body.

It is especially important in this context that individuals do not donate their bodies against payment and that they be aware of the fact that their bodies could be sold to third parties. Moreover, trade in bodily substances is already a reality in some areas - even though there is generally a stigma attached to this in society at large. One example of this is that blood donation centres take blood which was donated free of charge and sell it to hospitals[36]. This practice was not altered by the Transfusion Act passed in 1998.

The Organ Transplantation Act, on the other hand, places legal limitations on selling human organs. The ban on commercial activities is limited to selling bodily substances for the purpose of medical treatment, however. What it does not include is transferring ownership of specimens donated for other purposes, such as bodies donated for plastination. The principle intent of the ban is to prevent the critically ill from being exploited in a particularly reprehensible manner for selfish economic reasons and to prevent financial incentives from being offered to living donors - neither of these concerns bears any relevance to donations made for plastination.

Lawmakers, however, are threatening to criminalize the trade of any organs made available as a result of someone's death; human dignity and feelings of reverence on the part of the general public form the basis for this[37]. Because this aspect of the Organ Transplantation Act is relevant to plastination, it can be used as a starting point for determining whether or to what extent the sale of plastinated specimens can be reconciled with the current body of laws.

The term "commercial activity" is used in an identical sense in the Dangerous Drugs Act, where it is defined as any activity based on personal gain through the sale of "goods" and making a profit on a regular basis. According to this, an activity not aimed at personal gain would be one in which an appropriate sum is accepted for any necessary procedures involved in a particular medical treatment. This is especially pertinent with respect to removing, preserving, preparing, storing and transporting organs, as well as preventing infection. Furthermore, the ban on commercial activity does not pertain to medications prepared from human organs
within the bounds of laws regulating the manufacture of pharmaceuticals[38].

Were we to apply these standards to the sale of plastinated body parts to third parties, we would see the following: receiving appropriate reimbursement for plastinated specimens is not at variance with "accepted moral standards", provided these specimens were furnished to museums and research institutions free of charge and assuming the sale is

not the result of the intent to make a profit above and beyond the cost of dissecting the specimen[39]. These guidelines likewise pertain to entrance fees charged wherever plastinated specimens are exhibited. These are of course only a few preliminary points of departure for a legal assessment of the issue of monetary compensation for plastination. The fact that the Transfusion Act does not prohibit the sale of blood and blood components reflects a more flexible attitude towards the use of substances of human origin; the direction that future developments may take, however, is not yet foreseeable.

Conclusion

Objections and concerns raised against plastination indicate a potential danger when making use of human corpses and parts of human corpses. The statement that plastination and the exhibition of plastinated specimens touch upon human dignity can only be the result of careful, deliberate evaluation of the issue. It cannot, however, be used as a blanket criticism taking the place of specific arguments.

Making use of the aesthetic freedom that the new plastination technique provides does not violate the human dignity of the deceased, as long as the corpse has not been artistically distorted. The right to care for the dead as well as feelings of reverence on the part of survivors and the general public are likewise insufficient for justifying any other perspective on this question. Viewed in another way, protecting the body against the will of the deceased would mean imposing the values of others onto the donor. This would violate the right to self-determination of the donor, who, upon receiving information on plastination and on the uses of plastinated bodies, made a rational decision in favour of donation.

The donor has a moral and legal right to be respected in this highly personal decision, even after his or her death. With respect to the person preparing plastinated specimens, this conclusion corresponds to the right to use plastination techniques as a means of preserving bodies and/or body parts for long periods of time. This is true so long as the donor has given his or her consent, and provided that specimens are plastinated in keeping with the body's natural state and thus meeting the needs of human dignity. Such specimens may also be exhibited to the public for the purposes of providing information on the structure and function of the human body. This, however, must be done in a way appropriate to the dignity of the donor. Selling plastinated specimens to a very limited number of third parties, such as recognized research institutions and natural science museums, is permissible to the extent that this is in keeping with the original consent of the donor and that specimens are used within the context of both their original function and posthumous human dignity. Charging admission to exhibitions of plastinated specimens and selling such specimens to third parties are not in conflict with "accepted moral standards," provided reimbursement is commensurate with the time and expense involved.

[1] Because the Mannheim public prosecuter's office was already investigating similar charges, it abandoned plans to commence inquiries into charges of bodily injury, disturbing the peace of the dead, and violating the Children and Young Persons Act.

[2] Dr. Fischer, bishop of the Lutheran Church of Baden, as stated during a televised panel discussion broadcast November 27, 1997, on Südwest 3.

[3] Bieyl, quoted directly in: Der Pathologe, 1998, vol. 19.

[4] Von Hagens, "Das innere Gesicht." ("The Face Within."), in: the exhibition catalogue for Die Macht des Alters (The Power of Age), Cologne 1998, pp. 146 ff.

[5] For more information see Ruß·, Leipziger Kommentar zum Strafgesetzbuch. 11th edition, 1994, Article 242, Item 4.

[6] Article 1, Section 1 of the Constitution of Germany, "The duty of all public authority is to respect and protect the inviolable dignity of man."

[7] For more information regarding these terms, see Meer leau-Ponty, "Der Philosoph und sein Schatten", in: Das Auge und sein Geist. Philosophische Essays. ed. Arndt, Philosophische Bibliothek, vol. 357, 1984, pp. 45 ff.

[8] See, for example, Article 2 of the Feuerbestattungsgesetz (Cremation Act).

[9] Bundesgesetzblatt, vol. 1, 1997, no. 74.

[10] Article 2247, Paragraph 1 of the Bürgerliches Gesetzbuch (German Civil Code) instead of a series of laws: "The testator may draw up a will by means of a declaration written and signed by his or her own hand."

[11] Key decisions on this issue are that of the German Federal High Court, found in:
Neue Juristische Wochenschrift, 1968, pp. 1773 ff.
and that of the Federal Constitutional Court,
in: Neue Juristische Wochenschrift, 1971,
pp. 1645 ff.

[12] See also Schroeder/Taupits, Menschliches Blut: verwendbar nach Belieben des Arztes? Stuttgart 1991, pp. 42 ff.

[13] Eser, in: Schönke/Schröder, Strafgesetzbuch, Kommentar. 25th edition, Munich 1997, Article 242, Items 10 and 21.

[14] For additional information, see Bundestags-Drucksache (Bundestag Gazette) 13/4355, p. 16.

[15] Such as Article 42, Paragraph 1 of the legislation on interment of Baden-Württemberg: "Corpses may only be delivered to an anatomical institution for scientific purposes if the funeral documentation stipulated in Article 34 has been presented."

[16] Gesetz- und Verordnungsblatt für Berlin, June 26, 1996, pp. 237 ff., as well as the March 15, 1997, issue, p. 54

[17] Thiele, "Plastinierte Körperwelten, Bestattungszwang und Menschenwürde," in: Neue Zeitschrift für Verwaltungsrecht 2000, pp. 40-55;
Benda, "Von der Vergänglichkeit zum Plastinat," in: Neue Juristische Wochenzeitschrift 2000, pp. 1769 ff.

[18] Article 7 of the Berlin law on dissection.

[19] For further information, see Landtag von Baden-Württemberg, Drucksache (Gazette of the State Parliament of Baden-Württemberg) 11/2978 (Nov.11, 1993).

[20] Bundesgesetzblatt, vol. 1, 1997, p. 2631.

[21] For background: Federal Constitutional Court, Neue Juristische Wochenschrift 1971, pp. 1645 ff.

[22] For further information, see v. Münch, Grundgesetz Kommentar, vol. 1, Article 1 Item 6.

[23] See Entscheidungen des Bundesverfassungsgerichts, (Decisions of the Federal Constitutional Court) vol. 87, pp. 209, 228.

[24] See Entscheidungen des Bundesverfassungsgerichts, (Decisions of the Federal Constitutional Court) vol. 45, pp. 187, 228.

[25] See Entscheidungen des Bundesverfassungsgerichts, (Decisions of the Federal Constitutional Court) vol. 30, pp. 1, 16.

[26] For further information, see Bazon Brock, "Bildende Wissenschaft," ("The Educating Power of the Sciences") in: Die Macht des Alters, exhibition catalogue, pp. 142 ff.

27 See Wessels/Hillenkamp, Strafrecht Besonderer Teil 2. 23rd edition, Heidelberg 2000, Item 66.

28 See Entscheidungen des Bundesverfassungsgerichts, (Decisions of the Federal Constitutional Court) vol. 30, pp. 173, 189.

29 The objection has been raised against clinical dissection that it violates human dignity, because doctors performing the autopsies are frequently lacking in aesthetic sensibilities.

30 Fiedling in: Tijdschrift voor geneeskund en ethik, 1998, p. 8, discusses how public encounters with corpses have become interactive.

31 For further information, see von Hagens, Informationsblatt, p. 8.

32 Take, for instance, the German Museum of Medical History in Ingolstadt or the Berlin Museum of Medical History, which is located in the Charité Medical Centre and was "opened to the greater public" on July 27, 1899, for the purpose of informing and enlightening the public on pathological processes in the human body.
For further information, see Krietsch/Dietel, Pathologisch-Anatomisches Cabinet, pp. 2, 159.

33 Which, with respect to sale to third parties, should be ensured by means of appropriate stipulations contained within transfer agreements.

34 See "Entscheidungen des Bundesverfassungsgerichts," (Decisions of the Federal Constitutional Court) in Zivilsachen, vol. 69, pp. 295, 297.

35 Heinrichs, in: Palandt, Bürgerliches Gesetzbuch, 59th edition, Munich 2000, Paragraph 138, Item 2.

36 For further information, see Schröder/Laupitz, Menschliches Blut: verwendbar nach Belieben des Arztes?, pp. 10 ff.

37 See Bundestag-Drucksache (Bundestag Gazette) 13/4355, p. 29.

38 Compare with Article 17, Paragraph 2 of the Transplantationsgesetz (Organ Transplantation Act).

39 For further information regarding the parallel issue of doctors selling bodily substances, see Taupitz, Deutsches Ärzteblatt, 90 (1993), pp. B 785 ff.

Brigitte Tag, is a lawyer. After receiving her degree in administrative economics, she began her law studies at the University of Heidelberg, passing the first round of State law exams in 1987 and the second in 1990. She then earned her Ph.D under Prof. Hillenkamp at the University of Heidelberg. Her dissertation, which was awarded a mark of summa cum laude, dealt mainly with economic criminal law. At the Law Faculty of Heidelberg, Brigitte Tag acquired her credentials to become a professor in medical criminal law, criminal law, and criminal proceedings law in January 2000. The title of her postdoctoral thesis is: "Medical Treatment in the Dichotomy between Patient Autonomy and Lex artis. An Investigation of Medical Criminal Law." In addition to these activities, she has for many years been responsible for the organizational and substantive aspects of the Heidelberg initiative to reduce the amount of time needed by students to complete degree requirements. She has worked as an instructor preparing law graduates for the bar examination since 1990, and was honoured with the Baden-Württemberg Teaching Award in 1996.

Brigitte Tag's research and corresponding publications have focussed on general criminal law and criminal proceedings, medical criminal law, protection of autonomy (particularly with respect to medical law), medical and ethical questions at the beginning and end of life, the use of corpses, economic criminal law, interdisciplinary communication, legal education reform, and policy issues of higher education.

Bazon Brock

The Educating Power of the Sciences

Lending Permanence to Happiness

Jeremy Bentham (1748-1832) was a contemporary of Goethe who willed that his body be dissected in the presence of his friends and that his fellow faculty members enjoy his fortune for as long as he remained among them in body. There was more to the challenge of this radical reformer, philosopher, economist and lawyer than met the eye, and the professors met that challenge brilliantly — in keeping with Bentham's utilitarian teachings that the basis of moral codes lies in utility and that everyone recognizes what is to his own advantage. After their colleague died, they adorned his skeleton with a portrait bust and prepared a glass display case for it. This is how it remains to this day, outfitted with one of his hats, walking sticks and suits of clothes, preserved along with his mummified head at University College London.

Jeremy Bentham, the "auto-icon" University College London.

"The greatest happiness of the greatest number" was Bentham's general maxim as a social ethicist, and it would seem that he found his own greatest happiness in the knowledge that at least his virtually incorruptible remains would linger among the living for a long time to come. To the extent that this is true, this eccentric gentleman, were he alive today, would most definitely have welcomed Gunther von Hagens as a modern partner, as von Hagens' plastination process makes it (theoretically) possible for more and more confident individuals to follow Bentham's example.

Even as recently as the end of the 19th century, highly devout Catholic monks took those residents of Palermo whom they had comforted during their departure from this world and placed them in the catacombs of this Sicilian city, whose importance dates back to antiquity. The unique climatic conditions prevailing there naturally transform the dead into mummies. As a result, these pious entities sit, stand and lie about in eternity's vestibule, where thousands of calm tourists come each year to spend some time in quiet and, one would at least hope, inspiring communion with them.

Bentham, the residents of the Palermo catacombs, and those who have donated their bodies to the Heidelberg Institute of Plastination attest to the fact that members of early advanced cultures that seem alien to us today, such as those of ancient Egypt or pre-Columbian America, have not been the only persons prepared to use their own bodies to represent a central aim of every culture. Radical materialists, devout Christians, and many other modern Europeans have been and are likewise willing to represent that aim, i.e., to lend permanence to existence.

The primary aim of all of the cultural technologies known to us is to fulfill this goal of presenting the world of past, present and future generations as the only world. Mental efforts, at times manifested physically, bridge the vast gulf that we naively perceive between life and death, this world and the next, past and future. These efforts work because they are capable of enduring.

Cultures are a web of relationships between human beings. The less these relationships are dependent upon the discretion of the individual, the more binding they are. This discretion is the result of one's personal temporal horizons, which are, of course, temporary and restrictive. Opening and expanding these temporal horizons means capturing time, bringing it to a standstill; it means escaping time and its ravages, i.e., passing away without a trace.

Cultures make that possible for their members by guaranteeing repeatability, in other words by offering the chance of being able to begin and end what essentially has neither a beginning nor an end. This cultural guarantee of repeatability defines what we call permanence: the constant presence of the dead and their pasts in the present of the living. Cemeteries, monuments and memorials, museums, libraries and archives, trade routes, old city foundations and architectural styles, field names and city names all embody and represent this type of permanence as an opportunity to repeat, to fathom, to visualize — and to a certain extent, to resurrect.

Historians, archaeologists, theologians and philologists who have learned how to communicate properly with the dead are not the only ones who have the means to achieve permanence by repeating, i.e., by retrieving — today nearly everyone has access to video and audio recording technology. Video allows you to resurrect Marylin Monroe or Adolf Hitler; Enrico Caruso or Elvis Presley can be summoned up by CDs; scenes from your life are permanently available in photos; and at family gatherings you can weave resúmés into biographies, in which time and space can be fitted together or taken apart at will — just as only the cultural elite were able to do up until recently. People today have learned this by following the example of the arts and the mass media. The world of TV no longer complains when movies are reshown over and over and over. Instead viewers share in the satisfaction of seeing serial happiness return in infinite Warholesque repetition. And sports channel viewers have Friedrich Nietzsche's blessing, as slow motion allows them to watch moments deemed important three, four or an endless number of times, thus helping them achieve Master of Time status, i.e a cultural giant.

What is described is technical theology: Anyone can fulfill the Christian promise of resurrection with no Apocalypse, no Judgement Day. The mass media proves to us every day that we already have the end behind us. That is their Good News.

Gunther von Hagens' plastination is recognizable at first glance as a genuine cultural technology, lending permanence to a biological substrate using a means other than nature, i.e., other than by passing on the organism's intact genetic information.

Techniques aimed at selectively optimizing this natural process have thus far been highly successful. Protecting the frail, breeding specific animals, and collecting, selecting and reusing specific plant seeds are methods that have proven themselves to be so efficient that they have come to be the actual pattern for all cultural work — from obtaining a food supply and various forms of preservation, up to and including breeding efforts that reshape nature, thereby expanding useful resources. The requirements for this success are that there be some cultural benefit and that knowledge of the natural processes by which life regenerates itself be preserved. Possession of this knowledge, i.e., being able to apply it and pass it on to others, equates to power. Those desiring a share in this power must submit themselves to rules as they have applied and still apply to priests and doctors, scientists and artists. Yet historical experience shows that breaking rules is also a recognized cultural achievement, as breaking the rules does, in fact, mean having to codify new rules.

In this way, von Hagens is currently breaking the rules governing the knowledge and application techniques that lend cultural permanence to anatomy, medicine, theology and social ethics. At the same time, he is also demonstrating the new, modified rules that will result from this infringement. In so doing, he is acting in accordance with a tendency that has been clear in our culture (i.e., what we refer to as "Western" culture) for a good 250 years: the tendency towards professionalizing to the greatest possible extent the audience and/or clientele of priests, doctors, engineers, artists, craftsmen and those possessing power in democratic societies.

Ever since a large group of associates of French cultural pragmatists Denis Diderot (1713-1784) and Jean le Rond d'Alembert (1717-1783) published all of the practical and theoretical knowledge of their day in what they called an Encyclopedia, the principle addressees of such information have not been specialists, but rather all citizens in general. It went without saying that receiving this cultural knowledge would not make these citizens doctors or engineers; they would not be able to paint like an artist or sculpt or produce goods like a craftsman. They were instead to be put into a position to judge the work of artists, doctors or craftsmen, because they would be able to differentiate between what was reasonable (justifiable) and what was less reasonable, between what had been made well and what had been sloppily thrown together, between what was useful and what clearly was not, between effective but bitter medicine and the sweet consolations of a charlatan.

After all, what is the use in producing quality goods if potential buyers are unable to recognize quality? What is the point of performing medicine, painting, or governing according to the rules of the art if neither the ill, nor those who view the art, nor the voters know the existing rules or how to appreciate new ones? Ambitious business people need knowledgeable customers; serious doctors need informed patients; ingenious artists need a discerning audience possessing aesthetic sensibilities and open to new ideas — if not, business people, doctors and artists might as well abandon their efforts to produce achievements which really would have been worth their price.

The outstanding potential of plastination has been demonstrated by von Hagens' work, which not only educates the general public (i.e., makes it more discerning and perceptive) in matters that had previously been visually accessible through the use of only moderately useful models. It also prompts specialists, i.e., anatomists and surgeons, to link their perceptions with familiar ideas and concepts in completely new ways.

If we accept this offer, our trust in the happiness of permanence that culture promises ought to be greatly strengthened. Many of those who viewed the plastinated specimens (human bodies that have been transformed using various means of dissection and preservation) at the KÖRPER-WELTEN exhibition in Mannheim indicated in the visitor's book that only upon viewing those immortalised there did they regain a sense of awe for the highest of all cultural aims.

That may well be a melodramatic means of allaying feelings of irritation, even of horror, fear and mortality. Yet awe does, in fact, result from having overcome highly personal emotional responses in the face of overpowering impressions, and it is those cultural records that embody and represent

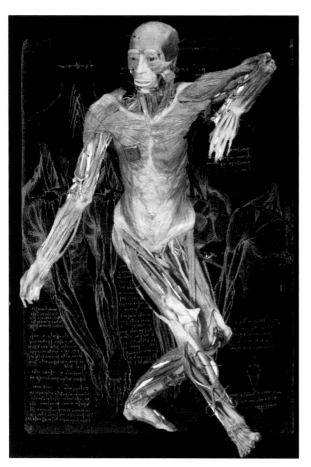

One of Gunther von Hagens' plastinated figures placed in front of an anatomical drawing by Leonardo da Vinci

a claim to permanence that make the most powerful impressions on us. It is in accordance with this premise that we assess not only the tombs of ancient Egyptian pharaohs, Gothic cathedrals and impressionist paintings in museums, but also disappearing rain forests, faded family photos and the loss of our homes. The plastination substrates have taken the core significance that assigning permanence has for all cultures and impressed it into the minds of exhibition visitors more conspicuously than any other medium presently does.

Real Virtuality

Bridges embody the idea of being able to travel at will from one shore to the other and back again, and represent that idea metaphorically whenever a mental step or leap is being described (bridging a gap between two people or societies, for instance). This unity of embodiment/animation and representation/symbolism is the hallmark of all truly effective cultural achievements, and allows us to recognize them as such.

Heinrich Lübke did, in fact, represent the function of head of state, but he did not embody that function. Gustav Heinemann embodied it, but appeared to have difficulties when it came to representing it. Roman Herzog, on the other hand, has that aura that tells us that he embodies what he represents and represents what he embodies — his body is a sign of his significance. The transformation cue in his case is given by the sirens of his police escort.

In other cases of cultural achievement, the transformation from embodiment to symbolic representation and vice versa ("this is my body, this is my blood") is marked by the ringing of a bell or through acclamation ("this is a work of art and not just material that represents an imaginary work of art"). And do the many voices cheering for a Nobel Prize not drown out the nagging doubts as to whether documentation on a subatomic decay chain reaction indicates the embodiment of a newly discovered particle or whether it merely represents a theoretical assumption formulated in terms of a physical experiment?

When it comes to thoughts, virtuality is conceded as a mere possibility; we evaluate embodiments/materializations, on the other hand, as something real. Great cultural achievements aim at turning thoughts into reality, but not in such a way that the achievement erases the thought. Instead, it is the unity of embodiment and representation that allows us to distinguish between both levels, i.e., between that which is virtual and that which is real. The product of culture is therefore a real virtuality.

There is, however, a large body of criteria we can use to assess how much reality is contained within an embodiment.

Authenticity is obviously the most highly valued criterion. When touring a castle, a tourist will tap a column to see whether it is really made of marble or simply painted to give the deceptive impression of marble. Is the singing on stage authentic or is it a case of lip-synching to a recording either of the singer's own voice or even of someone else's?

Despite all of the postmodern satisfaction that we get from simulations, fakes, substitutes, reproductions, and stylized recitations, we have not yet given up our demands for authenticity. On the contrary: you can only enjoy an imitation when you know how to distinguish it from the real thing.

In general we assign value to the things of this world based on the understandable claim that they really are what they claim to be, i.e., authentic. Was this van Gogh really painted by Vincent or is it the work of an imitator (copier or forger) who was able to make us believe that this van Gogh was real because he himself was extremely familiar with and appreciated the authentic works of van Gogh? Is this Buddha's tooth really an authentic part of the honourable man's earthly embodiment? And is it legitimate to preserve and honour Buddha's tooth? Does this actor really embody the playwright's character that he is currently playing? Or is he just delivering a text, even though he is not supposed to be reciting literature but authentically acting?

This self-evident demand for authenticity is voiced in all cultures, and any objections raised against it fall on deaf ears — such objections, in fact, strengthen the demand. If a relic should prove to be a forgery, the real relics are considered all the more valuable. If artists or architects or craftsmen consciously abandon any claim of embodying their ideas in an authentic manner, they are dismissed as cheap imitators, plagiarists or producers of kitsch or junk who are unable to keep the promises they seem to make.

Plastinated bodies are real virtualities; the extent to which they represent reality is verified to the greatest conceivable extent by their authenticity. One could say that they fulfill the function of relics both of scientific anatomy and of the artistic conceptualization involved in, for instance, sculpting. If we recall the statue of a runner by Italian futurist Umberto Boccioni (1882-1916), or the surreal, abstract works of French artist Germaine Richier (1904-1959) or the works of Spanish iron sculpture pioneer Julio Gonzáles (1875-1942), we see the conceptual precision with which Gunther von Hagens models his specimens. Their double justification of authenticity — a biological substrate on the one hand and genuine artistic figuration concepts on the other — is especially convincing to those who view the whole-body plastinates. Time and time again, when discussing their reactions to these exhibits, visitors to the KÖRPERWELTEN exhibition emphasize that they were particularly impressed by their authenticity.

Von Hagens does in fact work as a sculptor, creating models of his objects in order to determine how a body must be posed to show precisely what it is intended to show: the fascinating relationship between the external impression that the body makes and its internal structure. The relationship between surface and the functional logic of the human body has guided the conceptual work of sculptors and painters ever since the 4th century BC (as evidenced in Greek and Roman cultures). This work always revolved around two levels, which were used to demonstrate the relationship between internal and external processes. On the one hand artists wanted to illustrate how spiritual/intellectual efforts (such as the will to make a particular movement) manifested themselves through the body; in other words they wanted to show how mental activity or one's frame of mind (sadness or stoicism, enthusiasm or fear) can be embodied. On the other hand they wanted to make comprehensible and perceptible how individual components of the body (skin, muscles, tendons and ligaments, extremities and internal organs) work together to maintain its unity in all of the various states induced by the influence of external forces, particularly gravity.

Making the invisible interior realms of a living body perceptible attracted the attention of early anatomists and doctors who had developed the art of interpreting signs (symptomatology) as a means of drawing conclusions regarding the body's inner workings based on its exterior. This was more or less successful and fulfilled certain limited purposes such as assisting at a birth or healing the broken bones and open wounds that soldiers often suffered. Going a very large step further, however, i.e., creating openings in the body through which surgeons would have access to the inside of the abdominal cavity or chest, was dependent upon the mere possibility of visualizing what one had never seen before — insight gained by dissecting and cutting open corpses can only be applied to the living to a very limited extent. The ability to view dead bodies as if they were living was not achieved until plastination and, most importantly, the visualization concept that Gunther von Hagens developed out of necessity: he needed to give an appropriate form to his incorruptible anatomical specimens.

To authentically perceive dead bodies as living ones is an ancient goal of artists. Not only can that claim be substantiated by stories such as that of the mythical King Pygmalion of Cyprus, who fell in love with a statue of a woman that he himself had made; it is also attested to by countless actual historical accounts of efforts in the art of mimesis (the representation of natural reality) to go beyond purely formal mimicry of contours and surfaces. Michelangelo Buonarotti (1474-1564) would not have been one of the outstanding Renaissance sculptors had he, as a creator of human figures in marble, not attempted to breathe life into his creations — to animate them. "Moving pictures" were,

Plastinated voluntary muscles (a runner) by Gunther von Hagens; Unique Forms of Continuity in Space. 1913, by Umberto Boccioni (1882-1916)

after all, an exciting way to describe early silent films, and "talkies" described the first movies that had sound.

Animation, i.e., bringing life to a subject, is generally considered one of the loftiest goals of work with inanimate material. Not counting artists' and scientists' demands to create artificial life (a current priority of many cultural creators), plastination methods and concepts have been the most ambitious and successful attempts in the history of art and science at — authentically — perceiving dead bodies in the same way as living bodies.

Machines, for example, could also be understood as dead bodies that engineers can under certain circumstances equip with some of the features of the living. Non-trivial machines, such as self-programming computers and robots capable of learning, are what most often demonstrate astonishing signs of animation. Yet they only represent life simulated via programmes — they do not embody it. The substrate required for these machines (generally the chemical element silicon) may well be transformable into highly efficient electronic circuitry; nevertheless it remains far below the level of complexity characterizing even a single-celled organism. The machine's body, even for non-trivial machines, is not a sign to anyone, even when designers make an effort to give it a gestalt.

Gestalt, a term commonly used only in German, refers to the unity of embodiment and representation. Gunther von Hagens is an artist/scientist who has managed to lend inanimate matter the gestalt of the living — the gestalt of an authentic real virtuality.

Imaging Science

The ability to lend the real gestalt of the living to a thought process, to an idea, used to be the privilege of the arts, which, as doctor and poet Gottfried Benn (1885-1956) put it, moved in the realm of possibility in which gestalten are created (i.e., in virtuality).

Ever since the time of Goethe (1749-1832), this has been known as the educational power of the arts. A person becomes educated by appropriating the virtual constructs of others, whether in terms of insights, ideas or world views. Once one has embodied, has made completely one's own that which has been appropriated, i.e., once it becomes second nature and an expression of that individual's self, then one not only has an education, one is educated. In that sense, the individual has become a gestalt of the educational power of the arts.

Without doubt, there have been countless educated scientists and representatives of other trades. So why then was there an emphasis placed on the privilege of the gestalt-creating, educating power of the fine arts? If an artist were also to have a scientific education, he or she would have been known as a poeta doctus, a scholarly artist, as represented and embodied by author Thomas Mann (1875-1955; Nobel Prize winner in 1929). Examples of scientists with a sense for artistic creativity are, on the other hand, rare. A sophisticated career requiring an education, it seems, has most often been successfully combined with literary creativity; Arthur Schnitzler, Alfred Döblin and Hans Carossa all worked at least part-time in the field of medicine, just as Benn did; Theodor Storm and Franz Kafka worked in the field of law; Robert Walser was an engineer, and Max Frisch was an architect.

Scientists who place value on being professionals in the fine arts and whose artistic activity extends beyond simply doing it in their spare time or as a side-line have only begun to penetrate the public consciousness in recent times. Neuroscientist and biologist Carsten Höller and Detlef Linke took part in documenta X ("House of Pigs and People"). A large number of scientists working in the field of artificial life present their findings within institutional and objective contexts in the arts. Several excellent computer researchers see their screen representations as a form of "imaging," as a result of giving gestalt to scientific concepts (the term "imaging science" reflects this).

In a narrower sense, imaging science refers to methods and technologies such as positron emission tomography (PET) that produce images of the interior of a living body; these, however, can only be read, i.e., understood and interpreted, by specialists. In a more general sense, the term refers to processes that open up human perception to aspects of the world that would otherwise elude our natural sensory organs. (It is telling to note that "making the invisible visible" was a credo of painters such as Paul Klee, Wassily Kandinsky, Willi Baumeister and many others who also had their own ideas concerning the theory of art.) Scientists in the field of imaging use their computers to create new languages, and languages have since time immemorial been considered particularly efficient educational forces. Languages are characterized by the relationship that they construct between the internal world of the mind and the social external world of man. The creators of these types of languages are educating scientists in the truest sense. Gunther von Hagens, with his preservation technology and his plastination imaging concepts, is one of these scientists, one of the most interesting in fact. Anyone who puts forth the frequently raised objection that, precisely because of imaging science, von Hagens' process is no longer needed, that the presentation of anatomy that it aims to achieve is already outdated, those who raise this objection fail to see his fundamental achievement. Even the best results from imaging science are only useful in a meaningful way if they are applied in conjunction with displaying the anatomy of dead bodies as if they were living.

The educating power of the science of anatomical presentation can only be even somewhat appreciated if — as I have indicated here — it is understood as a cultural technology that makes it possible to fulfill the ancient cultural aim of presenting the unity of embodiment and representation as a real virtuality and does so in as permanent and authentic a way as possible. Plastination conveys the relationship between interiors and exteriors, between living organisms and inanimate matter, perceiving and making perceptible, viewing and comprehending, and does so at a previously unattained level of authenticity. It follows that plastination may be understood as a linguistic operation that uses artistic concepts to create a gestalt for scientific ideas — a gestalt for mankind living in a cultural context and demanding permanence.

Bazon Brock has been a Professor of Aesthetics and the Theory of Design at the Bergische Universität – Gesamthochschule in Wuppertal since 1981. He studied German literature, philosophy, art history, and political science at the Universities of Hamburg, Frankfurt and Zürich. In 1965 he received a teaching contract as a professor of non-normative aesthetics at the University of Fine Arts in Hamburg, and in 1978 he became a Professor for the Theory of Design at the University of Applied Art in Vienna. During his university studies he completed a course of studies in dramaturgy and worked as the Director of Dramaturgy at the Lucerne Municipal Theater. In the seventies he contributed to the establishment of an international design centre in Berlin. Brock has been instrumental in numerous events, "action teachings" and exhibitions (most recently "Wa(h)re Kunst. Der Museumsshop als Wunderkammer" and "Die Macht des Alters. Strategien der Meisterschaft"), and has produced films, programmes for radio and television, and videos. He has also published countless scholarly books and papers and has worked as an editor. His research is currently focussing on neuronal aesthetics and imaging sciences. The Swiss Federal Institute of Technology in Zürich awarded him an honorary doctorate in 1992.

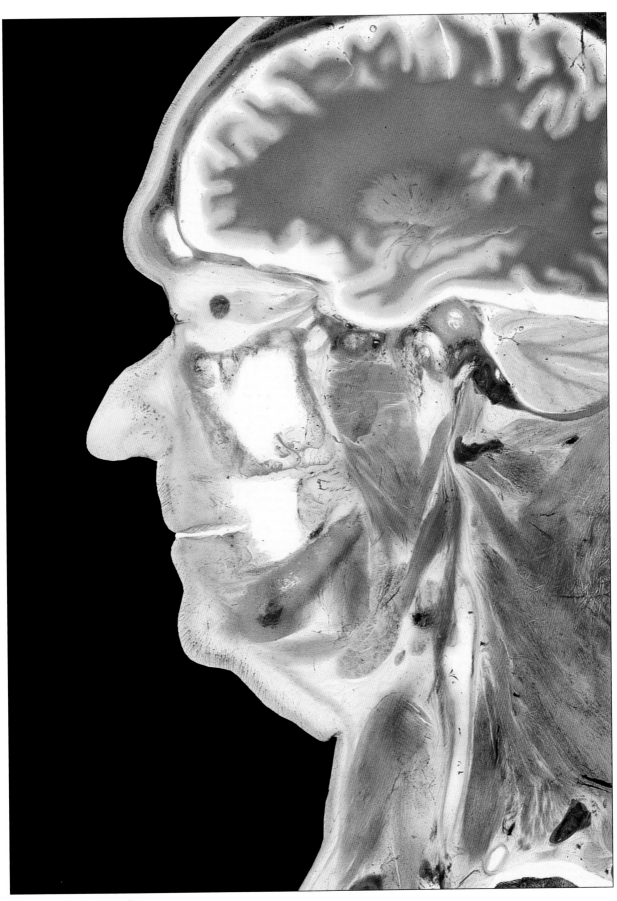

Transparente Kopfscheibe

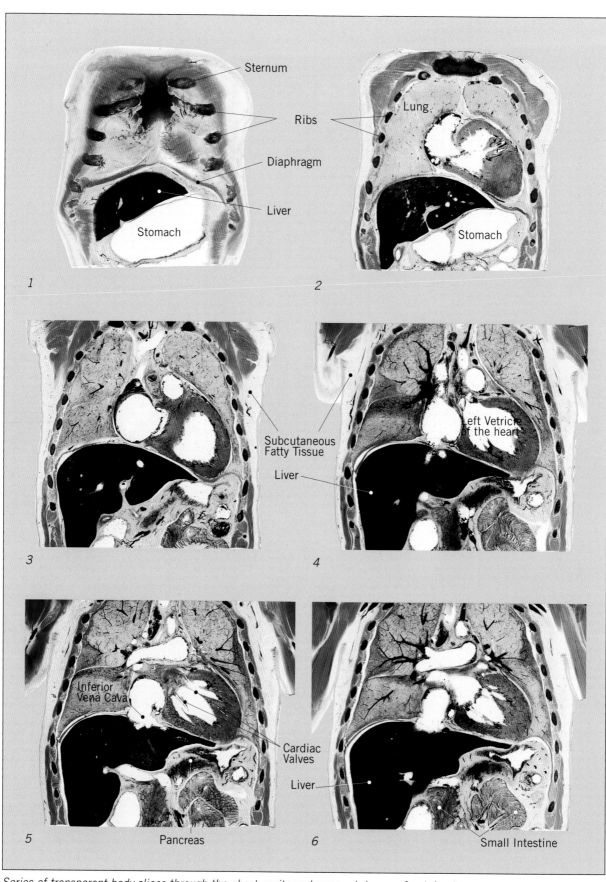

Series of transparent body slices through the chest cavity and upper abdomen, frontal cut

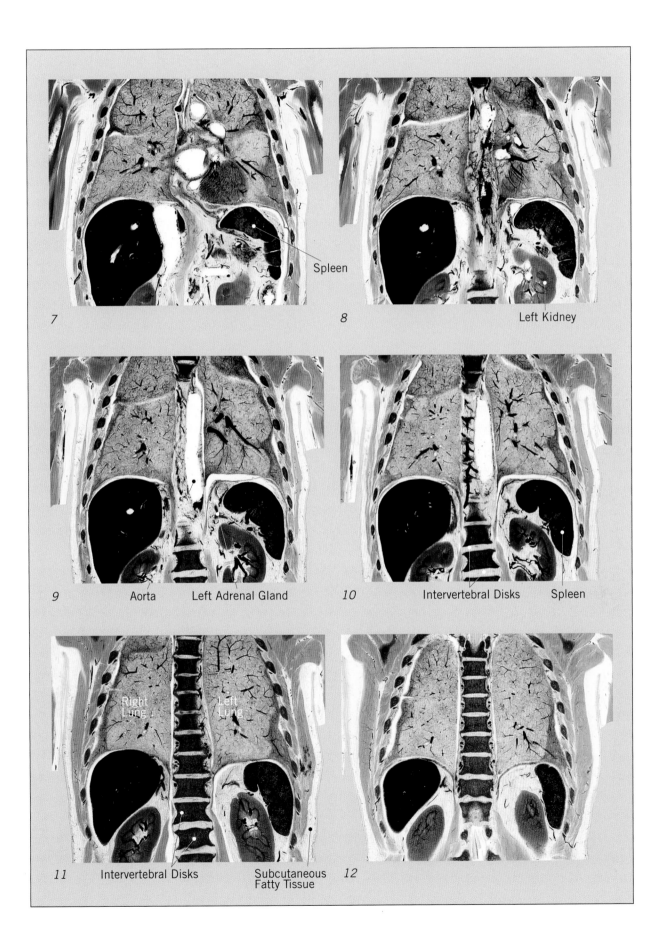

7

8   Spleen

          Left Kidney

9   Aorta   Left Adrenal Gland

10   Intervertebral Disks   Spleen

11   Right Lung   Left Lung

12

Intervertebral Disks

Subcutaneous Fatty Tissue

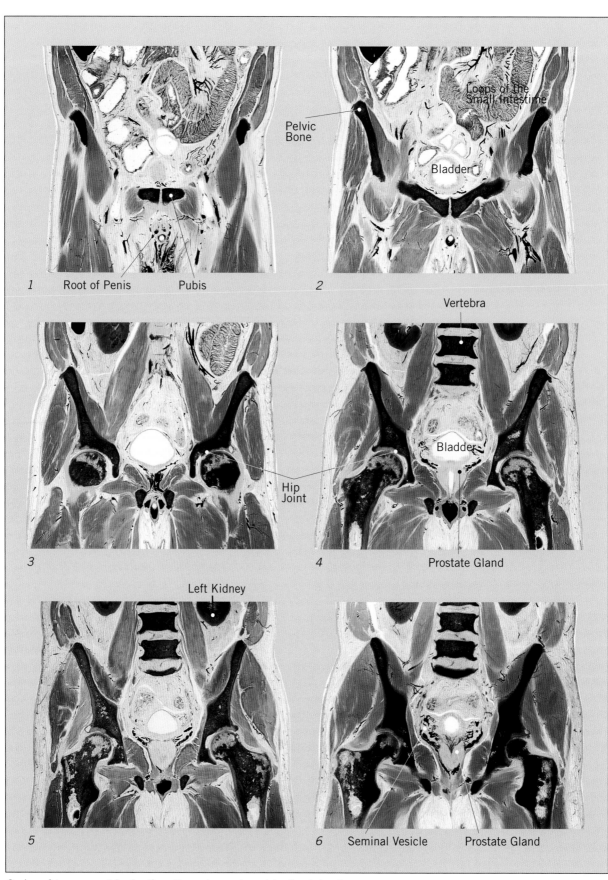

1 Root of Penis   Pubis

Pelvic
Bone

Loops of the
Small Intestine

Bladder

2

Vertebra

3

Hip
Joint

Bladder

4   Prostate Gland

Left Kidney

5

6   Seminal Vesicle   Prostate Gland

Series of transparent body slices through a male pelvis, frontal cut

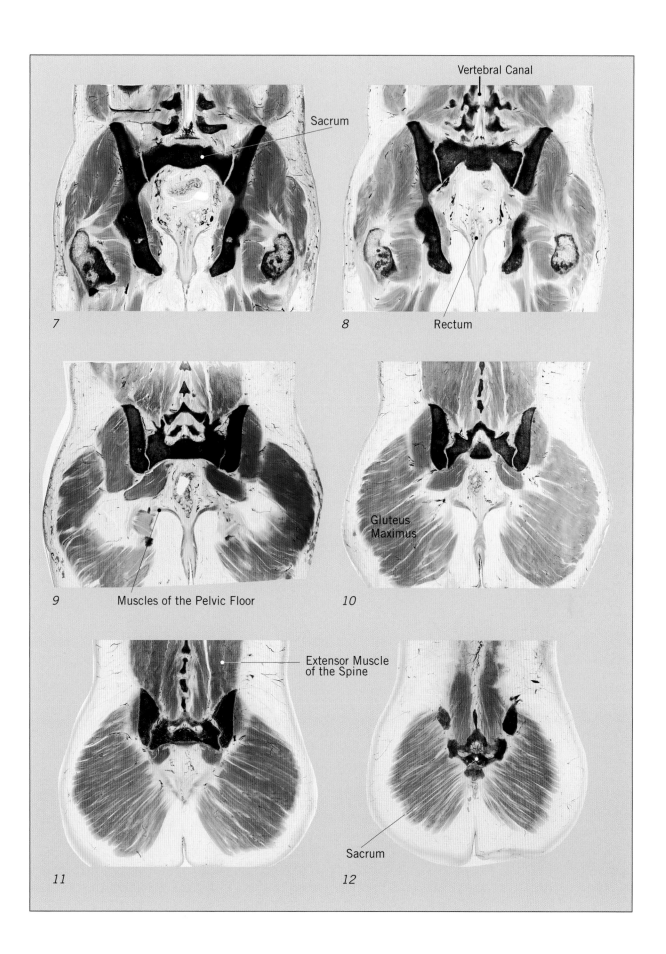

7

8   Vertebral Canal

Sacrum

Rectum

9   Muscles of the Pelvic Floor

10   Gluteus Maximus

11   Extensor Muscle of the Spine

12   Sacrum

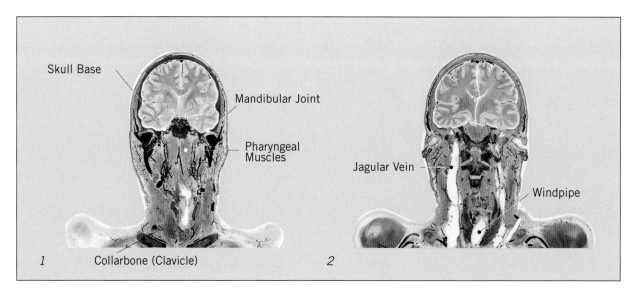

Skull Base

Mandibular Joint

Pharyngeal
Muscles

Jagular Vein

Windpipe

Collarbone (Clavicle)

1

2

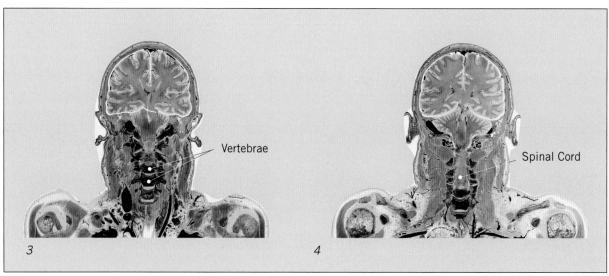

Vertebrae

Spinal Cord

3

4

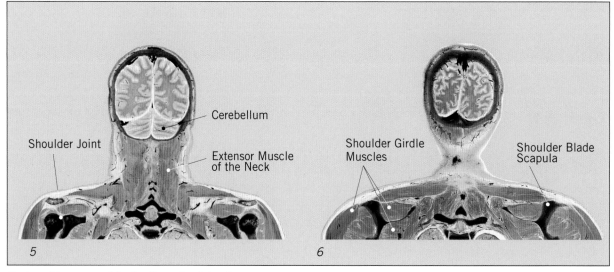

Shoulder Joint

Cerebellum

Extensor Muscle
of the Neck

Shoulder Girdle
Muscles

Shoulder Blade
Scapula

5

6

Series of transparent body slices, frontal cut

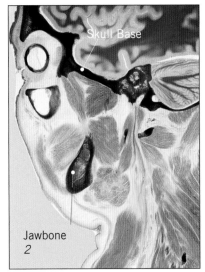

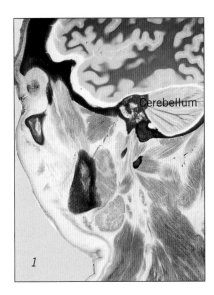

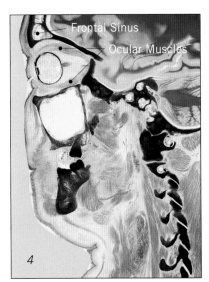

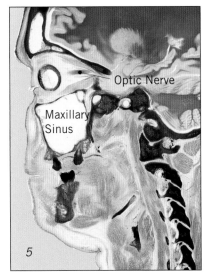

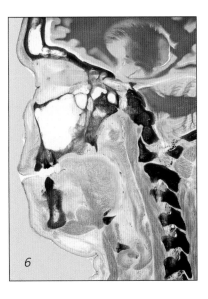

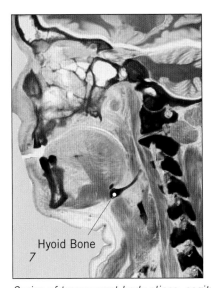

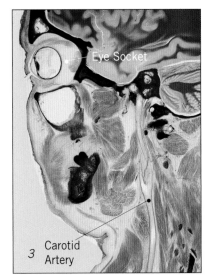

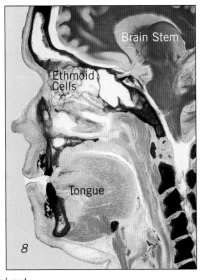

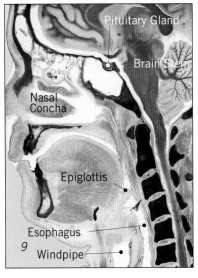

Series of transparent body slices, sagittal cut

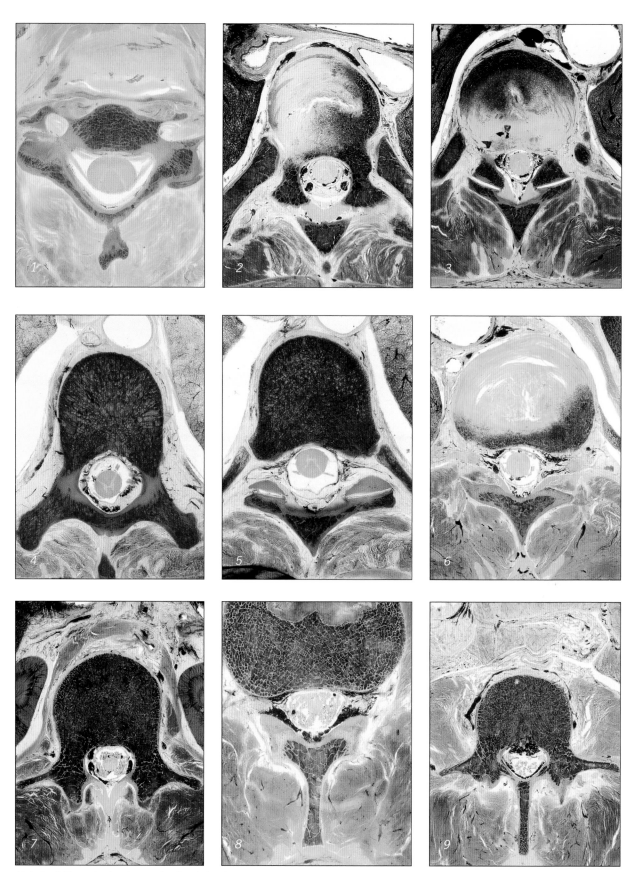

Detail of the spinal column, horizontal cut

Publishing Information:

Catalogue:
BODY WORLDS – The Anatomical Exhibition of Real Human Bodies
Prof. Gunther von Hagens, M.D.
Dr. Angelina Whalley, M.D.

Exhibition Design:
Gert Maruhn, Architect
Dr. Angelina Whalley, M.D.

Photographs:
Prof. Gunther von Hagens, M.D.

Scientific Consultant:
Prof. Eduard Bosiak, M.D.
(Institut für Plastination)

Editor and Publishing Consultant:
Albrecht Kunkel

Organisation of Exhibition:
Karen Schüssler-Leipold
(Institut für Plastination)

Published by;
Institut für Plastination, Heidelberg, Germany

Catalogue Design:
Andrea Birnkammer
(Institut für Plastination)

Translation:
Francis Kelly, Heidelberg

Printer:
Color Druck, Leimen, Germany

Copyright:
Institut für Plastination,
Rathausstrasse 18, 69126 Heidelberg, Germany

3nd printing 2002
(translation in English of 11th German Printing)